Physical Geography

Physical Geography

GORDON S. FAY

Associate Professor of Engineering
and
Lecturer in Earth Science
Los Angeles Valley College

A COLLEGE COURSE GUIDE

Doubleday & Company, Inc.
Garden City, New York

Library of Congress Catalog Card Number 64–19295

Printed in the United States of America

To the Reader

This book is written both for students who are formally enrolled
in a college course in physical geography and for the ever-increasing
numbers of readers who are studying "on their own."

It is designed to give the *nonscience major* a college-level view of
physical geography and at the same time an understanding of the
natural principles involved in the study of physical geography. In
satisfying these objectives the book developed, perhaps as a logical
consequence, into what should be a valuable aid for all students of
physical geography and associated subjects.

Some numerical examples have been used to explain thoroughly
some points. In general, however, I have tried to explain as many
principles and natural phenomena as possible in terms of everyday
or easily visualized experiences, and by describing simple experiments which the reader can perform in a matter of seconds with pencil, paper, string, etc. All readers will find at least some of the
mathematics and science fundamentals and "short cuts" of Chapter 2
to be helpful and interesting. Attention is invited to the review questions and exercises at the end of each chapter. Many readers will
find the exercises to be stimulating and informative. Answers to
selected exercises are given near the end of the book.

The inclusion of some of the historical background of physical
geography seems to be unique in a book on physical geography, as
does a chapter dealing with the effects of the earth's interior constitution upon our environment. Considerable emphasis has been placed
upon the cultural and economic aspects of physical geography. It
seemed rather unsatisfactory to explain what we know about our environment without at least describing some of our uses of it.

As far as possible I have tried to tie together the physical and cultural factors of the old and the new. In this way the reader can better understand what has been done, what is being done, and what will be done in the earth sciences which comprise physical geography.

Gordon S. Fay

Contents

Physical Geography

CHAPTER 1

Physical Geography and Man

Physical geography is the study of that portion of the earth which is man's natural environment. The word geography comes from the Greek *geographis*—"description of the earth." Physical geography is not a separate science, but it embodies several earth sciences.

The Earth Sciences of Physical Geography

The earth sciences of physical geography are those which deal with man's natural environment. The background earth science is *geodesy* which deals with the size and shape of the earth and with the sizes and areas of large portions of the earth's surface. With almost three fourths of the earth's surface covered by ocean water, *physical oceanography* is also a key science of physical geography.

Earth-sun relationships are of paramount importance to life on earth. These relationships, along with those of earth-moon and earth-sun-moon, bring *astronomy* into the realm of physical geography. Specific effects of sun energy upon natural environment are evidenced by weather and climate, concerns respectively of *meteorology* and *climatology*.

The actual locations of man's dwelling places are governed to a great extent by the availability of fresh water, a consideration of *hydrology*, and by landforms such as mountains and valleys which constitute the core of the science of *geomorphology*. General study of both the earth's exterior and interior is accomplished in *physical geology*, while *economic geology* deals with the occurrences and characteristics of mineral deposits.

Vegetation, or the apparent lack of it, is one of the most noticeable features of natural environment, as compare the tropical rain forests of Africa with the scrub vegetation of the Sahara Desert. *Plant geog-*

raphy is therefore included in physical geography as is the closely allied *pedology,* or soil science.

Finally, data in all of the above sciences can be presented concisely and graphically by means of maps, charts, and graphs, all within the scope of *cartography.* Cartography is not an earth science as such, but it is an indispensable allied science.

Relationships of Physical Geography to Cultural and Economic Geography

Cultural Geography.   Wherever he is, man's welfare, progress, and everyday living patterns depend largely upon how he reacts to his natural environment. Influenced in great part by physical elements of geography, such as weather, climate, topography, vegetation, etc., various cultures have developed. The study of man's distribution over the earth and the various ways in which he thus occupies his environment is called cultural—or "human"—geography.

Economic Geography.   The degree to which man utilizes available natural resources of his environment, plus the quantity and quality of such resources, has an all-important influence upon the resulting culture. However, the occurrences of these resources depend basically upon factors such as climate, soil formation, the hydrologic cycle, mineral deposit occurrence, etc., all elements of physical geography.

Further, an expanding culture goes hand in hand with an expanding economy which in turn means trade. Trade routes between peoples and areas are determined, other than politically, by characteristics of the intervening land, sea, or atmosphere, major elements of physical geography. The area of study outlined above—the areal differentiation of world production, consumption, and trade—is called *economic geography.*

It is readily seen that cultural geography and economic geography are intimately related. It is also evident that their common base is physical geography.

The History of Physical Geography

In a sense the first geographer was the first primitive man to realize that his survival was dependent upon his immediate environment.

However, it was not until man learned really to observe his natural environment, to record his observations, and to learn from them objectively that physical geography as a body of science began. This was less than three thousand years ago.

The Greeks. Physical geography had its recognized beginnings with the ancient Greeks. The first Greek geographer was Thales (625–545 B.C.) of Miletus. Thales solved many problems of a mathematical-geographical nature and lectured extensively concerning his travels.

The first map of the world was made by Anaximander, a friend of Thales. The map was based upon Thales' discourses, upon descriptions furnished by travelers, and upon Anaximander's own belief that the world was a cylinder hanging in a spherical universe. Ludicrous as such a concept may now appear, this cylinder in the stars was by far the closest that the Greeks had yet come to a correct visualization of the earth and its place in the universe.

Pythagoras (sixth century B.C.) advanced the premise, purely philosophical on his part, that the earth was round, an idea which was later substantially corroborated by Aristotle. Aristotle also believed that the northern and southern hemispheres could each be divided into climatic zones, or *klimata,* on the basis of temperature.

By then the terms longitude and latitude had also come into use. Herodotus (fifth century B.C.), the historian-geographer, thought that inhabitable areas of land had to be longer in the east-west direction than they were north and south. Thus in his writings Herodotus used *longitude* as a measure of the "longer" east-west dimensions and *latitude* as a measure of the "lateral" or "lesser" north-south dimensions.

The world's first geodetic scientist was Eratosthenes (third century B.C.) who measured the circumference of the earth by a method described in Chapter 3.

The Romans. The Romans were literally down-to-earth geographers. They were more interested, for example, in how mountains affected troop movements than how they affected the passage of clouds. Even so, two Romans had significant influence upon the development of geographic knowledge.

Strabo, who died within a few years of Christ, left his priceless seventeen-volume *Geography* which described the Mediterranean area at the beginning of the Christian era.

Ptolemy (second century A.D.) wrote several books, including a geography, and also made several maps. Following the Greek influence, Ptolemy's world map, for which he had calculated lines of latitude and longitude, showed an elongation of land masses in the east-west direction and a corresponding reduction in the widths of oceans. The mistake was compounded by the fact that Ptolemy used a figure for the circumference of the earth which was much less than that determined by Eratosthenes. The resulting major error involving ocean dimensions later played an amazing role in geographical exploration and discovery. It was precisely this feature of Ptolemy's map, the compressed oceans leaving no room for the American continents, which convinced Columbus that a sea voyage from Spain to China in an east-west direction was a highly feasible endeavor.

The Arabs.   It is evident from the foregoing that the science of mapmaking made little progress in Europe in the thirteen centuries between the time of Ptolemy and that of Columbus. The same is true of the majority of the other sciences. Fortunately, however, as Europe struggled through its Dark Ages, the Arab world preserved and even improved upon what was essentially a Greek heritage in mathematics and science.

In the realm of earth science, the Arabs studied landforms and the work of wind and rain. They calculated the height of what we know as the bottom of the ionosphere with an astonishing degree of accuracy and made great gains in astronomy. Necessity, in the form of an arid to semi-arid environment, also made them specialists in hydrology and to some extent in plant geography and soil science. The Arabs recognized that the earth was round and they were good navigators, but they somehow failed to make any significant contributions to the science of cartography.

Modern Physical Geography

Following the great voyages and explorations of the fifteenth, sixteenth, and seventeenth centuries, many countries of the Old World became landlords who knew little about the land they owned or even how to get to particular areas again. As a result the sciences of navigation and cartography both started to make great gains. In addition, visitors to the New World were encouraged to keep records of what they observed, but many of these accounts made up in fancy what they lacked in fact. Even by the beginning of the nineteenth century some American geography texts referred to certain unexplored lands in North America as being populated by lions, tigers, and unicorns. Descriptions of land and weather were equally fanciful.

At that same time, however, a matter-of-fact German, Baron Von Humboldt, was methodically exploring Mexico, Central America, and parts of South America. Humboldt's pioneer work in cartography, climatology, and plant geography represented the true beginnings of modern geography, for his work was based upon the scientific method of inductive reasoning following careful observation. Karl Ritter, also a German, who died in the same year as Humboldt (1859), also did much to help found modern geography. Ritter published many volumes on geographical subjects.

By the end of the nineteenth century, physical geography had made great advances. The concept of continental glaciation, as set forth by Louis Agassiz, was now widely accepted. Baron Von Richthofen and Sir Andrew Ramsay had made their important contributions to the study of marine erosion. A. Penck of Germany had published his work on the study of landforms, and in America W. M. Davis had started his important treatises on the "geographical cycle."

Thanks in part to the painstaking basic work of the nineteenth-century and early twentieth-century scientists, the twentieth century has already become the age of greatest discovery in many fields. The most spectacular advances in the earth sciences of physical geography have been made since World War II which, in itself, induced a great amount of activity in the sciences of oceanography, meteorology, and cartography. The International Geophysical Year (IGY) of 1957–1958 with sixty-six nations participating represented a world-wide assault upon the earth's physical secrets. Many of the studies made during that year are being carried forward today on a continuing, cooperative international basis.

History of Geography in the United States

The nineteenth century was a period of intensive geographical exploration in the United States. The Lewis and Clark expedition (1804–1806) traversed eight thousand miles of unexplored territory along a route which led from St. Louis to the headwaters of the Missouri and then across the Continental Divide to the Pacific Ocean. The expedition had tremendous influence upon United States growth, comprising as it did a solid base for later claim to the Oregon Territory.

At the same time the Lewis and Clark expedition was camped near what is now Bismarck, North Dakota, Lieutenant Zebulon Pike, under Army orders, was on his way to explore the upper Mississippi. After completion of that mission, Pike was sent on another exploration. Pike traced the Arkansas River to its source in the Rocky Mountains and explored near the base of the mountain now known as Pike's Peak. Further exploration subsequently brought him to the Rio Grande in New Mexico. Thanks to the explorations of Lewis and Clark, and Pike, the United States now knew considerably more about its recent Louisiana Purchase and the Oregon Territory which it was to acquire.

From 1843 to 1845, Captain John Frémont of the United States Topographical Corps made a series of remarkable explorations and mapping expeditions which included investigating the Sierra, the Rocky Mountain system, the Great Salt Lake area, many California rivers and valleys, and deserts of the West. Frémont's many contributions to geographical knowledge in the form of maps and descriptions reflected the facts that he covered more miles and mapped more area than any other American in the nineteenth century.

In 1871, Major John Wesley Powell's geographical studies in the Southwest culminated in the daring exploration of the Grand Canyon with a four-boat expedition. Although Powell's name is popularly associated only with this feat, he was a true scientist and one of the founders of American geography. He introduced several major concepts into the study of geology and eventually became the director of the newly-formed United States Geological Survey. Powell, a geologist, was actually the father of the American school of geomorphology.

The distinction of being America's first career geomorphologist goes to G. K. Gilbert (1843–1918), while C. E. Dutton (1841–1912) is noted for brilliantly extending some of Powell's original studies of areal erosion in the Grand Canyon area.

W. M. Davis (1850–1934), who founded the Association of American Geographers, based his painstaking analyses of erosional processes upon the work of Powell, Gilbert, and Dutton. The basic idea of Davis that differences in landforms reflect corresponding differences in geologic age, structure, and processes is now widely accepted. Some of Davis' other ideas concerning landforms were strongly challenged by the late Walther Penck of Germany and by advocates of his school of thought which includes some American geologists. However, Davis is still universally regarded as "the great definer and analyst."

Since the days of Davis, thought in geography has been strongly influenced by such men, to cite a few, as Richard Hartshorne whose scholarly analysis *The Nature of Geography* is a classic; by C. W. Thornwaite and his work in climatology; and by the W. W. Atwoods, Jr. and Sr., working in the field of physiography and physiographic history.

The Future and Physical Geography

Today, a fantastic array of instruments far beneath the ocean, buried in the earth's crust, measuring atmospheric elements, and hurtling through space are recording and transmitting priceless geographical data. These represent some of the first steps toward man's achieving maximum control and utilization of his environment. There seems little doubt now that hurricanes and tornadoes will some day be under at least limited human control. The oceans must be developed as major sources of food; the supply of fresh water in the United States must somehow be increased by 1980 to double that used in 1960.

Advances must be made in soil science in order that more land can be made more productive for regular crops. Plant geography and soil science will doubtless play a tremendous role in the use of land. The world's plant kingdom has been virtually untouched by man and many now little-known plants are potential sources of food, industrial fiber, and medicines. The United States Department of Agriculture already has a growing group of plant explorers who are combing the earth for such plants that can be grown in quantity on what would otherwise be unproductive land.

Another new and growing field of study deals with the effects that such factors as mineral occurrences, weather, and climate have upon the incidences of human disease, and even upon human behavior, in large geographical areas.

Perhaps the popularly most fascinating project at present is that of landing men on the moon. When that is done, the moon will become part of man's environment, even if *in absentia* for most of us. The consensus is that the first scientist on the moon will be an earth scientist, probably a geologist or a geophysicist.

The above are only a few examples of what the future will demand of the various sciences of physical geography. Other important developments and concepts are outlined in subsequent chapters in this book.

REVIEW

1. Discuss the significance of the scientific work done by the Arabs during Europe's Dark Ages.

2. Explain how the terms "longitude" and "latitude" and "climate" came into use.

3. Briefly discuss the high points of physical geography from the sixteenth century to the present.

4. What is the origin of the word "geography"?

5. Discuss some advances that lie ahead for the earth sciences of physical geography. Explain their significance in terms of your own life thirty years from now.

EXERCISES

(Answers are given in the answer section at the back of the book.)

1. Match each number with its correct letter:

(1) Astronomy	(a) Landforms
(2) Geodesy	(b) Maps
(3) Cartography	(c) Shape of earth
(4) Geomorphology	(d) Weather
(5) Hydrology	(e) Water supply
(6) Meteorology	(f) Earth-sun relationship

2. Match each number with the correct letter:

(1) Aristotle	(a) A cylindrical earth
(2) Humboldt	(b) The terms "latitude" and "longitude"
(3) Anaximander	(c) Measured height of stratosphere
(4) Herodotus	(d) Measured circumference of earth
(5) Arabs	(e) The scientific method
(6) Eratosthenes	(f) Showed earth to be a sphere

3. Answer the following as true or false.

    (1) Cartography is a true earth science.

    (2) A primitive man was history's first geographer.

    (3) Columbus' voyage in 1492 can be attributed largely to a major error in Ptolemy's maps.

    (4) Man now has good control of his environment.

    (5) Man is now making about 75 percent of maximum use of the world's plant kingdom.

CHAPTER 2

How to Study Physical Geography; Some Science Fundamentals; Solving Problems

Short Cuts in Mathematical Calculations

The average student taking a course in physical geography is not a science major. The usual course in physical geography, however, requires some mathematical solutions of problems. The methods of quick calculation explained below will be found extremely helpful by most students.

Accuracy, Significant Digits, Powers of Ten. These are not so much invented short cuts in calculation as they are principles of mathematics, but understanding and using these principles will materially speed up calculations and will help ensure proper answers.

To start, suppose that a student is measuring on a map the sides of a narrow, rectangular plot of ground. He scales one side as 83 feet and the longer side as 1216 feet. He multiplies the two figures and reports the area as 100,928. It is true that 83 multiplied by 1216 equals 100,928, but is this the area of the rectangle?

The chances are more than a thousand to one that it is not. Due to errors in the map and to errors in scaling, both measurements can be only approximate. It is generally considered that approximate measurements are such that the "83" length could be anywhere between 82.5 and 83.5, and that the "1216" length could be anywhere between 1215.5 and 1216.5.

If we take the lesser measurements, $82.5 \times 1215.5 = 100,278$ (approximate). Taking the greater measurements, $83.5 \times 1216.5 = 101,578$ (approximate). Obviously either one of these may be just as correct as the original value of 100,928. The apparent dilemma is resolved by using the principle of significant digits, and it will be necessary to depart from the problem for a moment:

A significant digit is a digit which "means something." There are two significant digits in 83, four in 1216, the reported lengths of the rectangle's sides. The last digits in each are, as shown above, in doubt but are still classed as significant because they result from estimation and not from guess. Decimal points have nothing to do with the number of significant digits in a number. The number 12.56 has four significant digits and so does 0.5898. Zeros are not significant unless they are "trapped" within a number. The number 15.003 has five significant digits while the number 0.00013 has two significant digits. The reason for this latter situation is that the decimal point merely expresses the units, in this case hundred-thousandths, and there are 13 of these units. Similarly, the number 3000 contains one significant digit unless it is indicated that it was measured to an accuracy of 2, 3, or 4 digits.

To get back to the problem, in multiplying or dividing two quantities, the rule is that the answer cannot usually contain a greater number of significant digits than the least number of significant digits contained in one of the quantities. In the example of 83 × 1216, the value of 100,928 would thus be "rounded off" to the correct answer of 100,000. In this case the first zero is significant and the quantity could be written as $1\bar{0}0,000$, the mark above the zero showing it to be the only significant zero. The work of multiplication may be speeded up by first rounding off to one more significant digit than is required in the answer. In the original example the 83 stays as it is; however, the 1216 could have been rounded off to 1220. (83 × 1220 = 101,260 which would then be changed to $1\bar{0}0,000$.)

It is important to note that, unless the principle of significant digits is applied in calculations, the answers will imply precisions and accuracies of measurement far from fact. Thus, what appear to be exact answers will actually be false and extremely misleading information.

To speed up calculation and to aid accuracy, "scientific notation" is commonly used, which means that numbers can be written in terms of significant digits and powers of ten. Using this system 365,000, for example, could be written as 365×10^3, or 36.5×10^4, or 3.65×10^5. As another example 0.0085 could be written as 8.5×10^{-3}, or $.85 \times 10^{-2}$, or 85×10^{-4}, etc. Suppose that it is required to divide 63 by

.015. The 63 could be written as 6.3×10, and .015 could be written as 1.5×10^{-2}. Then $\dfrac{6.3 \times 10}{1.5 \times 10^{-2}} = 4.2 \times 10^3$, or 4200.

Fractions. Some problems concerning the shape of the earth, map scale, etc. involve the use of fractions. A typical manipulation in such problems is that of reducing a given fraction to a fraction having "1" as a numerator. An example will help:

Problem: Reduce $\dfrac{8.5}{22560}$ to a fraction having "1" as a numerator.

Solution: Step 1. Unless otherwise indicated, these would be taken as approximate numbers. The fraction could not be written as $\dfrac{8.5}{22.6 \times 10^3}$.

Step 2. $\dfrac{22.6}{8.5} = 2.66$, approximately.

As the original numerator contained only two significant digits, the final denominator will contain two. The reduced fraction would therefore be $\dfrac{1}{2700}$.   (Answer)

Percent. Many areas of study require a knowledge of how to determine percent. The concept of percent is much used throughout the entire course in physical geography, in varied subject matter. An example is given below:

Problem: One cubic foot of air can hold 8.0 grains of water vapor at a certain temperature. The air at a certain locality was observed to hold 4.8 grains of water vapor at that temperature. What was the percentage of saturation of the air? (This quantity is called "relative humidity.")

Solution: The meaning of percent is "per hundred." The problem could be set up algebraically as $\dfrac{4.8}{8.0} = \dfrac{x}{100}$; $8.0x = 480$, and $x = 60$. Notice that the right-hand fraction can now be written as $\dfrac{60}{100}$, or 60 per hundred, or 60 *percent*.   (Answer)

To speed up the work, percentage problems, using the above example, may be done like this:

$$\frac{4.8}{8.0} \times 100 = 60 \ percent$$

                                                  (Answer)

Physics Principles

Density and Specific Gravity. The *density* of a substance is its weight per unit volume. In the United States, density is usually expressed in pounds per cubic foot, or grams per cubic centimeter.

The *specific gravity* of a substance is the ratio of its density to the density of, usually, water. To illustrate:

Problem: A certain rock weighs 187.2 pounds per cubic foot. Water weighs 62.4 pounds per cubic foot. What is (a) the density of the substance, (b) the specific gravity of the substance in relation to water, (c) the specific gravity of water with relation to itself?

Solution: (a) The density is 187.2 pounds per cubic foot.

(b) The specific gravity of the substance is

$$\frac{187.2 \text{ pounds per cubic foot}}{62.4 \text{ pounds per cubic foot}} = 3.00$$

(c) The specific gravity of water is

$$\frac{62.4 \text{ pounds per cubic foot}}{62.4 \text{ pounds per cubic foot}} = 1.00$$

Notice that whereas density is always expressed as some weight per some volume, specific gravity is expressed as an "absolute" value, without units. The units in the numerator and denominator of "pounds per cubic foot" may be thought of as canceling into each other just as, for instance, the number "5" would cancel in this equation: $\frac{187.2 \times 5}{62.4 \times 5}$. The reason, of course, is that 187.2 "pounds per cubic foot" and 62.4 "pounds per cubic foot" are as much quantities as are 187.2 "fives" and 62.4 "fives."

Mass, Gravity, Weight. Mass is the measure of the amount of material in a body. For us on earth, *weight* is the force with which the earth pulls on mass. *Gravitation* is the attraction between masses. It is this attraction between a body on or near the earth, and the earth, which determines the weight of the object.

Although, as shown by Einstein, mass can actually change at high velocities, this fact has no direct bearing upon any consideration in a beginning course in physical geography. As far as we are concerned then, mass or quantity of material in a body is constant.

On the other hand, what about weight? According to Newton's Law of Universal Gravitation, the force of gravitation between two bodies diminishes as the distance between the bodies increases. First advanced by Sir Isaac Newton, the Law of Universal Gravitation is the basis of many concepts in physical geography. Briefly, the law may be stated as follows: "Every particle in the universe attracts every other particle with a force which is proportional to their masses, and inversely proportional to the square of the distance between them." Thus a weight of one pound means that an object is attracted to the earth with a force of one pound. Therefore, as weight is dependent upon the force of gravitation, the weight of a body must decrease as the distance between the body and earth increases. Suppose, though, that the body remains on the earth's surface and certain tests show that the body does not weigh the same as it did in some other place on the surface. The weight has changed but the body is still on the surface of the earth, which means that, somehow, the force of gravitation differs in each of the two locations. This could be caused by several things including differences in distance from the earth's center, differences in the underlying rocks, or both. These important concepts will be referred to later, under several headings. The relationship between mass M, weight W, and the measure of gravitational force g is conveniently remembered by this equation: $M = \dfrac{W}{g}$. Remembering that M is constant, it is easily seen that as either W or g change, the other must also change.

Centripetal Force; Centrifugal Reaction. If a stone is tied onto a string and swung around in a circle, the force tending to move the stone toward the hand can be expressed mathematically as $\dfrac{W}{g} \dfrac{v^2}{r}$ where $\dfrac{W}{g}$ is the mass as explained above, v is the velocity of the stone, and r is the radius of the circle of rotation. This is the formula for the centripetal force acting upon a body moving at constant velocity in a circle, and trying to pull it in toward the center of the circle.

However, the stone of our example above is *not* moving in toward the center of the circle, which means that the stone must be pulling outward on the string with a reaction exactly equal to the centripetal force. This reaction is called the *centrifugal reaction.*

In the case of earth satellites, the force trying to pull the satellite in to earth is its weight or W. The reaction balancing this is $\dfrac{W}{g} \dfrac{v^2}{r}$

as shown above. Equating the two, $W = \dfrac{W}{g} \dfrac{v^2}{r}$ (the "weightless condition") and $v^2 = gr$. This final equation can be used to calculate very closely the velocity of an earth satellite.

At first glance there may seem to be a thin line, figuratively and literally, between our staying on the earth and being "centrifuged" into a weightless condition and thrown off the earth. The earth would have to turn about eighteen times as fast as it does now, however, in order to make any objects—and these would be at the equator—weightless.

Heat Transfer. The basic concepts involving heat transfer are very important to an understanding of the majority of natural processes studied in physical geography. To start, there are two ways to raise the temperature of objects: by doing work on them, as rubbing the hands together; or by adding heat from some other source, as holding the hands over a stove. The latter general process of adding heat from another source is by far the most important in the study of earth science phenomena involving heat transfer.

If heat is added from a source, it is apparent that that source is *releasing* heat. There must therefore be some system of *heat transfer* between the two objects or regions. There are three methods of direct heat transfer: conduction, convection, and radiation.

To illustrate these processes as they affect our natural environment, *radiation* from the sun produces heat on earth. Some regions will, for various reasons, become hotter than others. The air above these regions will become hotter by *conduction,* or heat transfer by contact, and will rise. As the air in this region now weighs less, the atmosphere pressure becomes lower. Cooler air from other regions then moves toward this "low," causing winds and breezes. The displaced hot air, now above, will move to a region or regions supplying the colder air, creating warm breezes aloft. Somewhere the hot air will become colder and sink because of increased density. It will then move on to an area of lower pressure, ideally the same one from which it came. In much the same way *convection* currents are set up in the air all over the world. It should be realized, though, that the above is a highly idealized picture of convection in the atmosphere as will be explained in a later chapter. In addition to the three direct methods of heat transfer outlined above, an important indirect method involving *latent heat* will be discussed in later chapters.

Specific Heat. The specific heat of a substance is the heat required to raise a unit mass of the substance one degree in temperature. The *British thermal unit* (Btu) is the amount of heat necessary to raise the temperature of one pound of water one degree Fahrenheit. The unit of heat in the metric system is the *calorie,* defined as the amount of heat necessary to raise the temperature of one gram of water one degree Centigrade. (Temperature scales are discussed in Chapter 8.) In both systems, then, the specific heat of water is 1.000.

The significance of specific heat in the study of physical geography lies mainly in the fact that the specific heat of water is much greater than that of land, as will be discussed in Chapter 8.

Graphical Solutions

Many problems in physical geography can be quickly solved by graphical methods. Others can be solved by combining graphics and mathematics into *semigraphical* solutions. The tools required for either method are simple and inexpensive: pencil, triangles, scale (a civil engineer's scale is suggested), a protractor for measuring angles, and a compass for drawing circles and arcs.

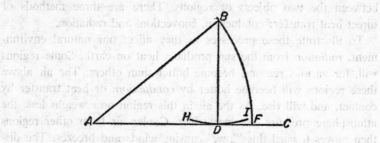

Fig. 1. Solution of right triangle.

Solving Right Triangles. Finding the unknown elements (sides and angles) of a triangle is often required in physical geography problems. If any two elements, other than the right angle, are known, the triangle can be solved. An example is given below:

Problem: Point *A* is at an elevation of 1230 feet above sea level on the side of a mountain. Point *B* on the same general slope is 1520 feet from *A,* the 1520 feet being measured along the mountain slope. Point *B* has an elevation of 2160 feet above sea level. What is the horizontal distance and the slope between A and B? (The horizontal distance is important because this is the distance that would be seen on a map between two points. The concepts of both horizontal distance and slope are encountered not only in mapping but also in the areas of earth-sun relationships, weather, drainage studies, structural geology, and others.)

Solution: (See Figure 1.) Draw a line AC through A, to represent a horizontal line. Using some convenient scale, set the compass for a radius of 1520 feet and draw arc FB. Set the compass for the difference in elevation of $2160 - 1230 = 930$ feet and by trial and error find point D where arc HI is tangent to AC. Point B is directly above. Draw BD. This completes the triangle. Length AD, the horizontal distance between A and B, may now be scaled off, and the angle of slope, DAB, measured with a protractor.

Square Roots, Graphically. The graphical method of determining square roots is extremely simple. As an example, suppose that it is required to determine the square root of 564:

(1) Express the number as one between 1 and 10, multiplied by some power of ten. In this case the number would be 5.64×10^2.

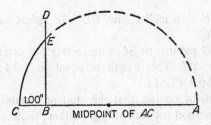

Fig. 2. Obtaining square roots graphically: $\sqrt{AB} = BE''$.

(2) Draw line AB, in Figure 2, 5.64 inches long.

(3) Make distance BC exactly 1 inch long.

(4) Erect perpendicular BD.

(5) Find midpoint of AC. AC is the diameter of the circle. Measure BE. This is the square root of 5.64, 2.38.

(6) Multiply the square root of 5.64 by 10 (the square root of 10^2). The product is the square root of 564, or 23.8.

If it had been required to determine the square root of, say, 56.4, this would have been written as 5.64×10 which means that the square root of 5.64 would be multiplied by the square root of 10, or

3.16. In cases like this, the multiplication is quickly performed graphically as shown in Figure 3, where B is a right angle:

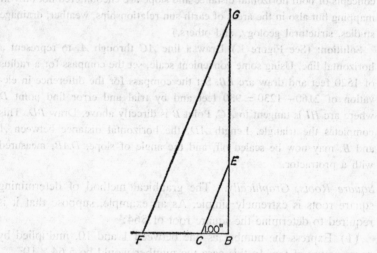

Fig. 3. Graphical multiplication of numbers: $BE \times BF = BG$.

(1) Make BF 3.16 inches long, BE 2.38 inches long.
(2) Draw EC.
(3) Draw FG parallel to EC, intersecting BE extended.
(4) Measure BG. This length is equal to 2.38×3.16, or the square root of 56.4 (7.51).

It is expected, of course, that the student is familiar with some mathematical method of extracting square roots. The graphical method shown, however, will give results correct to three significant digits if carefully performed.

Areas, Graphically. Some problems in the earth sciences of physical geography require that areas of certain plane figures be determined. Examples include areas bounded by lines of equal elevations on maps, areas of storm systems, and areal studies of vegetation and soil. Where areas can be broken up into triangles and rectangles, the problem is merely one of simple mathematics. However, the areas described are usually bounded by curved lines and the method often suggested in introductory courses is to transfer the curve to a grid of some kind and "count squares." The method is laborious and subject to much error.

If a student has access to a balance such as used in chemistry courses, such areas can be quickly determined. The outline of the area is transferred to a piece of paper whose weight per square inch has been found by weighing, to milligrams, ten square inches of the same stock of paper and dividing by ten. The "area" is then cut out and also weighed to milligrams. Dividing this weight by the weight of the paper per square inch will give the number of square inches in the area.

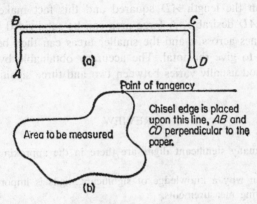

Fig. 4. Finding areas graphically. The bent wire shown in (a) is used to determine the area of a figure such as shown in (b).

For less precise determinations of area, a piece of heavy, stiff wire bent as shown in Figure 4 can be used. *AB* and *CD* are equal lengths from 1¼ to 1½ inches, while *BC* can be any length. A suggested length for *AD* is 10.0 inches. The end of the wire at *D* should be flattened out and filed or ground to a sharp edge. *D* is the center of the edge.

To find the area of a figure such as shown, a tangent line is drawn to the figure. The chisel edge is placed on this line and point *A* is placed over the point of tangency. Holding *AB* *lightly* between thumb and forefinger, end *A* is moved carefully around the figure, slightly above the paper, letting the chisel edge slide freely wherever it will. After the figure has been traced back to the starting point the perpendicular distance from the tangent line to the center of the chisel edge is measured. This distance multiplied by the length *AD* is theoretically equal to the number of square inches in the area. Right-handed people often find it convenient to place the chisel edge to the right of the diagram, on the tangent line, and to trace in a clockwise direction, holding AB between the thumb and forefinger of the left hand. Several readings should be made and averaged.

Even the wire of a paper clip bent in this manner, with one end smashed out to a chisel edge by a hammer blow, is capable of giving good results, but it must be carefully handled because of its light weight.

It will be seen that the area measured in one operation cannot be greater than the length AD squared and this fact makes a longer length for AD desirable. A large area can be subdivided by drawing a line or lines across it and the smaller areas can then be measured and added to give the total. The accuracy obtainable by the "bent wire" method usually varies between two and three significant digits.

REVIEW

1. How many significant digits are there in the approximate number .000367?

2. Explain why a knowledge of significant digits is important in any work involving measurements.

3. Explain the difference between specific gravity and density. How is each expressed?

4. Explain the difference between mass and weight.

5. Does a spring scale such as used in grocery stores for weighing vegetables, etc., measure weight, mass, or both? (Hint: Imagine the scale suddenly to be 1000 miles from the earth.)

6. Discuss the three methods of heat transfer.

7. Define "specific heat."

8. Explain how to obtain quickly the number of square miles in an irregular area shown on a map by (a) the chemist's balance method and (b) the bent wire method.

EXERCISES

(Answers are given in the answer section at the back of the book.)

1. Two sides of a rectangular area on a map are measured as 3.2 and 6.35 inches respectively. What is the area, in square inches?

2. Find the square root of 67,300 by the graphical method explained in this chapter.

3. Multiply 5320 by 69,500 by writing both numbers using powers of ten, and then using the graphical method of multiplication. Check your answer by mathematical multiplication.

4. Remembering the principle of significant digits, express the fraction $\frac{6.0}{9578}$ as a fraction having "1" as a numerator. Assume that both numerator and denominator of the original fraction are approximate numbers.

5. If exactly 1 cubic foot of air at a certain temperature can hold exactly 9 grains of water, but the relative humidity is actually 65 percent, how many grains of water does the air actually contain, per cubic foot?

6. Express both 3650 and 2,000,000 in scientific notation, and multiply them together. Express the product in scientific notation and also in the form of integers followed by zeros.

7. The specific gravity of a certain substance with relation to water is 4.00. Water weighs 62.4 pounds per cubic foot. What is the density of the substance?

8. In order for a body on the equator to become weightless a point on the equator would have to rotate with a velocity of approximately 25,800 feet per second. How many miles per hour is this? Use the exact relationship that a velocity of 88 feet per second is a velocity of 60 miles per hour.

CHAPTER 3

Shape and Size of the Earth: Latitude and Longitude

How Eratosthenes Measured the Earth

In the third century B.C., Eratosthenes, the librarian at the cultural center of Alexandria, devised a brilliant method for measuring the circumference of the earth. Having been informed that on a certain day each year the sun was directly overhead at Syene, south of Alexandria, Eratosthenes on that same day in Alexandria measured the angle made by the sun's noon rays with the vertical; the determination of this angle being based upon the height of a vertical stick and the length of its shadow. As nearly as Eratosthenes could determine with his crude field methods, the angle was one fiftieth of a circle. As is seen in Figure 5, this angle would also be equivalent to the

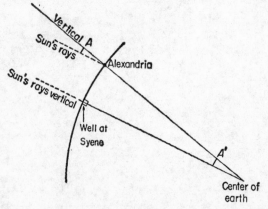

Fig. 5. The angle A at Alexandria equals the angle A' because they are corresponding angles formed by a line which intersects two parallel lines. (Not to scale)

angle at the center of the earth which subtends the distance on the earth's surface from Alexandria to Syene.

If the earth was a sphere, as he believed it was, Eratosthenes reasoned that this north-south distance was the arc of a great circle whose circumference was necessarily the circumference of the earth. The arc between Alexandria and Syene was one fiftieth of that circumference. All that was needed now was to determine the distance from Alexandria to Syene and multiply that figure by 50.

Eratosthenes calculated this distance with the help of the leaders of several camel caravans who had "logged" their journeys between Alexandria and Syene. Then, averaging time of actual travel between the two points, and observing the average speed of caravans on the outskirts of Alexandria, Eratosthenes multiplied the resulting values to obtain the distance from Alexandria to Syene. He then multiplied this figure by 50. His value for the circumference of the earth differs from the correct value of approximately 25,000 miles by little more than five percent, an astonishing accuracy considering the approximations he had to make. Since then, the method of Eratosthenes has become a basic procedure for geodetic measurements involving the size and shape of the earth. Today, however, due to our ability to determine longitude to a high degree of accuracy, the two points do not have to be on the same north-south line, and stars other than our sun are usually used.

The Earth Is an Oblate Spheroid

Spherical Appearance of the Earth. No one who has seen photographs of the earth taken from satellites can doubt that the earth is essentially spherical in shape. Actually, the earth's equatorial diameter is some 27 miles greater than its polar diameter due to a bulging in the equatorial region caused by the earth's rotation.

The Ellipsoidal Earth. If the earth happened to be homogenous, of the same density throughout, the form of the earth would be that of an *ellipsoid,* a solid figure whose cross sections are ellipses or circles.

The Earth as an Oblate Spheroid. However, the resulting solid is more nearly an *oblate spheroid.* Its variation from an ellipsoid, although physically slight, is of great scientific significance because this variation is caused by the fact that the earth's unit density increases toward the center of the earth.

The Equatorial Bulge. The effects of this bulging at the equator were detected in 1671 by Jean Richer, a French astronomer. Near the equator, in French Guiana, Richer noticed that his pendulum clock was losing a few minutes each day although it had been made by the best clockmakers in Paris. If the clock was not at fault, what was—gravity? That was Richer's conclusion. Gravity, for some reason, was weaker at the equator than it was in France. To many people this idea seemed preposterous until Isaac Newton's ideas became well known several years later: that the earth must bulge at the equator and therefore an object on the equator, being farther away from the earth's center, would have a lesser gravitational force acting upon it. What Richer and his clock had really discovered, then, was the equatorial bulge.

The prospect of an earth so "weak" that it actually deformed as it turned was alarming to many. More expeditions and investigations followed, and one party of famous French scientists finally "proved" by a remarkable series of faulty findings that the earth was egg-shaped, and longer in the north-south direction than in the east-west.

The scientific world then immediately split into two camps: those who supported the views of Richer and Newton, and those who favored the picture of an egg-shaped, ostensibly "stronger" earth. The Academy of Sciences of France, now in the middle of the dispute, sent an expedition to what is now Ecuador in 1735 and one to Lapland in 1736. Both expeditions, utilizing the basic method of Eratosthenes, measured north-south arcs and obtained the corresponding angles by astronomical observations. It was soon made clear to the world that the length of one degree of arc on the earth's surface increased as one went from the equator to the pole, and that the earth was in fact an oblate, or flattened, spheroid, the flattening being at the poles. (See Figure 6.)

The Oblateness of the Earth. The *oblateness* of the earth may be expressed mathematically as a fraction and is equal to the difference in lengths of the equatorial and polar diameters, divided by the equatorial diameter. The fraction is $\frac{27}{7927}$ or approximately $\frac{1}{300}$.

The internationally accepted value was $\frac{1}{297.3}$ until 1959 when the

U. S. Army Map Service calculated the value as $\frac{1}{298.24}$. As small as
the change may seem, it shows that the structural strength of the
earth as a whole is even greater than was formerly believed. (In the
outer zones of the earth, responses to stresses such as earthquake
shocks indicate an elastic strength equal to that of steel.)

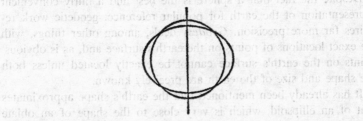

Fig. 6. The earth as an oblate spheroid. Deformation due to spinning is
much exaggerated in this diagram.

Satellites and the Shape of the Earth

Theoretical orbits of artificial earth satellites launched since 1959,
compared with their actual orbits, indicate that the long-held picture
of the earth as an almost perfect oblate spheroid has to be revised.
Near the north pole the earth's sea level is 50 feet higher than formerly believed, while the sea level in the Antarctic is 50 feet lower.
Other than in the polar regions, sea levels in the northern hemisphere
are 25 feet lower than previously believed, and sea levels in the
southern hemisphere are 25 feet higher. These variations all combine
with the spheroidal shape to give the earth a very faint suggestion of
a pear shape, the widest part of the "pear" being in the southern
hemisphere.

Apart from its importance to geodetic studies, this "new look" of
the earth has also been interpreted as being even more evidence, in
addition to that of the new value for the oblateness of the earth, that
the earth is far stronger structurally than previous estimates held.

It should be emphasized here that this "pear shape," and other
deviations of the earth from the form of a sphere, can be detected
only by very precise methods and that the earth's best popular representation, other than for purposes of advanced study, is that of a
globe. The 50-foot difference mentioned above would be indiscerni-
ble on a 2-foot diameter globe. Even Mt. Everest, almost 6 miles

above sea level, would, on the same globe, be a speck only $\frac{2}{100}$ inches high. The 27-mile difference between the equatorial and polar diameters would be represented by a length of $\frac{1}{10}$ inch.

The Geoid

Despite the fact that a sphere is the best and a fairly convenient representation of the earth for popular reference, geodetic work requires far more precision. *Geodesy* deals, among other things, with the exact locations of points on the earth's surface and, as is obvious, points on the earth's surface cannot be exactly located unless both the shape and size of the earth are precisely known.

It has already been mentioned that the earth's shape approximates that of an ellipsoid, which is very close to the shape of an oblate spheroid and thus is also very close to the actual shape of the earth. It will probably immediately occur to the reader that an ellipsoid would be a better reference for geodetic work than a sphere, and that an oblate spheroid would be better than both. This would be true if we knew the shape of the oblate spheroid. Lacking that knowledge, an assumption of the earth's shape can be made and then an ellipsoid, a relatively easily calculated figure, may be developed to represent the average surface of the earth. Ellipsoids—several, as will later be seen—have thus been calculated to represent the average surface of the earth.

The situation, however, in precisely mapping the earth is that we still do not know enough about the shape of the earth to be able to determine the exact positions of points in relation to any ellipsoid. An illustration of this is the fairly recent determination mentioned previously of the "pear shape" of the earth. We do know this, though: as Newton outlined and as Richer found out, the gravitational force between two objects decreases with distance and increases with increase in mass. Therefore, measuring the gravitational force at a point on the earth's surface should help to tell us two things: the distance from the center of the earth to that point, and the density of the rock mass in the region.

Now imagine that a geographer tries to do some precise surveying and mapping without taking into consideration the gravitational forces in that region. In other words, he is going to use the surface of the ellipsoid as a reference surface. He sets his surveying instrument over a point—which, let us assume, is directly on the ellipsoid surface—and observes the vertical angle to a star. As shown in Figure 7, his plumb bob is deflected toward the mountain mass according to

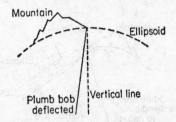

Fig. 7. Deflection of plumb bob due to mountain mass.

Newton's principle of gravitation and the angle he actually measures is not from a tangent to the ellipsoid assumed passing through his position but is from a line perpendicular to his plumb bob which does *not* now point toward the center of gravity of the ellipsoid.

Next, if some of the rock mass were now removed to form an ocean basin, so that the geographer is now on the edge of a continent, the plumb bob would swing even further toward the continent because the attraction of the less dense water on the plumb bob is less than the attraction of the removed rock. This is shown in Figure 8. It is thus seen that using only the ellipsoid as a reference base for

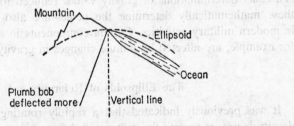

Fig. 8. Increased deflection of plumb bob due to relatively lighter weight of ocean water. Note depression of ocean surface below ellipsoid.

mapping or for astronomical observations will cause very serious errors under almost any conditions.

The reference surface that geodesists really want as a base is that of the *geoid,* a complex up-and-down surface formed by the hypothetical projection of sea level into the continental masses. Due to the attraction of those parts of the continental masses above mean sea level, the force of gravitation at the hypothetically projected sea level is lessened and the geoid surface beneath the continents rises above the surface of the ellipsoid as shown in Figure 9.

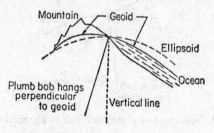

Fig. 9. The geoid and the ellipsoid.

This brings about a corresponding basin-like depression in the hypothetical surface of the geoid over the ocean basins as shown in the diagram. This latter is actually what happens physically. The continents with their excess of mass do pull the fluid, less-dense ocean water toward them and up, creating an actual "flattening" of sea level, below the ellipsoid, over ocean basins.

A plumb bob will always hang normal to the geoid surface. Therefore the shape of the geoid surface is of great importance in the fields of geodesy, astronomy, and geophysics. As will occur to some readers, exact determinations of gravity values reduced to sea level—and these mathematically determine the geoid—are also of importance in modern military activities. Certain components in missile systems, for example, are affected by minute changes in gravity.

The Ellipsoids of Reference

It was previously indicated that a rapidly rotating sphere whose density increases toward the center will deform to an oblate *spheroid* and that an ellipsoid can be calculated to give a close approximation to the shape of the spheroid.

At first glance it might seem that there is no problem: everyone is to agree on the shape of the oblate spheroid and therefore everyone will use the same ellipsoid of reference. That happens to be the exact difficulty. The calculated shape of a spheroid depends upon what hypothesis is used concerning its internal structure. If five people each use a different hypothesis, five different spheroids will result.

The resulting ellipsoids will then also all be different. Substituting the term "world regions" for "people" gives us the present condition: several different ellipsoids of reference used around the world. In 1924 the International Geodetic Congress in Madrid adopted one of these, the ellipsoid computed in 1910 by J. F. Hayford of the U. S. Coast and Geodetic Survey, as the *International Ellipsoid*.

Adoption of an "international ellipsoid" does not in itself solve the problem. For example, America has always used an ellipsoid calculated by Clarke in 1866; Great Britain has used several; Russia has used the ellipsoid of Krassovski since 1940; other countries have used others. Pulling these ellipsoids into a common shape, into a cartographic "one world" as it were, would be a tremendous task involving new maps for approximately half of the world's continental areas. It is much more practical, as is now being done, to maintain the already established ellipsoids and their maps, and to "bridge" between the International Ellipsoid and the other ellipsoids and their maps for which basic data is politically and otherwise available.

Effects of the Earth's Curvature

All natural phenomena studied in earth science, such as climate, weather, internal forces of the earth, etc., are accentuated or modified to varying degree by the earth's surface being essentially the surface of a sphere. Many of these effects of the earth's curvature will be discussed later, in their proper chapters. One effect should be discussed here.

To a person near or on the ocean, or traveling in an airplane on a clear day, one effect of the earth's curvature is very apparent: the horizon is not very far away. Even at an altitude of 30,000 feet, the approximate altitude of Mt. Everest, the horizon is only about 200 miles away. The horizon of a man standing on an ocean shore is about 3 miles distant from him. It is apparent that man's view of his immediate physical environment has, until very recently at least, always been severely limited even with optimum conditions of topography and vegetation. This fact, of course, played a key role in the history of man and of governments.

Figure 10 illustrates the physical effect and its cause. A surveying instrument is leveled and a horizontal line *AH,* perpendicular to the plumb bob, is established by the telescope of the instrument. However, a *level* line would actually be along the arc *AL* as any point on

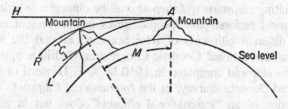

Fig. 10. The top of the mountain at the left appears to the surveyor on mountain *A* to be at the same elevation as his surveying level, but it is actually *"C"* feet higher in elevation.

AL would have the same elevation above sea level as the telescope of the instrument. Further, due to atmospheric refraction, the actual line of sight will not be along the horizontal line *AH* but will be below it, along the curve *AR*. The corrections for curvature and refraction are usually combined into one correction which can be expressed approximately by the formula $C = .57\ M^2$ where *C* is the correction in feet and *M* is the distance in miles between the two points. Examples of problems involving this relationship are given below:

Problem: A television camera is in a weather satellite which is orbiting the earth at a mean altitude of 400 miles above the earth's surface. Several pictures taken by the camera show the horizon. Assuming that the combined correction for curvature and refraction can be expressed by $C = .57\ M^2$ for a photograph showing the horizon, how far away was the horizon from the satellite?

Solution: The "correction" for curvature and refraction is here the satellite's altitude in feet: $400 \times 5280 = 2,100,000$ feet, approximately. $M^2 = \dfrac{2,100,000}{.57} = 3,700,000$ feet, approximately. (Notice the use of the significant digits principle which materially shortens the calculations.) The square root of 3,700,000 is approximately 1900. (See *Square Roots* in Chapter 2.) The horizon in the photograph was therefore approximately 1900 miles from the satellite when the picture was taken.

NOTE: The approximate value of $C = .57\ M^2$ is based upon average refraction for average observations made in the lower part of the atmosphere but it is used in this problem to familiarize the student with its numerical value. The answer of 1900 obtained above is within 5 percent of the true value, however.

Problem: The objective lens of a submarine periscope is approximately 6 feet above the surface of the ocean. With his line of sight tangent to the ocean horizon, an observer at the periscope notices that the line of sight is also almost tangent to the top of a small island on the other side of the horizon. If the island is known to be approximately 150 feet high, how far is it from the submarine?

Solution: The distance to the horizon from the submarine, M, in miles, is equal to the square root of $\frac{6}{.57}$, or 3 miles, plus. The distance from the ocean horizon to the island, in miles, equals the square root of $\frac{150}{.57}$, or 16 miles, plus.

Adding the two distances together gives the total distance from the submarine to the island: 19 miles, plus. Considering the degree of approximation of the quantities and observations involved, the distance would be expressed as "approximately 20 miles."

Latitude and Longitude

Longitude. If planes are passed through a sphere, the curves formed by the intersections of the plane and the sphere are circles. If planes are passed through the *center* of a sphere, the curves formed are *great circles,* the largest possible circles that can be constructed on that sphere. Great circles which pass over the poles of the earth, considering the earth as a sphere, are thus divided into half-circles called *meridians*. An infinite number of meridians can be constructed on a sphere. On the earth, these meridians are lines of *longitude*. (See Figure 11.)

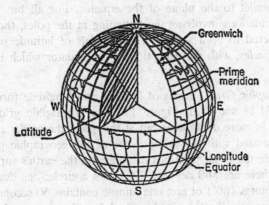

Fig. 11. Latitude and longitude. (Adapted from the Department of the Army)

At this point it may occur to the reader, after having considered the earth as an ellipsoid, oblate spheroid, and geoid, that it is now somewhat of an analytical retreat to consider the earth as a sphere again, the shape which we definitely know it does not assume. Actually, the earth's shape is so close to that of a perfect sphere that the only major differences between the shape of a circle and that of the earth's true cross section occur in the polar regions. These differences, as will be recalled, are due to the "flattening" at the poles and thus have nothing to do with the east-west positioning of the meridians, or lines of longitude.

The *prime meridian,* at 0° longitude, passes through Greenwich, England. Directly opposite it, on the other side of the globe, is the meridian whose longitude is 180°. All other meridians have values between 0° and 180° and are also designated as being either east or west of the prime meridian. The longitude of a point is the angle, measured in a plane parallel to that of the equator, between the prime meridian and the point. As is seen in Figure 11, all points on the same meridian have the same longitude.

Latitude. In view of the above, it is obvious that if only the longitude of a point is known, the point could be anywhere between the north and south poles, on a certain meridian. If the angular distance of the point north or south of the equator is known, however, this, in conjunction with its longitude, would fix the point. The angular distance north or south of the equator is a point's *latitude.* So-called *parallels* of latitude are formed by passing planes through the "earth-sphere" parallel to the plane of the equator. For all but the most refined calculations involving the flattening at the poles, the earth is still considered to be a sphere. The parallels of latitude so formed are *small circles,* with the exception of the equator which is a *great circle.*

The Geographic Grid. Lines of latitude and longitude form a *geographic grid* as shown in Figure 11. The geographic grid will be referred to in more detail later but at this point the reader should be made acquainted with the primary use of the geographic grid, that of describing the exact positions of points on the earth's surface.

Briefly, there are 360 degrees (360°) in a circle; one degree contains 60 minutes (60′) of arc; one minute contains 60 seconds (60″) of arc. A point's location is described in this manner: Longitude 118° 20′ 35″ W, latitude 34° 19′ 58″ N. The grid itself, being of geometrically perfect construction, is precise. If the latitude and longitude are determined to the nearest second, a point's location—theoretically at least—is known to within 150 feet of its true position.

Lengths of Arcs on the Earth's Surface.   It will be apparent from Figure 11 that the arc length between two given meridians is a maximum at the equator and diminishes to nothing at the poles. On the other hand the meridional arc lengths between successive parallels of latitude spaced, say, 15° apart will change very little, the change being due mainly to the flattening at the poles. The actual differences seem inconsequential: the arc length of 1 minute of latitude at the equator being only about 60 feet less than the arc length of 1 minute of latitude at a pole, both being about 6100 feet in length.

The *nautical mile* was determined by measuring arcs at certain latitudes on the earth's surface and, very closely, 1′ of longitude measured in the plane of the equator equals 1 nautical mile on the surface. The nautical mile is also, very closely, the average length of arc of 1 minute of latitude. The nautical mile is approximately equivalent to 1.15 statute miles; or 1 statute mile is approximately equal to .870 nautical miles. The nautical mile also equals 6076.10333 (the 3 "repeats") feet or precisely 1852 meters. (The meter itself was originally intended to be one ten-millionth of the distance from a pole to the equator, measured along a meridian.)

Great Circle Routes.   If latitude and longitude are known for two points on the earth's surface, a *great circle route* can easily be calculated between the points. Arcs of great circles represent the shortest surface distance between two points on a sphere and are used in navigation and in similar activities.

On a globe, the great circle route between two points can be determined by stretching an elastic band between the points and then lightly "flicking" the band so that it will adjust itself into its position of least strain, which will be along the shortest route and thus along the arc of a great circle. This simple procedure also emphatically demonstrates that the shortest surface path between two points having the same latitude is not along that parallel of latitude, unless the two points are on the equator. Even then the flattening at the poles and the equatorial bulge must be considered for precise determination of the shortest distance between two widely separated points. For example, the shortest route between two points on the equator, but whose longitudes are 180° apart, would be over a pole.

REVIEW

1. Explain how Eratosthenes measured the earth.

2. Explain the "equatorial bulge."

3. Who was Jean Richer? How were his observations related to ideas expressed by Sir Isaac Newton?

4. Differentiate between "sphere," "oblate spheroid," "ellipsoid," and "geoid."

5. Explain why several ellipsoids of reference have been calculated as an approximation of the earth's shape.

6. Discuss a course of events in history which would have been altered if the earth's curvature were such that men with telescopes could have seen advancing armies and ships 100 miles distant.

7. Define "latitude" and "longitude." How is each measured? In what units?

8. Define "great circle course." Along what parallel of latitude can one travel a great circle course, assuming the earth to be a sphere?

EXERCISES

(Answers are given in the answer section at the back of the book.)

1. Assuming the average width of the United States, measured along a great circle, to be 3000 miles, what fraction of the earth's circumference does this represent?

2. The oblateness of the earth is mathematically described in the approximate fraction $\frac{1}{300}$. Express the oblateness in percent.

3. State what your answer to (2), above, means.

4. How far away is the ocean horizon for an astronaut in an earth-orbiting space vehicle whose altitude is 150 miles?

5. How many seconds of arc are there in one degree of arc?

6. A man whose eyes are 25′ above sea level is standing on a seashore cliff. His line of sight is tangent to the horizon so that he can just see, on the side of the horizon, the top of an island. If the island is 15 miles distant from the man, what is the elevation of the top of the island?

CHAPTER 4

Map Projections and Map Grids

What Map Projections Are

A map *projection* is a representation of all or a number of the earth's parallels and meridians, drawn on a plane surface. The pattern formed by the lines of longitude and latitude of a particular projection is called the *map grid*. Ideally a map projection should show true areas, true sizes, and true directions and distances between points but no one projection shows all of these. The reason, of course, is that the surface of a globe cannot be peeled off and made into a flat surface, any more than a flat sheet of paper can be fitted around a globe, without wrinkles, bulges, and overlaps.

Some map projections are true projections in that they can be constructed by drafting procedures alone. Other projections are both graphical and mathematical, while others are purely mathematical. As a matter of fact, even if a particular projection can be obtained by purely graphical means, it is much more convenient to plot it by using mathematical tables. In many instances, however, the chief characteristics of a particular map projection can at least be illustrated by a graphical projection.

There are many possible map projections and the mathematics of map projection is often fairly complex. This section of the book is designed to give the reader a nonmathematical working knowledge of several important map projections.

How to Analyze Map Projections

Before even studying map projections it is very easy to determine most of the faults and virtues of any projection used on a map which shows an extensive portion of the earth's surface. Then, if the type of projection used is stated on the map, we can immediately arrive at most of the characteristics of that projection.

How are the characteristics of a particular projection determined from a map? The *geographic grid,* consisting of lines of longitude and latitude, was explained in Chapter 3. Any distortion of this grid—and at least one kind of a distortion must occur in any projection—results in a distortion of size or shape or direction, or distance, or a combination of these. Therefore, by inspecting the changes in the grid, we can deduce, for any particular projection, what is happening to sizes and shapes of land masses and ocean basins, and what is happening to directions and distances.

The first step, then, is to determine the characteristics of the geographic grid as it exists on the sphere. From Figure 11 of Chapter 3, and assuming the earth to be a perfect sphere, the following listed facts are evident:

1. All lines of longitude intersect all lines of latitude at right angles.

2. All lines of longitude are of equal length.

3. All lines of longitude converge toward the poles and meet at the poles.

4. All lines of latitude are parallel.

5. The circumferences of all lines of latitude decrease in length from the equator toward the poles.

6. The distance between two given lines of latitude, measured along a meridian, is the same all over the world.

7. The distance between a given difference in longitude, measured along the same parallel, is the same all over the world.

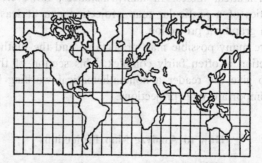

Fig. 12. Mercator projection, from latitude 60° south to latitude 78° north. (Adapted from the U. S. Department of Commerce, Coast and Geodetic Survey)

Consider, now, the Mercator projection illustrated in Figure 12. The grid of this particular projection does not agree with items 3 and 5. Therefore, land masses and ocean basins are stretched both north and south, and east and west, the distortions becoming greater as the poles are approached. This projection therefore does not show true distance except in one instance: it should be noted that this would apparently be a satisfactory projection for regions on the equator.

If distance is distorted on this projection, then it might seem reasonable to assume that the direction between two points on the earth's surface will also change. This, however, is an assumption and it happens that one of the things that the Mercator projection does preserve is the direction between points on the earth's surface.

Map Projection Classification

Map projections in general may be classified in two ways: according to the related geometry of their construction, and according to their most evident desirable characteristics such as the preservation of areas, distances, etc. According to their actual or approximate geometry, many map projections can be described as *cylindrical, conic,* or as *flat plane* projections. In the cylindrical projections, the earth's spherical grid is considered to be projected upon a cylinder tangent to, or intersecting, the earth. The conic projections are based upon the earth's grid being projected upon a cone or cones tangent to, or intersecting, the earth. The flat plane projections result when the earth's grid is projected upon a flat plane.

As formerly expressed, the second general classification of projections is based upon those desirable characteristics preserved by the projection. Thus we have *equal-area* projections; equal shape, or *conformal* projections; *azimuthal* projections; and *equidistant* projections. As already stated, no one map projection can possibly have all of the above desirable characteristics. However, many map projections have more than one of these characteristics to high degrees of precision and have others to lesser degree. On the other hand, some projections are a complete compromise between all major characteristics. The Van der Grinten projection, for example, is not conformal, equal-area, azimuthal, or equidistant. It is very pleasing to the eye, however, and is much used for presentation of data. A Van der Grinten projection is used in Figures 52, 53, and 64 of this book. It can be said that any kind of map projection is some kind of a compromise and that the choice of a projection depends upon what features are the most important to preserve in a particular map. For example, certain projections are better suited for certain areas. Some projections are better for areas whose longest dimensions are essentially east-west while other projections are used for states whose longest dimensions are approximately north-south.

Explanation of "Equal-Area," "Conformal," "Azimuthal," and "Equidistant." The term *equal-area* signifies that a projection having this characteristic shows equivalent specified areas in any part of the map. The meaning of this can best be grasped by imagining a map, say a world map, spread out upon a table. Now imagine a penny placed somewhere on the map representation of India while another penny is placed somewhere on the map representation of Canada. If the map is "equal-area," the *ground area* beneath both pennies, in square miles, must be equal. This is true for any positioning of any number of pennies, if the map is a true equal-area map.

"Conformal" means that small areas shown on a projection must *conform,* or show the same shape as on a globe. This brings up this point: suppose that the coastlines of a hypothetical small island coincide with two meridians and two parallels, that is, two coastlines are east-west and two are north-south. If the island is to be shown in true shape, then the projection used obviously must have its meridians and parallels intersecting at right angles, a feature of conformal maps. The fact that a projection's meridians and parallels intersect at right angles does not, however, necessarily mean that the projection is conformal. It is possible, for example, to stretch a rectangular piece of rubber so that, while its sides are still perpendicular to each other, its shape is considerably altered.

"Azimuthal" means that a line drawn from a central point of the projection to any other point will have the same direction as the line has on the earth. The term *zenithal* is often used to describe this type of projection. The feature of being able to determine correct directions from just one point to other points may seem to make azimuthal projections of little general use. It so happens, however, that some projections designed chiefly to show equal-area or other features are automatically also azimuthal in character.

"Equidistant" projections are those in which the distances in a particular direction or along a particular line are exactly proportional to their corresponding distances on the ground. Some equidistant maps are equidistant along parallels and some are equidistant along meridians while others are equidistant along great circles, etc. Some readers will recognize that "equidistant" along certain lines means that the scale is constant along these lines. The subject of map scale is discussed in Chapter 5.

Cylindrical Projections

One type of cylindrical projection is easily visualized by assuming that a translucent cylinder is tangent to the earth, also translucent, at the equator and that a light at the center of the earth or at some other position projects the shadow of the geographic grid onto the cylinder. The shadows of the lines of latitude and longitude, traced onto the outside of the cylinder, constitute the projection. In this, and in all geometric projections, the reader must imagine that the resulting projection is between himself and the light source. The cylinder is then unrolled to make a flat map. A second type of cylindrical projection is made by intersecting the cylinder by the planes of the parallels as well as those of the meridians. Two other types of cylindrical projection involve arbitrary spacing of the parallels.

The Mercator Projection

The Mercator projection (Figure 12) is a mathematically derived projection. It can, however, be explained in terms of a general cylindrical projection relationship.

The cylindrical projection, as described above, results in an east-west stretching which becomes greater as the poles are approached. At latitude 60°, for example, the distance between two given meridians, measured along a parallel, is only half the distance between the same meridians, measured at the equator. So, on a cylindrical map, with its parallel meridians, a land mass at latitude 60° will appear to be twice its actual east-west length.

Now suppose that we wish to preserve the shape of a small area. The situation is much like that of partially inflating a balloon (the earth) and drawing, say, a small triangle (land mass) on it, and then cutting out a "square" of rubber which has the triangle on it. If we stretch the rubber one inch in an east-west direction, it also has to be stretched one inch in a north-south direction in order to preserve the shape of the triangle as much as possible. This, in effect, was what Mercator—his real name was Gerhard Krämer—did in 1569. He stretched his map just as far north and south at a particular latitude as the cylindrical projection pulled it east and west at that latitude.

What may seem to have been a more or less mechanical procedure on Mercator's part is actually fairly complicated, the actual amount of "stretching" at a particular location being dependent upon a number of factors. For instance, when curved pieces of rubber are stretched as described above, wrinkles, bulges, depression, and overlaps develop. These were some of the things that Mercator had to iron out mathematically. It should be pointed out, however, that areas within 10° of the equator are automatically mapped very well on the Mercator projection.

The Mercator projection, like the true cylindrical projection, cannot of course show the poles and, due to the tremendous scale change in high latitudes, is usually carried only to about the 80° latitudes. The Mercator is popularly used as a world map even though it is in general extremely misleading from the standpoint of area size. For example, Greenland on a Mercator projection appears to be larger than South America. Actually South America is eight times larger than Greenland.

In that the map shapes of small areas on the Mercator projection are similar to their global shapes, the Mercator is a conformal projection. It is not an equal area projection. The chief virtue of the Mercator projection is that a *rhumb line,* or *loxodrome,* a line which intersects all meridians at the same angle, appears on the Mercator as a straight line. The great use of the Mercator projection described is therefore in navigation, as, to get from one place to another, all a navigator has to do is to keep on the same bearing. For long distances, however, the use of the Mercator is combined with that of another type of map, as will be explained below.

Flat Plane, or Azimuthal, Projections

The flat plane projections are usually called *azimuthal,* or *zenithal,* projections. Neither term describes the actual or approximate geometry of the projection, which may be referred to as projecting the earth's grid onto a flat translucent plane. Again, the earth is considered to be a translucent, hollow sphere with the grid painted upon it. The light source may be in the center of the sphere, or some distance from the earth. The translucent flat plane may be tangent to the earth, or some distance from it or it may intersect the earth. The center of a flat plane projection is the center of the particular circle bounding the entire projection. Directions measured from this point to any other point will be true bearings at that point, hence the name "azimuthal," the term "azimuth" referring to direction. This is discussed in detail in Chapter 5.

The Gnomonic Projection. A *gnomonic* projection is a so-called "central" projection in that the light source is at the center of the earth. Figure 13 illustrates a gnomonic projection with the plane of projection tangent at the equator.

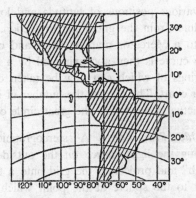

Fig. 13. Gnomonic projection of part of the western hemisphere. (Adapted from the U. S. Department of Commerce, Coast and Geodetic Survey)

It is seen that the meridians on the gnomonic projection are straight lines. This is because the intersection of two planes is a straight line. The intersections referred to are those of each meridional plane with the plane of projection. Similarly, *all* great circles will appear as straight lines, on the gnomonic projection.

It will be noticed that the lines of latitude in Figure 13 are curved with the exception of the equator. This effect, which is common to all gnomonic projections, is also a common, everyday sight: a lamp whose shade has circular openings at the top and bottom throws shadows upon a nearby wall in true gnomonic projection. The light bulb represents the light at the center of the earth while the edges of the upper and lower openings in the shade represent parallels of latitude in the northern and southern hemispheres, respectively.

The gnomonic and Mercator projections are combined in navigation. As a great circle is the shortest distance between two points on the earth's surface, great circle courses are commonly followed, as far as practicable, by transoceanic ships, and airplanes on long flights. A great circle, as explained above, appears on the gnomonic projection as a straight line. However, the gnomonic projection gives true directions only at its center. On the other hand, a true-course line on the Mercator projection appears as a straight line, while a great circle other than a meridian appears as a curved line on the Mercator projection. A great circle course on the gnomonic will therefore, except in the case of meridians, appear as a curve on the Mercator.

In navigation, the great circle course is laid out on the gnomonic projection and various positions of latitude and longitude are read off the straight line, from the gnomonic projection. These positions are transferred to a Mercator map or chart and connected with a curved line. The curve is then approximated by a series of straight chords, the bearings of which can now be taken directly from the Mercator map or chart. The greater the number of chords, the more closely will the actual route follow the great circle course.

The Stereographic Projections. A stereographic projection is formed by holding the light source *on* the outside surface of the translucent "earth" and projecting the grid onto a translucent plane which is tangent to the sphere at the point which is diametrically opposite from the light source; that is, on the same diameter and on the opposite side of the sphere. (The reader is reminded that the resulting grid is considered to be traced onto the *outside* of the translucent plane, the plane being between the observer and the "earth.") The polar case of the stereographic projection is illustrated in Figure 14.

The characteristics of the polar stereographic projection can be understood by holding one hand like a "claw," palm toward you, the back of the hand close to a door or wall. The curved fingers represent lines of latitude or longitude. Hold a flashlight near the middle of the hand and project the "grid" onto the wall. Note the increase in size of the shadows toward the edges. Also note that the shadows of the fingers become increasingly more widely spaced as the edges of the "projection" are approached, the spaces between the shadows of the fingers becoming disproportionately wider than the actual spaces between the fingers. This explains the increase in size of the land masses shown in Figure 14 as the edge of the projection is approached. (In this experiment, the observer is of course viewing the "grid" in reverse.) The equatorial case of the stereographic projec-

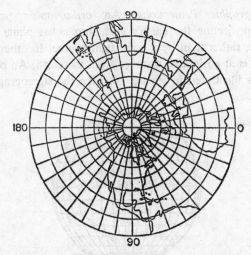

Fig. 14. Polar stereographic projection. (Adapted from the U. S. Department of Commerce, Coast and Geodetic Survey)

tion is shown in Figure 15. There are also *oblique stereographic* projections, in which the light source is at any position other than at a pole or on the equator.

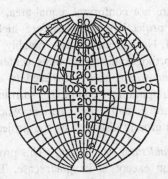

Fig. 15. Stereographic projection of the western hemisphere. (Adapted from the U. S. Department of Commerce, Coast and Geodetic Survey)

The stereographic projections are azimuthal in that true directions can be measured from the center point of the projection to any other point. They are conformal, small areas on the map being the same shape as the same small areas on the globe. The stereographic projections are not equal-area, nor are they equidistant except for small distances.

The Orthographic Projections. An *orthographic* projection is formed by projecting the earth's grid onto a flat plane by *parallel rays* of light, rather than by a point light source. In other words, the light source is at an infinite distance from the earth. An orthographic projection is illustrated in Figure 16. Like the stereographic projec-

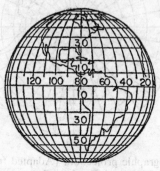

Fig. 16. Orthographic projection of the western hemisphere. (Adapted from the U. S. Department of Commerce, Coast and Geodetic Survey)

tions, orthographic projections can be of the polar, the equatorial, or the oblique case. The orthographic projections are azimuthal, of course, but they are not conformal, equal-area, or equidistant. Certain orthographic projections are therefore highly misleading. Before World War II, Nazi propagandists, notably Major General Karl Haushofer, used orthographic projections centered on Germany as "proof" that Germany was being squeezed to death by ominously large nations which apparently completely surrounded Germany. The "large" nations were actually small nations whose sizes and actual positions had been grossly distorted by the projection used.

The Azimuthal Equidistant Projection. This projection is not a true geometric projection except in its polar case. The equatorial cases and the oblique cases are computed. An oblique case of this projection is shown in Figure 17. The azimuthal equidistant projection is equidistant along lines drawn from the center of the projection, as these lines represent great circles. The projection is not equidistant along the parallels, nor is it equal-area.

Lambert's Azimuthal Equal-Area Projection. This projection is the most important of the azimuthal projections. It also has a polar, an

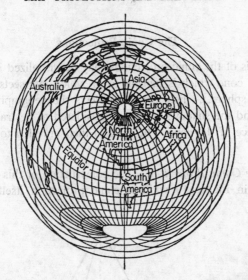

Fig. 17. Azimuthal equidistant projection of the world. (Adapted from the General Electric Company)

equatorial, and an oblique case. The polar case can be constructed geometrically. The equatorial and oblique cases are computed. The equatorial case of this projection is shown in Figure 18. The projection itself is azimuthal and equal-area. It is not conformal and it is not equidistant.

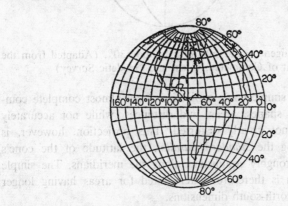

Fig. 18. Lambert equal-area projection of the western hemisphere. (Adapted from the U. S. Department of Commerce, Coast and Geodetic Survey)

The Conic Projections

The basis of the conic projections may be visualized in terms of a translucent cone which is tangent to or which intersects the translucent earth sphere. A light source projects the geographic grid onto the cone and the shadows are then considered to be traced onto the outer surface of the cone. The cone is then unrolled to make a flat plane.

The Simple Conic Projection. The construction of this projection is illustrated in Figure 19 while a conic projection itself appears in

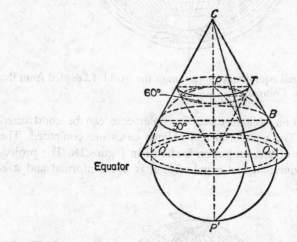

Fig. 19. Cone tangent to the sphere at latitude 30°. (Adapted from the U. S. Department of Commerce, Coast and Geodetic Survey)

Figure 20. The simple conic projection is an almost complete compromise in that shapes, areas, and distances, while not accurately preserved, are not greatly distorted. This projection, however, is equidistant along the *standard parallel,* the latitude of the cone's tangency. It is roughly equidistant along the meridians. The simple conic projection is therefore better suited for areas having longer east-west than north-south dimensions.

The Polyconic Projection. The construction of the polyconic projection is illustrated in Figure 21. Instead of one cone, many, or *poly,*

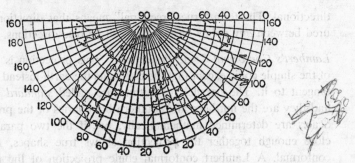

Fig. 20. Central perspective projection on cone tangent at latitude 30°. (Adapted from the U. S. Department of Commerce, Coast and Geodetic Survey)

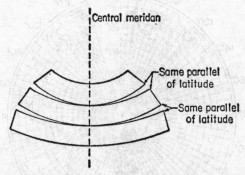

Fig. 21. Why the polyconic projection continually changes scale in a north-south direction as the projection is carried to the east and west. Notice that there is no scale change along the central meridian.

cones are used and the resulting grid strips tied together mathematically. It will be seen from Figure 21 that the resulting east-west grid strips become more and more separated to the east and west of the central meridian of the projection. The polyconic projection should therefore be used for areas having greater north-south than east-west dimensions.

The polyconic projection is a compromise projection. It is equidistant along the central meridian. The polyconic projection is used by the U. S. Geological Survey for its well-known topographic maps. Within the confines of one of these quadrangles, which represents a rough square of ground from 7½ to 60 miles on a side, the projection may be *considered* to be conformal, equal-area, equidistant, and true-directional. The term "true-directional" means that directions measured between *any* points on the map will be true directions.

Lambert's Conformal Conic Projection. This projection is like that of the simple conic except that the cone cuts the earth instead of being tangent to it. The parallels of cutting are called *standard parallels* and they are the northern and southern boundaries of the projection. Scales are determined mathematically, but if the two parallels are close enough together the projection shows true shapes, hence is conformal. A Lambert conformal conic projection of the northern hemisphere is illustrated in Figure 22.

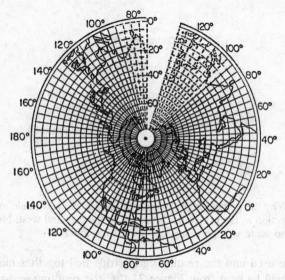

Fig. 22. Lambert conformal conic projection, northern hemisphere, with standard parallels at 30° and 75°. (Adapted from the U. S. Department of Commerce, Coast and Geodetic Survey)

Other Projections

Many map projections have been devised, some of which are valuable contributions to cartography and some of which seem to be of little practical use. The projections which have been described in detail in this chapter are only some of the most used projections. Some others are briefly described below.

The Transverse Mercator Projection. If the transparent cylinder referred to in the discussion of the Mercator projection is tangent to a meridian, rather than the equator, the resulting transverse projection will possess very good properties of area and shape near the meridian, just as the regular Mercator projection maps areas within 10° of the equator with very little distortion. So, if the cylinder is now rotated about the earth's polar axis, the whole world can thus be mapped in narrow north-south strips which are then joined mathematically. The transverse Mercator projection, made essentially in this manner, is also mathematically made conformal.

The Transverse Mercator Projection and the Military Grid. One type of *transverse Mercator* projection makes use of a cylinder cutting slightly into the earth, rather than being tangent to it. The scale is therefore the same along two lines which are parallel to the central meridian and equidistant from it. These lines differ in longitude by about 6°. For *military grid zone* purposes the latitudinal boundaries are 8° apart while the meridians mapped are therefore 6° apart. For military mapping, and as done by the U. S. Army Map Service, between 80° south latitude and 84° north latitude the world is divided into areas which measure 6° east-west and 8° north-south. The columns are numbered 1 through 60 starting from the 180° meridian and progressing eastward. The 8° rows are lettered by starting at 80° south and proceeding to 84° north, using the letters C through X, I and O omitted. As an example, the military grid reference system (MGRS) designation of the Fort Knox, Kentucky, area is 16*S*. The grid system associated with the above described military use of the transverse Mercator projection is called the Universal Transverse Mercator (UTM) military grid.

Military Use of the Polar Stereographic Projection. The Polar stereographic projection is used by the U. S. Army Map Service for the regions of from 80° S to the south pole, and from 84° N to the north pole. A military grid system also using squares, as in the case of the Universal Transverse Mercator grid, is employed in conjunction with the projection to form the *Universal Polar Stereographic Grid.*

Other popular projections are the *sinusoidal* (Figure 23), the *Mollweide homolographic* (Figure 24), and *Aitoff's equal-area* projection (Figure 25). For discussion of these and other projections, the reader is directed to the references dealing with map projection, in the bibliography.

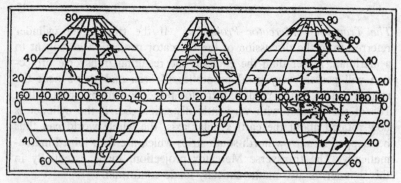

Fig. 23. Sinusoidal or Mercator equal-area projection. (Adapted from the U. S. Department of Commerce, Coast and Geodetic Survey)

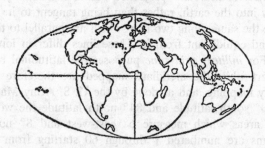

Fig. 24. The Mollweide homolographic projection of the sphere. (Adapted from the U. S. Department of Commerce, Coast and Geodetic Survey)

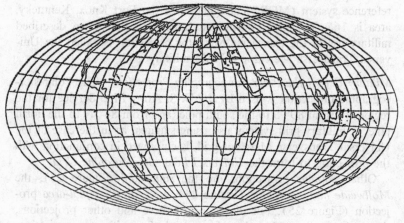

Fig. 25. Aitoff's equal-area projection of the sphere. (Courtesy of the U. S. Department of Commerce, Coast and Geodetic Survey)

The United States Public Land Survey

In addition to its inclusion on the military grid, much of the United States has been mapped on what might be called a civilian grid. The system of subdivision to be described originated in Congress in 1784 and has been little changed since then. The system, a so-called rectangular system, is based upon the laying out of near-squares in all directions from an *initial point* whose precise latitude and longitude are known. These near-squares are laid off in one direction until they meet the near-squares coming the other way, which were laid off from another initial point.

To start, through each initial point a *principal meridian,* a true north-south line, and a *base line* in a true east-west direction are established. The base line is kept perpendicular to *all* meridians. Next, lengths of 24 miles are measured along the principal meridian and along the base line. True parallels of latitude are constructed through the 24-mile points on the principal meridian. These parallels are called *standard parallels,* as in projections. Points 24 miles apart are placed on the standard parallels. Through each one of these points a *guide meridian* is constructed. Referring to Figure 26 it will

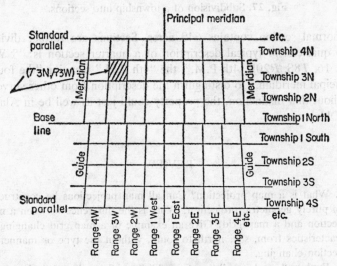

Fig. 26. Townships and ranges, United States Public Land Survey. Convergence of meridians accentuated for clarity.

be seen that each guide meridian is actually a series of meridian segments due to the fact that all meridians converge toward the pole.

Each 24-mile block is then divided into 16 blocks called *townships*. A township measures 6 miles, more or less, on a side. Vertical rows of townships are called *ranges,* while horizontal rows are called by the same name and are *township* rows. Ranges are numbered consecutively to the east and west of the principal meridian while township rows are numbered to the north and south of the base line. (See Figure 26.) In descriptions, range is designated by *R* and township by *T.*

Each township is divided into 36 sections, numbered as shown in Figure 27. Each section is therefore one mile, more or less, on a side.

6	5	4	3	2	1
7	8	9	10	11	12
18	17	16	15	14	13
19	20	21	22	23	24
30	29	28	27	26	25
31	32	33	34	35	36

Fig. 27. Subdivision of a township into sections.

A normal section contains 640 acres. Sections are further divided into quarters. A typical description of a quarter section is: "NW¼ Sec. 16, *T*8S, *R*20E, 4th P.M.", the "4th P.M." meaning "the fourth principal meridian," to distinguish the description from other surveys. Without that distinction, the property could just as well be in Alaska or Oklahoma.

REVIEW

1. What is a map projection? Can all map projections be constructed from purely geometric projection? What is the difference between a map projection and a map grid? Give an example of a map grid changing its characteristics from, say, north to south, without the type or manner of projection changing.

2. Explain "equal-area," "conformal," "equidistant," and "azimuthal," with respect to map projections.

3. Explain how the existence or absence of some of the characteristics listed in (2), above, can be quickly determined for a particular map.

4. What is the chief virtue of a regular Mercator projection?

5. Explain how the Mercator and gnomonic projections are used together in navigation.

6. Explain how stereographic projections are made. What are their desirable characteristics?

7. For what kind of areas are simple conic projections used; polyconic projections? Name one popular use of the polyconic projection.

8. Explain how the transverse Mercator projection is made. For what is it used?

9. Discuss the United States Land Survey system, ending with the subdivision of sections.

EXERCISES

(Answers will be found in the answer section at the back of the book.)

NOTE: All exercises given below, with the exception of Exercise 7, may be worked graphically. See Chapter 2.

1. A straight line on a certain Mercator map makes a smaller angle of 70° with a meridian at a point whose latitude is 35° N and whose longitude is 140° W. At what smaller angle will the line cross the 180° meridian?

2. A certain polar stereographic projection has a diameter of 30 inches and shows the entire northern hemisphere. What are the map distances, in inches, between the circles representing the 20° parallel and the 10° parallel, and between the circles representing the 10° parallel and the equator?

3. Repeat Problem 2, but for a polar orthographic projection whose diameter is 30 inches. Compare the results with those of Problem 2. Which projection therefore compresses land masses which are nearer the equator?

4. For a certain simple conic projection, the cone is tangent at the 30° parallel. Suppose that you are to make such a cone out of a circular piece of paper by cutting out a wedge-shaped piece and then bringing together the edges of the remaining piece. What fraction of the circular piece of paper will be used to make the cone?

5. What is the Military Grid Reference System designation of the square which contains a point whose latitude is 45° N and whose longitude is 115° W?

6. What is the straight-line distance in miles between the SW corner

54   PHYSICAL GEOGRAPHY

of Sec. 31, *T*2S, *R*4E and the SW corner of Sec. 31, *T*3N, *R*7E? Assume a perfectly rectangular system, with no convergence of meridians.

7. A transverse Mercator projection cylinder "intersects the earth" to form vertical strips which are about 6° wide, as explained in this chapter. Assuming the earth to be a perfect sphere whose radius is 3960 miles, what is the radius of the cylinder?

CHAPTER 5

Map Fundamentals

The most-used tools of the geographer are maps. The science of map-making is called *cartography*. In the office, one of the cartographer's most important duties is to determine the kind of map projection to use to map a particular area. In the field, the cartographer must be able to establish a grid system or to utilize an already existing grid system and to make his map fit into it. As has been pointed out in Chapter 4, the type of local grid system employed is governed by the type of projection used for an area.

Maps may be broadly classified as either *planimetric* or *topographic*. Planimetric maps show only the *plan* view of features in an area while topographic maps, discussed in Chapter 21, also show topography, or relief.

Horizontal Control

Whether a map is of the planimetric or topographic type, the points on the map must be correctly located on some kind of a planimetric grid. If a grid system already exists on the ground as well as on paper, the mapper already has points of *horizontal control*, points whose positions in some coordinate system are known.

Triangulation. Horizontal control is of *first* order, *second* order, *third* order, or of lower accuracy, depending upon the degree of refinement used to establish it. The most widely used method of extending horizontal control has been that of *triangulation*. If the coordinates of A and B, in Figure 28, are known, the distance AB is also known or can be calculated. Horizontal angles at either end of *base line* AB are measured to point C, a new point. The triangle ABC is solved by trigonometry and the coordinates of C are calculated. Now using both AC and BC as base lines, points D and E can

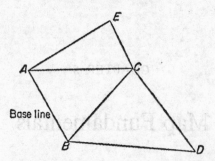

Fig. 28. Triangulation proceeding from the base line *AB*.

be established. As seen, the establishment of each new point gives two new base lines, and the work proceeds in this manner. Most triangulation nets really become *quadrilateral* nets, the quadrilateral being the base figure used for adjustment of errors, etc.

In the cases where horizontal control must be established in areas which are a considerable distance from any actual ground points of a grid system, a base line may be constructed by measurement. Local control is then established as above and referenced to some grid system at a later date. In some situations it is necessary for a geographer or explorer to determine latitude and longitude by astronomical observations, determine the direction of true north by the same methods, and then proceed with his mapping or with his establishment of control.

When the United States began its federal control surveys, it was precisely the above method which government surveyors used to establish triangulation nets. When it was attempted to tie the nets together, discrepancies due to the individual determinations of latitude, longitude, and direction became evident. The problem then was to arrive at an average latitude and longitude somewhere in the middle of the country and to readjust the nets from there. The station known as *Meade's Ranch,* in Kansas, was selected as being close to both a geographical and mathematical average and was given the coordinates of 39° 13′ 26.686″ North Latitude and 98° 32′ 30.506″ West Longitude. This location is the origin of the network called the *North American Datum of 1927,* used by Canada, the United States, and Mexico, and stretching into Central America.

Triangulation Methods. Since World War II many advances have been made in the instruments and methods used in precise triangulation work. Whereas the *theodolite,* essentially a telescope with a graduated circle beneath it, was almost universally used for geodetic work in establishing horizontal control, instruments utilizing other principles are rapidly coming to the fore. In general these new instruments are based upon an induced wave from an instrument at one station. In some instruments the wave is a radio wave while in others it is a light wave.

Horizontal control is also being extended on a world-wide basis by the use of satellites. The precision of the method is such that the distance between two points on the east and west coasts of the United States can be determined to an accuracy of 33 feet or better. The U. S. Coast and Geodetic Survey, in charge of the program, is in this way extending precise horizontal control to all of the continents, rapidly bridging the oceans where, formerly, purely electronic triangulation had failed because of the long distances involved.

Vertical Control

Points of *vertical control* are points whose elevations above some datum plane are known in what might be called a vertical grid system, as opposed to the horizontal grid associated with points of horizontal control.

Elevation of points may be obtained in a number of ways, depending upon what accuracy is desired. *Precise leveling,* accomplished with an instrument equipped with a spirit level, is at the present time the most accurate, widely used method. Essentially, precise leveling directly measures small vertical differences in elevation which are added together to give the total difference in elevation between two points. Precise leveling is the most refined form of *differential* leveling. A quicker method but one of less accuracy is *trigonometric leveling,* which involves the solution of the vertical side of a right triangle. A still faster method is that of *barometric leveling,* accomplished by means of altimeters designed for surveying and exploratory work. This method, based upon change in barometric pressure due to elevation, is subject to considerable error, however, unless the user fully understands the many factors which may influence its accuracy.

As with the triangulation nets for horizontal control, discrepancies also occurred between the first federal precise level nets. The *Sea Level Datum of 1929* was subsequently established and all precision level nets were adjusted to it. Leveling, like triangulation, is of either first, second, third, or lower order. Permanent points of known elevation are called *bench marks*.

Map Scales

A *map scale* may be defined as the mathematical or graphical ratio of a distance on the map to the corresponding distance on the ground.

Kinds of Map Scales. There are three main methods of presenting map scales: the *representative fraction,* the *equality,* and the *graphic scale.*

An example of the *representative fraction* (R.F.) method of expressing scale is the fraction $\frac{1}{4800}$ which may also be expressed as 1:4800. This means that one unit on the map represents 4800 of the same units on the ground. It does *not* mean, as is sometimes assumed, that 1 inch on the map represents 4800 feet on the ground.

The statement on a map that $1'' = 5000'$ (1 inch equals 5000 feet) means that 1 inch on the map represents 5000 feet on the ground, and is an example of the *equality* method of expressing map scale.

The *graphic scale* method, sometimes called the *bar scale* method, is familiar to most readers. A bar divided into map miles and fractions of miles is a widely used method of expressing scale, an example being road maps.

Calculating Scale. If the ground distance between two points shown on a map is known, the scale of the map can be calculated, at least roughly, as the example below illustrates:

Problem: The distance between two points is known to be 2.2 miles. If the map distance between the points is 8.3 inches, express the scale of the map as a representative fraction.

Solution: $\dfrac{8.3}{2.2 \times 5280 \times 12} = \dfrac{1}{17000}$

NOTICE: (a) That the denominator in this case cannot logically be expressed to more than 2 significant digits, according to the principles explained in Chapter 2. (b) That the map scale fraction is always expressed with a "1" as the numerator. A map scale is never given, using the above example, as $\dfrac{2}{34000}$.

Converting Scales. It is often necessary to change an expressed map scale to another form. The examples below cover the usual general cases.

Problem: A map scale is expressed as 1:126,720. Express the scale of the map in terms of inches on the map and miles on the ground.

Solution: The original scale can be written as $\frac{1 \text{ inch}}{126,720 \text{ inches}}$. There are 5280 × 12 or 63,360 inches in one mile. Division will show that there are exactly 2 miles in 126,720 inches. The equality for expressing a scale for this map would be given by "one inch equals two miles."

Problem: A map scale is expressed as $1'' = 2000'$ (one inch equals 2000 feet). Express the scale of the map as a representative fraction.

Solution: The equality may be written as 1 inch = 2000 × 12 inches, or as $1'' = 24000''$. As the units are now the same, the representative fraction is expressed as 1:24000 or as $\frac{1}{24000}$.

Problem: Make a graphic scale for a map whose scale is expressed as 1:500,000. The graphic scale is based on the ratio of inches on the map to miles on the ground.

Solution: The original fraction can be written as $1'' = 500,000''$. Dividing, $\frac{500,000}{12 \times 5280}$ = number of miles in 500,000 inches = 7.9 miles. The scale could now be stated as one inch on the map represents 7.9 miles on the ground. However, bar scales whose divisions represent an uneven number of miles are inconvenient to use. The following proportion could be made: $\frac{1''}{7.9 \text{ miles}} = \frac{x''}{10 \text{ miles}}$ where x is found to be 1.27. This means that 10 miles on the ground is represented by 1.27 inches on the map. A bar scale 12.7 inches long could now be drawn and divided into 10 equal parts, each division representing 10 miles on the ground.

Small Scale, Intermediate, and Large Scale Maps. The definitions of *small, intermediate,* and *large scale* differ widely among organizations. For actual field work done in geography, maps may be conveniently placed in the following listed categories:

> Large scale, 1:1000 (or less than 1000)
> Intermediate scale, 1:1000 to 1:10,000
> Small scale, 1:10,000 (or more than 10,000)

Note that the larger the denominator of the representative fraction, the smaller the scale. The reason for this is illustrated by the example of $\frac{1}{10,000}$ being a smaller fraction than $\frac{1}{1000}$. *The reader is reminded, however, that the terms of "small," "intermediate," and "large scale" are not consistent in usage.* For example, all of the ratios expressed above are considered by some agencies to be in the category of large scale maps.

Map Scales and Ground Areas

It will be intuitively evident that if two maps cover equal areas of paper, and have the same scale, the maps will show equal amounts of ground area. If two maps cover equal areas of paper but have different scales, then the ratio of the two ground areas depicted on the maps can be easily determined. An example in the form of a stated problem is given:

Problem: Two maps, A and B, have the same area in square inches. The scale of map A is $\frac{1}{4000}$ while that of map B is $\frac{1}{12000}$. What is the ratio of the two ground areas shown?

Solution: Let the "paper area" of both maps be "a" square inches. One square inch on Map A represents 4000×4000 square inches on the ground, and one square inch on Map B represents 12000×12000 square inches on the ground. The total ground area shown by Map A is $4000 \times 4000 \times$ "a" square inches, while the total ground area shown by Map B is $12000 \times 12000 \times$ "a" square inches. The ratio of the two ground areas, $\frac{12000 \times 12000 \times a}{4000 \times 4000 \times a}$ reduces to 9, which means that Map B shows 9 times the ground area shown by Map A.

This leads to the rule that, for maps covering the same number of square inches of paper but with different scales, the smaller denominator is divided into the larger and the result squared. This gives the ratio between the ground areas shown on the maps. In the above example, $\left(\frac{12000}{4000}\right)^2 = 9$.

It is sometimes necessary to calculate a scale so that a map of a certain paper area will show a fixed ratio of ground area to another map of the same paper area:

Problem: Map A has a scale of $\frac{1}{5000}$. Map B, covering the same number of square inches of paper as Map A, is to show 5 times the ground area shown by Map A. What will be the scale of Map B?

Solution: $\left(\frac{\text{Larger denominator}}{\text{Smaller denominator}}\right)^2 = (5)$

$(\text{Larger denominator})^2 = 5 \times 5000^2$

$\text{Larger denominator} = \sqrt{5} \times 5000 = 11,200$

The scale of Map B will be 1:11200.

Direction on Maps

Geographic, Grid, and Magnetic Directions. A statement such as "A is directly south of B on this map" means very little and may be extremely misleading unless it is known what north-south reference system is being used. The situation is this: directions of lines on maps may be given with respect to *true* or *geographic* north; with respect to *map grid* north, which will differ from true north, according to the type of map projection used; and with respect to the magnetic north-south direction which is usually different from the other two.

Bearings and Azimuths. A *bearing* expresses a line's direction in terms of one of the four direction quadrants. A typical bearing would be, for example, "S 39° 15′ W" which means *39° 15′ west of south.* Bearings always start with either N or S, never E or W. The angular value will always be less than 90° except where it is exactly 90° and then the bearing would be given as "due East" or "due West."

The second way of expressing a direction is by *azimuth.* The azimuth of a line is the angle, measured in a clockwise direction from north to the line. (Sometimes azimuth is measured from the south for astronomical calculations, etc., but the more general procedure of measuring azimuth from the north will be followed here.) The azimuth of the line whose bearing is S 39° 15′ W would be, then, 180° + 39° 15′, or 219° 15′. (See Figure 29.)

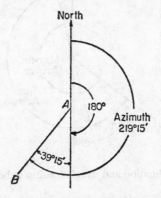

Fig. 29. The bearing of *AB* is S 39° 15′ W. Its azimuth is 219° 15′.

It has probably already been noted by the reader that, in the light of what has been said about geographic, grid, and magnetic directions, the above bearing and azimuth could be either geographic, map grid, or magnetic. This is true and some maps indicate the directions of all three "norths" by three converging lines and by showing the angular values between the lines. In the usual beginning field work, however, it is the relationships between true (geographic) and magnetic directions which must be thoroughly understood; hence the following discussion will be limited to magnetic directions and geographic directions.

The Earth's Magnetic Field; and Magnetic Declination. The earth has a magnetic field much like that of a bar magnet; however, the earth's magnetic poles do not coincide with its geographic poles. On or above the earth's surface a compass needle will align itself with the magnetic force lines and thus indicate the directions of magnetic north and south. As the magnetic poles do not coincide with the geographic poles, a compass needle over a point on the earth's surface will usually point to one side of the true north-south line passing through that point.

At any locality the angle between true north and magnetic north is called the magnetic declination. (See Figure 30.) Lines along

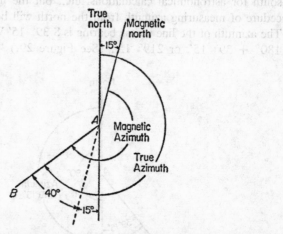

Fig. 30. Magnetic declination and its relationship to bearings and azimuths.

which the values of declination are equal are *isogonic* lines. The line along which there is no apparent magnetic declination is an *agonic* line. The values of declination in an area are always changing because the magnetic north and south poles are always shifting their positions. The resulting *changes in declination* can be measured and are often expressed on maps, for the particular areas shown by the map. In 1960 the U. S. Coast and Geodetic Survey determined the present magnetic north and south poles to be at 74.9° N, 101.0° W; and 67.1° S, 142.7° E respectively, the change for each amounting to about 100 miles from their designated position in 1955.

Calculating Bearings and Azimuths. A sample calculation will be helpful in demonstrating the relationships between the "two norths" and the resulting directions of a line:

Problem: The magnetic declination in a certain locality is 15° E. The magnetic bearing of line AB is S 40° W. Find: (a) the true bearing of AB; (b) the magnetic azimuth of AB; (c) the true azimuth of AB.

Solution: Figure 30 shows the relative positions of the magnetic and true north-south lines, and line AB, and also shows the angles involved. From the figure: (a) the true bearing of $AB =$ S 55° W; (b) the magnetic azimuth of $AB = 180° + 40° = 220°$; (c) the true azimuth of $AB = 180° + 40° + 15° = 235°$.

It is important to remember that *magnetic* bearings and azimuths are measured from the *magnetic* north-south line while geographic or *true* bearings are measured from the *true* north-south line.

Map Symbols and Conventions

In order to present as much pertinent data as possible on a map, extensive use is made of symbols and conventions. Where color is used on a map, works of man are usually shown in black or red, water in blue, and vegetation in green. Cultivated land may be shown in brown. Various symbols are used to represent orchards, forest lands, salt marshes, etc.

In addition, conventional representations for the works of man, such as railroads, bridges, tunnels, mines, buildings, etc., appear on many maps. Some maps print a *legend* either on the face of the map or on the reverse side, which includes an explanation of the symbols and conventions used. Usually, however, due to the close similarity or association between map symbols and conventions, and their counterparts on the ground, the correct interpretation is almost automatic.

REVIEW

1. State the chief difference between planimetric and topographic maps.

2. Discuss the general procedure in triangulation.

3. What is the *North American Datum of 1927*?

4. Outline the basic principle of each of the three principal methods of leveling.

5. Assuming two maps of the same size but with different scales, explain the relationship between the two scales and the two ground areas shown.

6. Is there any difference between "true" north and "geographic" north? Between "true" north and "grid" north?

7. Define "the azimuth of a line."

8. Can bearings exceed 90°? Can azimuths exceed 90°?

9. Do the earth's magnetic poles coincide with the earth's geographic poles?

10. Explain "magnetic declination."

EXERCISES

(Answers are given in the answer section at the back of the book.)

1. The distance between two points on a map is 5.6 inches. The corresponding ground distance is 7.2 miles. Express the approximate scale of the map as a representative fraction.

2. Convert the scale of 1:240,000 to an equality in terms of inches on the map and feet on the ground.

3. A student expresses a map scale as 3:45000. How should it be expressed?

4. Two maps of the same size have scales of 1:4000 and 1:16000 respectively. What is the ratio of their ground areas shown?

5. Two maps are of the same size. Map A has a scale of 1:20000; Map B shows twice the ground area shown by A. What is the approximate scale of Map B?

6. The magnetic bearing of line *AB* is S 30° W. The magnetic declination is 10° W. Find the true bearing of the line.

7. If the magnetic declination at a point is 15° E, what is the magnetic bearing of the earth's magnetic north pole from that point?

CHAPTER 6

Earth-Sun and Earth-Moon Relationships

The sun is a natural, unshielded thermonuclear furnace whose radiant energy is the chief source of the earth's illumination and atmospheric heat. Over a period of one year all regions of the earth are exposed to direct solar energy for approximately the same total amount of time. This yearly balance of hours of daylight and darkness is governed mainly by the combined rotation and revolution of the earth, and by the fixed "tilt" of its axis in space.

Chiefly due to the same three factors, regions of the earth, although exposed to solar radiation for nearly the same number of hours in a year, do not all receive or retain the same amount of solar *energy* in a year's time. The tilt of the earth's axis, for example, brings about differences in the slant of the sun's rays at various latitudes, resulting in differences in the receipt of solar energy. Thus, although the north pole and equatorial Africa experience nearly equivalent numbers of hours of daylight and darkness in one year, their atmospheric temperatures are very different.

Differences in temperature throughout the world's atmosphere, aided by the earth's rotation, set up pressure belts or cells. The pressure cells induce giant wind systems which transfer heat from one region to another, determine world-wide precipitation patterns, and strongly affect the temperature and the circulation of the oceans. The oceans, in turn, are strong controls of climates.

In addition to earth-sun relationships, earth-moon relationships are of significance not only from the standpoint of tides, but also from the view that men will some day land on the moon. As already pointed out, when that happens man's environment will include that of the moon.

From the standpoint of daily living, earth-sun relationships bring about phenomena of interest and importance to us: daylight and darkness, the varying lengths of daylight and darkness through the year, weather, climate, winds, and temperature. Earth-moon relationships induce several tidal effects on earth and there is recent evidence to suggest that certain rainfall patterns are strongly influenced by the moon.

Rotation of the Earth

The earth *rotates* on its axis, a complete rotation taking approximately 24 hours. The actual time of rotation is discussed in Chapter 7, but for purposes of this chapter the approximate time of 24 hours is sufficiently close.

Although the earth's velocity of rotation was long considered to be constant, measurements within the last decade indicate that not only is the earth slowing down in its rotational velocity, but also that it occasionally demonstrates bursts of speed followed by periods of subnormal speed. These minor variances, which may be related to changes in the earth's magnetic field, are beyond the scope of this chapter, other than noting that they do exist.

Direction of Rotation. A general statement concerning the direction of the earth's rotation would be that the earth rotates from west to east. That is, in any hemisphere the sun seems to rise in the east and set in the west. To a person in the northern hemisphere who imagines himself looking down upon the north pole, however, the earth would turn in a counterclockwise direction. For a person looking down upon the south pole, the earth is rotating in a clockwise direction. These facts and the fact that the earth's rotational velocity decreases from a maximum of a little more than 1000 miles per hour at the equator to zero at the poles, have great influence upon several phenomena, including global wind systems. These effects will be discussed in other chapters.

Rotational Velocities and Centrifugal Reactions. The decrease in rotational velocity of the earth as one goes from the equator to the poles is not directly proportional to the changes in latitude. For students familiar with trigonometric functions the approximate velocity at any latitude may be expressed by $v = 1000$ cosine latitude, where v is the velocity in miles per hour. The velocity of the earth's rotation at any latitude may easily be found graphically by constructing a right triangle as shown in Figure 31.

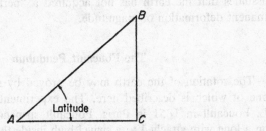

Fig. 31. The cosine of a particular latitude is given by $\dfrac{AC}{AB}$. The sine of the latitude is given by $\dfrac{BC}{AB}$. If AB is made 10 units long, the rotational velocity of the earth at the constructed latitude equals the length of AC, in the same units, multiplied by 100. If AB is made 15 units long, the length of BC, in the same units, equals the apparent change in degrees per hour of the plane of swing of a Foucault pendulum.

The rotation of the earth brings about other major effects involving centrifugal reaction. First, an object near the poles will have less tendency to fly off the earth than an object of the same mass nearer the equator because of their relative velocities. (The principle of centripetal force and centrifugal reaction was outlined in Chapter 2.) To put it another way, an object on the equator, in general, would weigh less than an object of the same mass anywhere else on the earth's surface, even without the equatorial bulge.

The equatorial bulge, as a matter of fact, results from these differences in weight or gravitational pull. Consider the earth as an undeformed sphere which is rotating but has not yet reached its maximum rotational velocity of 1000 miles, plus, at the equator. Particles in the equatorial zone are relatively tending more and more to move outward as the velocity increases. Particles at the same depth below the surface but in higher latitudes are trying to move toward the equator, nearer the center of gravity of the earth. As they do so, just as a finger pressing down on an angle to a table surface exerts some force perpendicular to the surface, so all these particles exert some force at right angles to the equatorial plane. The result is that the equatorial region, its resistance to deformation already weakened, is caught in an enormous squeeze which results in the equatorial bulge.

Supposedly, if the earth gradually stopped rotating, it would return more or less elastically to the shape of a near-perfect sphere. This assumes that the earth has not acquired a "permanent set" or permanent deformation of magnitude.

The Foucault Pendulum

The rotation of the earth may be proved by several experiments, one of which is described here. The experiment was performed by L. Foucault in 1851 in Paris. Foucault suspended a heavy weight on a long wire attached to a swivel high inside the rotunda of a large building. The weight was set swinging close to the floor and in a few minutes it became evident that the plane of swing of the weight was moving relative to the positions of stationary objects in the room. Either the plane of swing was actually changing or the room was revolving about an axis. As Newton had proved, an undisturbed pendulum would not change its plane of swing, therefore the room must be turning. If a fixed point on a solid sphere moves, the sphere must be in motion. If the point travels in a circle, as the pendulum showed it did, the sphere is rotating around a fixed axis. So, probably, went his reasoning, and Foucault had proved the rotation of the earth.

Why the Foucault Pendulum Seems to Change Its Plane. Foucault pendulums are now common sights in planetariums and observatories, but the average observer probably does not understand the relationship of the earth's rotation to the plane of swing of the pendulum.

Figure 32 represents a simple map view of the floor of an observatory in the northern hemisphere. The Foucault pendulum is suspended at P some distance above the floor. An observer A is on a parallel of latitude a few feet north of P. A second observer B is on a parallel of latitude a few feet south of P. A, P, and B are all on the same meridian. Assume that the pendulum is swinging from B toward A at a particular instant.

Within one or two seconds, due to their different velocities of rotation, A, P, and B will have moved through space to A', P', and B' respectively. Assume that the pendulum weight is then at P''. To the observer at B', the plane of the pendulum seems to be moving clockwise. As for the observer at A', the pendulum has not yet reached his latitude. However, as it started from a lower latitude it has a greater eastward velocity than does the observer at A'. Thus it

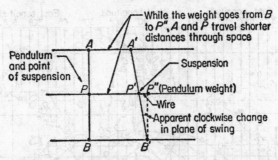

Fig. 32. The Foucault pendulum. The apparent change in the plane of swing of the pendulum is due to the different rotational velocities at different latitudes. The weight, starting at B and at the same eastward velocity, will travel to, say, P''. For the observer now at B', the weight has moved to the east of his meridian and the plane of swing seems to be changing clockwise.

also seems to the observer at A', when the pendulum does reach his latitude, that the plane of the pendulum is moving clockwise as the pendulum is east of his former position.

At the poles a pendulum will of course seem to change its plane of swing through 360 degrees in one day, or 15 degrees per hour. At the equator no apparent change is possible because the velocities of points an equal distance north and south of the equator are equal. Apparent clockwise motion of the plane is in effect canceled by a counterclockwise "motion" of the same magnitude. For any latitude, the apparent change of swing in degrees per hour is equal to 15° multiplied by the sine of the latitude.

The sine of any latitude may easily be obtained graphically. In Figure 31 the sine of the latitude is equal to $\dfrac{BC}{AB}$. The sine of any angle is the ratio of the side opposite the angle, divided by the hypotenuse. The sine of 60°, for example, will be found graphically to be 0.87.

The "Up-and-Down" Paths of Satellites on Maps

Figure 33 is a chart showing the path of one of the United States Tiros weather satellites, over a seven-hour period. Questions are often asked as to what causes the "up-and-down" curves, what determines their shapes, and why satellites seem to wander around between the hemispheres. Due to ever-increasing use of satellites in

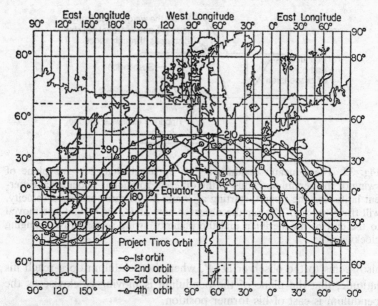

Fig. 33. The map trace of one Tiros weather satellite. (Adapted from the U. S. Department of Commerce, Weather Bureau)

geographical work, an explanation of satellite paths on maps is presented below.

The first thing to realize is that earth satellites do not wander up and down, and around. They travel in planes which cut the center of the earth and whose intersection with the earth's surface are therefore great circles or nearly so. As outlined in Chapter 2, the orbit of a satellite is dependent upon fixed physical laws. These laws remind us of the Foucault pendulum in that the orbital plane of a satellite theoretically also does not change with respect to the plane of the earth's equator. Similarly, the "wandering paths" of satellites, like the "change in the plane of swing" of pendulums, are relative. In the case of satellites, apparent displacements are further accentuated by projecting the paths onto the plane surface of a map.

Consider Figure 34, which represents an orbital plane making an angle of 30° with the plane of the equator. Now imagine a satellite at *A*, going toward *B*. Remember that the length *AB* approximates an arc of a great circle curving away from the reader, into the plane of the paper.

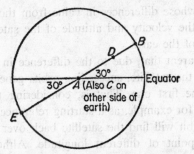

Fig. 34. As seen on a map, the northernmost and southernmost latitudes of a satellite's path are approximately equal to the angle between its orbital plane and the plane of the equator.

As is evident from the diagram, a satellite's north and south boundaries on a map will be approximately equal to the angle between the orbital plane and the plane of the equator. In this example the satellite's boundaries will be 30° N latitude and 30° S latitude.

If the earth did not rotate, the satellite would, theoretically at least, pass over points A, D, E, B, and C time after time and the path of its flight projected onto a map would look something like Figure 35.

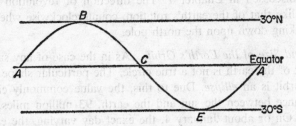

Fig. 35. The mapped path of the satellite of Figure 34, assuming that the earth is not rotating. Vertical scale is exaggerated.

The "loops" in the northern and southern hemispheres can easily be understood by putting a rubber band around a globe or ball, to represent the equator, and then placing another rubber band around the ball, at an angle to the first, to represent the path of a satellite.

Referring to Figure 34 again, and now considering the rotation of the earth, point D on earth will not be in the orbital plane by the time the space vehicle reaches the latitude of point D. The same is true of the other points. The points actually traversed by the satellite will all have longitudes whose differences in value from those of *D, E,* and *B* depend upon the velocity and altitude of the satellite and the rotational velocity of the earth.

It may be apparent that, due to the difference in the velocities of the earth and of the satellite, succeeding orbits generally will be out of phase with the first one. That is, considering the equator and longitude 75° E, for example, as a starting reference point, the completion of one orbit will find the satellite back over the equator but passing over a point of different longitude. Although succeeding curves will be of the same pattern, they will be displaced as in Figure 33.

It will be noticed that rotation of the earth has no effect upon the north-south component of space travel. The latitude being passed over by the satellite at any instant would be the same no matter whether the earth was rotating or not.

The Earth in Its Orbit

As the earth rotates on its axis it also *revolves* about the sun. The time for one revolution is approximately 365 days. More exact values will be discussed in Chapter 7. The direction of revolution of the earth is like that of the earth's rotation, counterclockwise when seen as if looking down upon the north pole.

Shape and Size of the Earth's Orbit. As in the case of any satellite, the orbit of the earth is not a true circle. The particular shape of the earth's orbit is an *ellipse.* Due to this, the value commonly cited as the distance between the sun and the earth, 93 million miles, is an average. On or about January 4, the exact day varying, the earth is in *perihelion,* at its closest approach to the sun, and the distance between the two bodies is about 91½ million miles. On or about July 4 the earth is in *aphelion* and at its greatest distance—93½ million miles—from the sun. The fact that the earth's orbit is elliptical means that, like all satellites, the earth must speed up at times in its orbit and slow down at other times. The significance of this is discussed in the next chapter.

The completion of one orbit with respect to the stars is known as the *sidereal year.* The completion of one orbit with respect to the sun is a *tropical year.* As the tropical year has about 365¼ days and the calendar year has 365 days, one day is added to the calendar year in every fourth year, or *leap year*. All leap years are evenly divisible by 4. For instance, 1968 and 1972 are leap years.

The Tilt and Parallelism of the Earth's Axis. The *plane of the ecliptic* is the plane of the earth's orbit. The plane of the ecliptic therefore passes through the center of the sun and the center of the earth. The axis of the earth maintains a fixed angle of about $66\frac{1}{2}°$ with the plane of the ecliptic and the axis also maintains a very close *parallelism*. The parallelism of the axis can be demonstrated by holding a pencil (the earth's axis) at any angle, and then, holding the wrist rigid, moving the hand around in a small horizontal circle (the plane of the ecliptic). It will be seen that the pencil is always parallel to its former positions and that it may be considered to be pointing toward the same spot, if that spot is as far away, relatively, as the stars are from earth. This concept of treating an area in space as a point is usually one of the most difficult for students to accept. This may help: If the earth's orbit were represented by a small dot made by a pencil point, an average star would be represented by a similar dot over 100 miles away!

General earth-sun relationships resulting from this combination of tilt and parallelism are illustrated in Figure 36. The diagram also

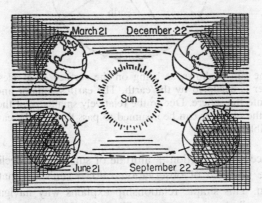

Fig. 36. Effect of inclination of the earth on seasons. (Adapted from the U. S. Navy Department)

graphically explains the origin of the popular expressions of the sun being "below the equator" for half of the year and "above the equator" for the other half.

Declination and Altitude of Sun, and Latitude

The concept of the sun being above, below, or on the equator is also used in certain astronomical observations. The angle of the sun above or below the equator is called the sun's *declination*. The angle of the sun above the horizon is called the sun's *altitude*. If the sun's declination and altitude are known as the sun crosses a meridian, the latitude of the place of observation may easily be calculated as the poles, the observer, and the sun are all on the same meridian at that instant.

In Figure 37 the right angle *ZOH* may be expressed as 90° = lati-

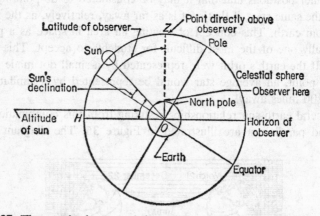

Fig. 37. The sun is shown as being on the surface of a celestial sphere whose center is occupied by the earth. The earth's equator and poles are projected onto the sphere. Due to the relatively small size of the earth, the horizon of the observer can be assumed to pass through the earth's center with negligible error.

tude of place of observation + altitude of sun − sun's declination, or as: latitude of place of observation = 90° + sun's declination − altitude of sun. This simple relationship explains why navigators commonly "shoot" the sun at noon. The altitude of the sun is determined by a sextant or octant, or by some other instrument; the sun's declination is taken from tables, and calculating the latitude is then only a matter of simple addition and subtraction. The algebraic sign of the sun's declination is (+) if the sun is "above" the equator, and (−) if "below." In using the formula, the altitude and the latitude are both taken to be positive and the sign of the declination depends upon whether the sun is between the observer and the equator (+), or on the other side of the equator (−). An example of this type of calculation is given:

Problem: An explorer in the northern hemisphere in winter measures the noon altitude of the sun on a certain day as 20° 46′. The sun's declination at that instant was −18° 23′ (sun on other side of equator from observer). What was the latitude of the place of observation?

Solution: Latitude = 90° − 18° 23′ − 20° 46′ = 50° 51′ N.

The Sun's Vertical Rays. Further application of the above formula leads to interesting results. Suppose that it is desired to find the latitudes of all places where the sun's rays are vertical at noon at least once during the year. Now, if the sun's rays are vertical, the altitude of the sun is 90° and the above formula reduces to: Latitude = 90° + declination − 90°, or: Latitude = declination. Because of the tilt of the earth's axis, the declination must always be somewhere between −23½° S and 23½° N. As will be discussed in some detail in a later chapter, this is of paramount importance in the heating of the earth's atmosphere, the area described above being the *tropics*. Its northern boundary at 23½° North is the Tropic of Cancer. Its southern boundary at 23½° South is the Tropic of Capricorn.

It can also be deduced from the above that, when the sun's noon rays are vertical at a point on the earth's surface, the angular value of the declination of the sun must be equal to the angular value of the latitude of the point. This gives us another way to express the declination: *the declination of the sun is equal to the latitude of the place where the sun's noon rays are striking vertically.*

The Circle of Illumination

Figure 38 illustrates various positions of the earth in its journey around the sun. At any instant, half of the earth is illuminated and the other half is dark. The circle separating the illuminated and unilluminated portions of the globe is called the *circle of illumination*.

The Equinoxes and Solstices. It will be noticed that the sun is illuminating the northern and southern hemispheres equally at two times during the calendar year. These are the times of the *equinox* (equal night). The vernal or spring equinox occurs on March 20 or

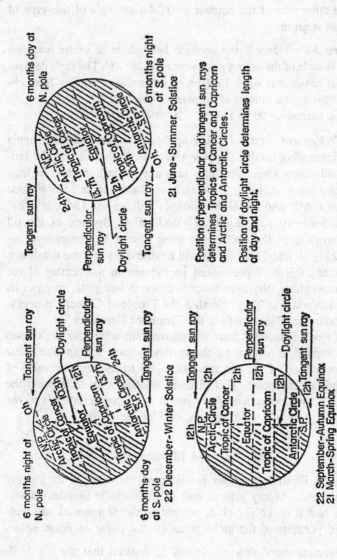

Fig. 38. The circle of illumination. (Adapted from the U. S. Navy Department)

21; the autumnal equinox occurs on September 22 or 23. The different dates result from the ¼-day difference between the calendar year and the tropical year and the subsequent addition, during leap year, of one whole day.

The diagram also shows that when the northern half of the earth's axis is tilted away from the sun, the northern hemisphere is receiving less illumination than is the southern hemisphere. The minimum illumination received at one time by the northern hemisphere is on December 22 or 23, when the northern portion of the earth's axis is tilted directly away from the sun by a full 23½°, and the sun's rays are vertical at the Tropic of Capricorn. For the northern hemisphere, this is the *winter solstice,* the "shortest day" in the year. For the southern hemisphere this is the *summer solstice,* the "longest day" in the year. On or about June 21, the summer solstice in the northern hemisphere, the situation is completely reversed, as shown. The northern hemisphere is now receiving its maximum amount of illumination as the northern part of the earth's axis is tilted *toward* the sun by a full 23½°. The sun's noon rays are vertical at the Tropic of Cancer.

The Arctic and Antarctic Circles.   As seen in Figure 38, at the times of the solstices, the sun's most oblique rays are tangent to the parallels of latitude at 66½° North and South. These parallels are the northern hemisphere's *Arctic Circle* and the southern hemisphere's *Antarctic Circle.* The region between the Arctic Circle and the north pole is called the *Arctic*; that between the Antarctic Circle and the south pole is called the *Antarctic.*

Hours of Daylight and Darkness during One Day.   It is only at the instant of the equinoxes that every parallel of latitude is half in darkness and half in light. At the time of the equinoxes the circle of illumination passes through the poles, flooding one half of each (northern and southern) hemisphere with equal amounts of light and plunging the other half into equal darkness. At all other times, in any given latitude except that of the equator, the hours of direct daylight in 24 hours exceed those of darkness or *vice versa.* Also, if a given latitude in the northern hemisphere is experiencing a certain number of hours of daylight during a 24-hour period, its corresponding latitude in the southern hemisphere is experiencing the same number of hours of darkness during the same 24-hour period. The term "direct daylight" is used here to distinguish between unrefracted light directly received from the sun, and twilight.

The duration of daylight and darkness for a particular latitude and date can be obtained from diagrams or tables published by government agencies. Many newspapers publish the times of sunrise and sunset for every day, the information usually being obtained from federal government sources. The values given locally usually take into consideration such factors as atmospheric refraction, etc.

For any given latitude, the higher the noon sun is above the horizon, the greater will be the number of hours of daylight. (To the reader: Why?)

It will be helpful at this point to review principles involved in the illumination of the earth, by solving some typical problems. A thorough mastery of earth-sun relationships can be obtained only by (a) studying and understanding diagrams illustrating the relationships; (b) being able to show these relationships by means of sketches; and (c), by solving problems illustrating the relationships.

Problem: On the day of the summer solstice in the northern hemisphere, what will be the sun's noon altitude (above the northern horizon) at the south pole?

Solution: The sun is $23\frac{1}{2}°$ *below* the equator as it would appear to people in the southern hemisphere. Therefore the declination is negative. Using the previously developed relationship involving altitude, declination, and latitude: Altitude $= 90° +$ declination $-$ latitude. Substituting, Altitude $= 90° - 23\frac{1}{2}° - 90° = -23\frac{1}{2}°$.

The sun is therefore not visible from the south pole on this date. Further, this day must be the middle of the "6-month Antarctic night" as the altitude in the above equation cannot have a plus value until the declination is more than $0°$. This will occur at the equinox on or about September 22, three months later. Thus the 6-month Antarctic night begins on or about March 21 and ends on or about September 22. During the same period the Arctic is experiencing a "6-month day," its "6-month night" starting on or about September 22 and ending on or about March 21.

Problem: At what latitude in the northern hemisphere will the noon sun be on the horizon on December 22?

Solution: On December 22 the sun's declination with respect to the northern hemisphere is $-23\frac{1}{2}°$. The altitude is $0°$. Substituting in: Latitude $= 90° +$ declination $-$ altitude, Latitude $= 90° - 23\frac{1}{2}° - 0° = 66\frac{1}{2}°$, the Arctic Circle.

Problem: On what date will the sun's noon altitude at the south pole be 23½°?

Solution: The date cannot be solved, directly, but the declination can be solved, and then the date corresponding with that declination can be determined: Declination = latitude + altitude − 90°; Declination = 90° + 23½° − 90° = +23½°, the (+) sign meaning that the sun is between the place of observation and the equator. This places the sun directly over the Tropic of Capricorn, as the declination of the sun equals the latitude of the place where the sun's noon rays are vertical. The sun is over the Tropic of Capricorn on or about December 22, the answer.

Twilight. Daylight and darkness do not occur suddenly, and it may be said that the circle of illumination literally has a fuzzy edge. By the time the sun rises over the horizon in the morning there is already considerable light. The same thing is true between the times of sunset and total darkness. This second light or *twilight* (twi-, *two*) of both morning and evening is caused by particles of dust and moisture in the atmosphere which act as tiny mirrors to deflect and reflect the sun's rays onto the earth's surface.

Other than basic earth-sun relationships, the length of twilight in a particular region is affected by three things: the thickness of the atmosphere, the vertical and horizontal distribution of dust and moisture, and the latitude of the region. As will be discussed in a later chapter, the thickness of that part of the earth's atmosphere which contains most of the atmospheric dust and moisture particles is greatest at the equator and least at the poles. Secondly, the vertical and horizontal concentration of these particles is not the same in all latitudes. However, the most important factors determining the length of twilight are latitude and the position of the earth with respect to the sun. These, combined, determine the apparent speed of the sun in a certain locality and therefore also determine the length of twilight.

Astronomical twilight encompasses the period of time from sunset until any discernible glow due to the sun finally disappears. The average value of the sun's angle below the horizon at the end of astronomical twilight is commonly assumed to be 18°. Thus at the equator, with the sun sinking below the horizon at a velocity of 15° per hour at the time of the equinoxes, astronomical twilight lasts $\frac{18 \text{ hours}}{15}$, or a little more than one hour.

The duration of twilight in general increases as the poles are approached. The reason is that the plane of the sun's path becomes increasingly less vertical as the poles are approached and thus it takes longer for the sun to reach its level of 18° below the horizon. The situation is much like that of a person crossing a street. The shortest distance is at right angles to the street line; the more the deviation from this path, the longer it takes to cross. Similarly, the longer it takes the sun to travel between the horizon and 18° below the horizon, the longer will twilight last.

The above statement needs one important modification. During the year in each hemisphere, in the areas bounded by 50° latitude and each pole, each parallel of latitude will witness the phenomenon that the sun at times does not fall more than 18° below the horizon in that latitude. The result is that, although the sun is not visible, high latitude regions experience "twilight" nights at various times of the year.

Earth-Moon Relationships

Although earth-sun relationships are of far greater natural importance to us than are earth-moon relationships, the latter do affect man's physical environment in several ways.

The Moon's Orbit. The moon, about 2160 miles in diameter, revolves around the earth at an average distance of approximately 240,000 miles. The orbit of the moon is an ellipse. The moon completes one revolution around the earth in about 27⅓ days, with respect to the stars. This period of time being known as the *sidereal month.* It takes, however, approximately 29½ days, or a *synodic month,* for the moon to complete one revolution with respect to our sun. The reason is that while the moon is revolving about the earth, the earth is revolving about the sun, carrying the moon with it. Thus the moon will not be lined up with the earth and sun again until it revolves for about two days more. Figure 39 shows this relationship, and also shows the directions of rotation and revolution for the moon and the earth as if looking down upon the earth's northern hemisphere. It is seen that from this viewpoint the earth and the moon are both rotating and revolving in a counterclockwise direction. The differing west-east velocities of revolution of the earth and the moon result in the moon's rising about fifty minutes later each day.

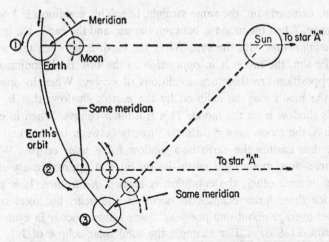

Fig. 39. Sidereal and synodic months. Position 1 is the beginning of both a sidereal and a synodic month. In position 2 the distant star and the moon are again in the plane of the meridian and a sidereal month has been completed. In position 3 the moon and the sun are in the plane of the meridian and a synodic month has been completed.

The plane of the moon's orbit does not coincide with the plane of the ecliptic, but it makes an angle of approximately 5° with it.

This relationship may be visualized by imagining a dinner plate half submerged in water, at a shallow angle. The water represents the plane of the ecliptic and the earth is at the center of the plate, on the water line. The orbit of the moon is represented by the edge of the plate. Tracing this around, as if moving a finger along the edge of the plate, the moon is seen to be on one side of the plane of the ecliptic half of the time and on the other side the rest of the time. It will be noticed, however, that there are only two places where the moon's orbit intersects the plane of the ecliptic. These places are called nodes. In terms of the dish in water, these would be where the finger, following the rim edge of the plate, goes into the water and comes out, and thus one node is called "descending" and the other is the "ascending" node.

Eclipses; Two Conditions of Syzygy; Quadrature. An eclipse can occur only when the moon is in the plane of the ecliptic and thus only when the moon is in or near a nodal position. The other requirement for an eclipse is, of course, that the sun, earth, and moon are on, or nearly on, the same straight line. This condition is known as *syzygy*. When the moon is between the sun and the earth, the moon is in *conjunction* with the sun. When the earth is between the moon and the sun, the moon is in *opposition* to the sun. Both conjunction and opposition are therefore conditions of syzygy. When in opposition, the moon may be eclipsed by the earth's shadow; that is, the earth's shadow is on the moon. This is a *lunar* eclipse. When in conjunction, the moon may get almost directly between the sun and the earth, thus casting the earth into shadow for a *solar* eclipse. When the three—sun, moon, and earth—lie on lines at approximately right angles to each other, the condition is termed *quadrature*. It is possible for three lunar eclipses to occur in one year, but total solar eclipses average about one per year. Solar eclipses occur in cycles of 18 years, 11½ days. For example the total solar eclipse of July 20, 1963, will have as its cyclic counterpart a total solar eclipse on August 1, 1981.

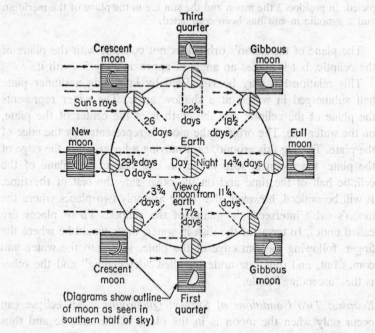

Fig. 40. Phases of the moon. (Courtesy of John Wiley & Sons, Inc. Adapted from A. Strahler's *Physical Geography*, 2d edition, 1960)

Phases of the Moon. One half of the moon is always illuminated by sunlight but a full moon is seen only during the aspect of opposition, when the earth is between the moon and the sun. During conjunction, we are facing the dark side of the moon. This is the beginning of the synodic month. Between conjunction and opposition, and between opposition and conjunction, at quadrature, we see one half of a hemisphere, or one quarter of the moon, illuminated. These are the *first* and *last quarters* of the moon. Figure 40 shows the various phases.

Rotation of the Moon. Like the earth, the moon rotates on an axis. Due to the strong gravitational pull of the earth, the moon's period of rotation is equal to its period of revolution of one synodic month. Thus the moon always shows the same face to the earth. This effect may be visualized by imagining one person walking in a circle around another. As he walks he keeps turning, or rotating, his body so that he is always facing the person in the middle of the circle. Halfway around the circle, the traveler is also facing the point from which he started. His body therefore rotated through 180° while he revolved through the same angle.

Precession and Nutation. It would be dynamically more stable, as may easily be imagined, if the earth's equatorial bulge rotated in the plane of the ecliptic. The gravitational and accelerative effects of the sun tend to bring this about. On the other hand, the moon is in effect trying to get the equatorial bulge into the plane of the lunar orbit. The rotation of the earth resists any change, the result being that the earth's axis *precesses,* as if moving around a giant cone in space. This movement can be observed on a small scale by watching a top. As its rotational velocity decreases the top tends to fall toward the earth because gravity is pulling on its "bulge." However, as the top is still rotating, it does not fall, but its axis will precess, describing a cone.

If the top is now given a slight tap, a slight wobble will be introduced but the top will continue to precess, although wobbling. A similar wobble, called *nutation,* is induced in the earth's axis by a combination of several phenomena including the fact that the moon itself precesses in its orbital plane due to solar attraction. Nutation affects the position of the axis very little. Due to precession, however, the earth's axis points to different space coordinates over a period of time. In 13,000 years, Vega instead of Polaris will be our north star but, 13,000 years from then, the cone will have been completed and the axis will be back to its present orientation.

Ocean Tides. The moon *appears* to be moving eastward through between 12 and 13 degrees a day, with respect to the sun. This effect is due to the moon's revolution about the earth. From the standpoint of time, this is roughly equivalent to $\frac{12.5}{360} \times 24 \times 60$, or 50 minutes. The moon therefore makes two successive appearances over the same meridian in 24 hours and 50 minutes. Or, to put it another way, the moon rises approximately 50 minutes later each day.

At a given point two high tides and two ebb tides will also occur in a given approximate period of 24 hours and 50 minutes. It may correctly be reasoned therefore that, although the sun exerts great gravitational pull upon the earth, the phenomenon of ocean tides in general is mostly controlled by earth-moon relationships. This results from the fact that although the mass of the sun is 27 million times that of the moon, the sun's distance from earth makes its gravitational pull upon earth much less than that exerted upon the earth by the relatively close moon. This is in accordance with Newton's Law of Universal Gravitation, mentioned in Chapter 2.

Also, the tidal bulge—high tide—results from the fact that, on the side of the earth closest to the moon, a unit mass of ocean water, because it is closer to the moon, will be attracted to the moon with a greater force than will a unit mass of solid earth. (The mass of the earth may be thought of as being concentrated at the earth's center.) At the same time, on the other side of the earth, the ocean water is 4000 miles farther away from the moon than is the earth's center of gravity. This makes the force of attraction between the moon and the solid earth greater than that between the moon and the ocean water on the far side of the earth. In response to this difference in forces, the ocean water bulges out on that side of the world also. Between these bulges of high water are two regions of low water. The earth rotates beneath bulges of high water and in a period of 24 hours and 50 minutes, a given "port" passes through two periods of high tide and two of low tide.

The combined gravitational pull of the sun and moon is of course a maximum when the sun, moon, and earth are in approximately a straight line, and least when the three bodies are in quadrature. Thus, abnormally high tides, or *spring* tides, occur at full moon and new moon, while abnormally low tides, or *neap* tides, occur at the quarter phases of the moon.

Earth Tides. Although the earth is extremely rigid, tides also occur in the earth's crust due to solar and lunar attraction. This tidal bulge in the solid earth has been measured as being about one foot high during the time of ocean spring tides. Although theoretically interesting from several viewpoints, perhaps the greatest significance of this phenomenon is that the earth must be at least as elastic as steel in order to resume its shape after such deformation.

Tides in the Earth's Atmosphere. As the earth's atmosphere has mass, it must also be attracted by the pull of the sun and the moon. This attraction sets up tides in the atmosphere called *lunar winds* whose velocities are very low, about $\frac{1}{20}$ mile per hour. It has been known for some time that these lunar winds attain higher energies during periods of new and full moon, just as do ocean tides. Statistical studies completed in 1962 also indicate that rainfall is considerably heavier during or near these periods. Although at time of writing there is no proved link between heavy rainfall and these "spring tides" or surges in lunar winds, it is a promising new field of research in physical geography. Incidentally, this particular phenomenon of atmospheric tides is also being studied from the standpoint of its possible association with the processing of ultraviolet radiation within the atmosphere.

REVIEW

1. Distinguish between "rotation" and "revolution" of the earth.

2. Describe Foucault's experiment and draw a sketch to explain the apparent change in direction of the plane of the pendulum's swing.

3. What is the plane of the ecliptic? Is the moon ever in the plane of the ecliptic? If so, how often?

4. Define "parallelism of the earth's axis."

5. Distinguish between the declination of the sun and its altitude.

6. Explain the relationship of the declination of the sun to the latitudes of the places where the sun's noon rays strike vertically.

7. Upon what three main factors does the illumination of the earth depend at any given instant?

8. What is the cause of twilight? On what does the length of twilight chiefly depend?

9. Discuss the precession of the earth's axis in terms of cause and effect.

10. Explain the cause of ocean tides in terms of Newton's Law of Gravitation.

11. How many calendar days are there in a tropical year? A leap year?

EXERCISES

(Answers are given in the answer section at the back of the book.)

1. An artificial weather satellite is to be launched so that its northern boundary will be the Tropic of Cancer and its southern boundary the Tropic of Capricorn. What approximate angle should its orbital plane make with the plane of the equator?

2. The sun's altitude as observed at noon at a certain place is $30° 45'$. The sun is between the observer and the plane of the equator, its declination being $+20° 19'$. If the observer is in the southern hemisphere, what is his latitude?

3. For what place or places does the sun's noon altitude above the horizon equal the sun's positive declination at the same instant? (Remember that the declination is [+] if the sun is between the observer and the plane of the equator.)

4. The sun's noon rays are directly overhead in a certain place on a certain day. The declination at that time is $0° 00'$ and the sun is climbing into the northern hemisphere. What is the latitude of the place of observation? What is the date?

5. When the sun's noon rays are vertical at the Tropic of Capricorn, what will be the noon altitude of the sun as observed from the Tropic of Cancer? From the equator? From the south pole?

6. Through what angle will the plane of a Foucault pendulum seem to turn in one hour at latitude $35°$?

7. State which of the following are leap years: (a) 1963; (b) 1968; (c) 1970.

CHAPTER 7

Time

Sidereal Time and Solar Time

We could have as may kinds of time as we wished, by establishing any number of reference systems. One such established reference system is that of the stars. On the average, the earth completes one rotation with respect to the stars in 23 hours, 56 minutes, and 4.091 seconds, a period of time known as the *sidereal day*. The average time for the earth to complete one rotation with respect to the sun is precisely 24 hours. Figure 41 shows the relationship between the

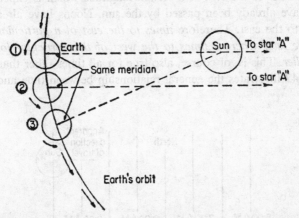

Fig. 41. In position 1, the sun and a distant star are on the meridian at true noon. In position 2, the distant star is again on the meridian, and a length of time (23 hours, 56 minutes, 4.091 seconds) equal to a sidereal day has elapsed. In position 3, the sun is again on the meridian, and a noon-to-noon 24-hour period of rotation equal to a solar day has ended. Arc length between positions 2 and 3 is greatly exaggerated.

solar and sidereal day, the relationship being analogous to that between the synodic and sidereal month.

It is often puzzling to students that the time for one complete rotation of the earth with respect to the sun is exactly, and very nicely, 24 hours, while the sidereal day is expressed in hours, minutes, seconds, and decimals of seconds. The reason for the exact 24 is, simply, that 24 was chosen by the Anglo-Saxons, some time prior to A.D. 1100 to represent a convenient number of divisions in a day. The number 24 could conceivably have resulted from dividing the three watches from sunrise to sunrise into 6; then 12; and then 24.

Longitude and Time

As the earth rotates once on its axis in 24 hours, it also rotates through $\frac{360°}{24}$, or 15° of longitude per hour. In studying time-longitude relationships it is recommended that the student visualize the sun moving around a stationary, nonrotating globe, from east to west, or across a map from east to west. In this way it is easy to see that all meridians to the east of a certain longitude which is experiencing noon have already been passed by the sun. Noons have already occurred to the east. Therefore *times to the east of a particular longitude are later whereas times to the west of the particular longitude are earlier*. This is, of course, also true for all times other than noon. Figure 42 illustrates the general relationship between time and longitude.

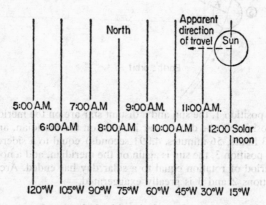

Fig. 42. Times to the east of a particular longitude are later. Times to the west of the longitude are earlier.

The Sun as a Clock

Nothing has been said so far in this discussion to indicate that our sun is commonly referred to as an indifferent "timekeeper." Actually, of course, it is the earth which is not a good timekeeper. To maintain its elliptical orbit about the sun, the earth must constantly increase its velocity of revolution over one half of the year to a maximum at perihelion, and then decrease it over the other half, to a minimum velocity of revolution at aphelion.

To understand how this affects the measurement of time, consider the earth near aphelion. It is moving through space at a less-than-average velocity of revolution. Its rotational velocity is the same, however, hence near aphelion the earth does not have to rotate quite as far to bring the sun over the same meridian again. Near perihelion, its velocity near to a maximum, the earth has to rotate for a slightly longer period to bring the sun over the same meridian again.

In addition to these effects, the tilt of the earth's axis also makes the sun seem to run either slow or fast during certain times of the year, in relation to passing over the same meridian on successive days. This effect, combined with the others, makes the sun an inexact clock.

True Solar Time, Mean Solar Time. Any measurement of a time unit based upon the true sun will, as can now be seen, vary with the time of year. A clock which indicated sun time would have to speed up during some portions of the year and slow down during others. In order to make solar days of uniform length, a fictitious sun called the *mean* sun is assumed to move at a constant velocity, completing its "orbit" in one year. The time kept by this mean sun is variously called *mean solar* time, or *civil* time, or *mean* time. The three terms are interchangeable, each meaning the time kept by the fictitious sun and by clocks and watches. The time kept by the true sun is called *true solar* time, *apparent* time, or *true* time. It is of course rather unfortunate from the standpoint of word association that, with respect to time, the words "apparent" and "true" are synonymous.

Time Zones, Standard Time, and Local Time

Time Zones. As a logical extension of the fact that rotation of the earth through 15° requires one hour of time, the 360° of longitude around the world is divided into 24 time zones, the governing or "standard" meridian of each zone usually having a longitude which is a multiple of 15° or of 7½°. The usual reason for the latter is that some smaller countries or possessions happen to be about halfway between the standard 15° division. The reference meridian for all of the world's time zones is that of 0° Longitude, passing through Greenwich, England. The majority of standard times around the world can therefore be expressed as Greenwich time plus or minus an even number of hours, or plus or minus some number of half-hours.

Larger countries in general use the multiple-of-15° system. The United States, for example, has Eastern Standard, Central Standard, Mountain Standard, and Pacific Standard times, the standard meridians being, respectively, 75° W, 90° W, 105° W, and 120° W. The standard meridians in the United States are, very roughly, in the middle of each time zone. The reasons that they are not precisely in the center, and that the limits of the time zones are not themselves meridians, result from consideration of state boundaries, natural boundaries, etc.

Standard Time; Daylight Saving Time. In each time zone of the world, then, watches and clocks give the mean solar or civil time for the standard meridian of that zone. This is the time being experienced by the standard meridian of that zone, hence the term "standard time." For example, a clock in the state of Maine will not indicate the time of 12:00 noon until the mean sun is over the 75° W meridian, which is far to the west of Maine. (Daylight Saving Time differs from standard time by one hour, the relationship being expressed by: Daylight Saving Time = Standard Time + 1 hour or, Standard Time = Daylight Saving Time − 1 hour.)

Local Time. The above brings up the point that by the time the clocks in a certain locality indicate standard time noon, that locality, if to the east of the standard meridian, has already experienced mean solar, or civil, noon. It may also have experienced true noon. In this case, the true sun also is now west of the local meridian. If a locality in a certain time zone is west of the standard meridian of the zone, the clocks of that locality will indicate 12:00 noon before the mean sun arrives over the local meridians. If the true sun also is to the east of the local meridian, local true noon has not yet occurred, either. (See Figure 43.)

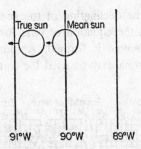

Fig. 43. All watches on all meridians in the time zone read 12:00. The mean sun and the true sun crossed the 89° W meridian before 12:00 by watch time. The true sun crossed the 90° W meridian before 12:00 (as in illustration) by watch time. The true sun may cross the 91° W meridian either after or before 12:00 watch time, followed within a few minutes by the mean sun. The true sun is ahead of or behind the mean sun according to the time of year.

The time when the mean or civil sun crosses a local meridian is called *local civil* noon, and *local civil* time is based upon this crossing of a local meridian by the fictitious sun. The time based upon the true or apparent sun's crossing of a local meridian is called *local apparent time.*

The Equation of Time; The Analemma

The Equation of Time. Some observations such as those for determining latitude and longitude require knowing the watch time of local apparent noon; that is, the watch time of the instant that the true sun crosses a certain meridian. For calculations of this type, the number of minutes that the true sun is running ahead of or behind the mean sun at that time must be known. This value is called the *equation of time.* In formula form, *equation of time = true solar time − mean solar time.* The value of the equation of time can be calculated from astronomical tables, for any instant of any day of the year, and may be of positive or negative sign depending upon the comparative magnitudes of true solar and mean solar time. It will be evident upon reflection that if the true sun is traveling ahead of the mean sun, the equation of time is positive; if the true sun is behind the mean sun, the equation of time is negative. At four instants during the year the mean and true suns are traveling together, and the equation of time is zero.

The Analemma. If the declination of the sun for each day of the year is plotted against the equation of time for each day, a figure-8 curve called the *analemma* is formed. An analemma is shown in Figure 44. The analemma may be used for certain rough determina-

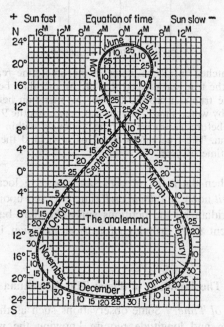

Fig. 44. The analemma. (Courtesy of John Wiley & Sons, Inc. Adapted from A. Strahler's *Physical Geography,* 2d edition, 1960)

tions of astronomical nature, as will be shown later. Some globes display analemmas on them, in the vicinity of the equator.

Longitude and Time, Equated

All time-longitude relationships can easily be calculated from the basic fact that every 15° of longitude swept over by the true or by the civil sun represents a one-hour change of time. Degrees, minutes, and seconds of longitude are represented by °, ′, ″, respectively. Hours, minutes, and seconds of time are represented by ^{h}, ^{m}, ^{s}, respectively:

$$15° \text{ longitude} = 1^h \text{ time}$$
$$1° \text{ longitude} = 4^m \text{ time}$$
$$1' \text{ longitude} = 4^s \text{ time}$$
$$1'' \text{ longitude} = \frac{1}{15}^s \text{ time}$$

and

$$1^h \text{ time} = 15° \text{ longitude}$$
$$1^m \text{ time} = 15' \text{ longitude}$$
$$1^s \text{ time} = 15'' \text{ longitude}$$

Problems Involving Time, Longitude, Declination of the Sun, and the Equation of Time

Example calculations involving some or all of the above topics have been left until now in order that a logical sequence ranging from simple to more involved types of problems might be presented in integrated form. *It is strongly recommended that the student sketch a few pertinent meridians, placing their corresponding times on them, as an aid to visualization of each problem.*

Problem: It is 2:00 P.M., Eastern Standard Time. What is the standard time in Greenwich, England? (This is known as Greenwich Civil Time, abbreviated GCT.)

Solution: $2:00 + \dfrac{75° - 0°}{15°} = 7:00$ P.M.

Problem: It is 3:00 P.M., GCT. What is the Pacific Standard Time?

Solution: Express 3:00 P.M. as $12 + 3 = 15$ hours after midnight, or 15^h.

$$15 - \frac{120° - 0°}{15°} = 7^h, \text{ or } 7 \text{ A.M.}$$

Problem: It is precisely $10^h\ 20^m\ 36^s$ A.M. Central Standard Time. What is the local civil time at a place in the Central Standard Time zone and whose longitude is 96° 20′ 15″ W?

Solution: As it is $10^h\ 20^m\ 36^s$ A.M. on the meridian of longitude 90° W, it is earlier than this at 96° 20′ 15″ W.

The difference in longitude between the two meridians = 6° 20′ 15″. Converting this to time, using the conversions given under "Longitude and Time, Equated":

$$6° = 6 \times 4^m = 24^m$$
$$20' = 20 \times 4^s = 80^s$$
$$15'' = 15 \times \frac{1}{15}^s = 1^s$$

Total time differences = $25^m\ 21^s$

The local time on the 96° 20′ 15″ meridian is therefore:

$$10^h \ 20^m \ 36^s - 25^m \ 21^s = 9^h \ 55^m \ 15^s \text{ A.M.}$$

Problem: At what standard time on December 10 will the true sun cross the meridian passing through Cape Kennedy, Florida?

Solution: From a map, the longitude of Cape Kennedy is about 80½° W. From the analemma printed in this chapter, the equation of time for December 10 is about +7½ minutes. The true solar time is 12:00 noon. Using the equation of "equation of time = true solar time — civil time," $+7½ = 12^h$ — civil time. (Notice that the true solar time of solar noon is always 12^h.) Solving algebraically, civil time = $12^h - 7½^m$ $= 11^h \ 52½^m$ = local civil time of true noon at 75° W. The difference in longitude between 80½° and 75° $= 5½° = 22^m$ of time. The watch time of the sun's crossing the 80½° W meridian will be:

$$11^h \ 52½^m + 22^m = 12^h \ 14½^m \text{ EST.}$$

Due to the inexactness of the values as obtained from the analemma, longitudes should be approximated to the nearest ½ degree. The same is true for values of declination obtained from the analemma, as in the following problem:

Problem: (a) At what standard time on February 15 will the sun cross the meridian passing through Iquique, Peru? (b) What will be the altitude of the noon sun at Iquique on this date? (Note: Iquique, Peru, is the site of an international astronomical observation station.)

Solution: (a) From a map, the latitude of Iquique is 20° S; its longitude is 70° W which places it in the Eastern Standard Time zone. From the analemma, the equation of time for February 15 = -14^m. "Equation of time = true solar time — civil time," so $-14^m = 12^h$ — civil time. Solving algebraically, $12^h + 14^m = 12^h \ 14^m$ = local civil time of the sun's crossing the meridian passing through Iquique. The difference in longitude between 75° and 70° $= 5° = 20^m$ of time. Therefore, the time at which the sun will cross the meridian through Iquique = $12^h \ 14^m - 20^m = 11^h \ 54^m$ EST.

(b) From the analemma, the sun's declination on February 15 is +13°. Using the relationship, developed before, that "altitude = 90° + declination — latitude," and substituting: Altitude = 90° + 13° — 20° = 83°. Note again that the sign of the latitude of the place of observation is always (+) for use in the equation. Also the sign of the sun's declination is (+) if the sun is between the observer and the equator; otherwise it would be (−).

Time, Longitude, and Dates

So far, this discussion has been in terms of time-longitude relationships during the same day. Suppose, however, that it is required to find the Eastern Standard Time corresponding to a Greenwich Civil Time of 3^h (3:00 A.M.), Tuesday.

The general procedure, in line with the solution of previous problems, would be this: $3 - \dfrac{75}{15} = 3 - 5 = -2^h$. But what does "$-2^h$, Tuesday" mean? The answer will be apparent if the student will here sketch 6 vertical lines to represent meridians 15° apart. The meridian farthest to the right is labeled 0° and the time of 3^h Tuesday is placed on it. The meridian to its left is labeled 15° W, and the time of 2^h Tuesday is placed on the 15° W meridian. Proceeding in this manner it will be found that the 45° W meridian has a time of 0^h Tuesday which is the same thing as 24^h Monday, or midnight. Thus the 60° W meridian will have a time of 23^h Monday, and the 75° W meridian will have a time of 22^h (10:00 P.M.) Monday. In a problem of this type, then, the correct time can be found by algebraically adding 24^h to the negative value obtained. Further, when a negative value is obtained, such as the -2 above, and the 180° meridian has not been "crossed" in the calculations, the day will be one less, as from Tuesday to Monday in the example.

The International Date Line

What happens if the 180° meridian *is* crossed in the calculations? Imagine that the time on the 150° E meridian is desired at the instant of 8:00 P.M., Eastern Standard Time, Thursday. If the student draws a series of lines as before to represent meridians, and places the longitudes and times on them, an interesting fact develops: Proceeding to the right from the line representing 75° W, the times increase until midnight Thursday occurs on the 15° W meridian. It is 1:00 A.M., *Friday,* on the meridian of Greenwich, and it will be found that the meridian of 150° E has a time of 11:00 A.M., Friday. Expressing 8:00 P.M. as 20^h: $20 + \dfrac{75 + 150}{15} = 35$; $35 - 24 = 11^h$ *Friday*.

Now, graphically proceeding to the *left* of the 75° meridian, plac-

ing longitudes and times on the meridians, it will be found that the
time on the 180° meridian is 13^h (1:00 P.M.) Thursday and, still
keeping on to the left, that the time at 150° E longitude is evidently
11^h (11:00 A.M.) *Thursday*. To sum up, going around to the east
gives us 11:00 A.M. Friday on the 150° E meridian; going around to
the west gives us 11:00 A.M. Thursday. The difference is precisely
24 hours. Somewhere a new day has begun.

To understand this, imagine the sun in a position over the Greenwich meridian on, say, Monday. It is therefore 12:00 noon Monday
at Greenwich, 0° longitude. At the same instant a curious condition
is present on the 180° meridian. Calculating the time on the 180°
meridian by going around to the east from Greenwich gives: 12^h
$+ \dfrac{180}{15} = 24^h$ Monday. The time on the 180° meridian, going around

to the west, is: $12^h - \dfrac{180}{15} = 0^h$ Monday. At the precise instant of
Greenwich noon Monday, then, it is Monday all over the entire
world. The instant the sun is slightly to the west of the Greenwich
meridian, however, a new day, Tuesday, begins on the 180° meridian
and starts sweeping around the world in an east-west direction. In
crossing the 180° meridian therefore, a ship's calendar is either set
ahead or put back by a full 24 hours.

The preceding statement has to be modified somewhat. It so happens that the 180° meridian passes over the Siberian Peninsula and
some Pacific islands. Therefore the *International Date Line,* instead
of being synonymous with the 180° meridian, is actually a jagged
and in some cases a curved line in order that people living in the
same general areas will not have times differing by 24 hours.

An example involving time-longitude-International Date Line relationships is given:

Problem: It is 5:00 P.M., Eastern Standard Time, Wednesday. What
time is it in a place whose longitude is 135° E?

Solution: Going eastward from the 75° meridian and expressing 5:00
P.M. as 17^h (after midnight); $17 + \dfrac{75}{15}$ (time difference between GCT
and EST) $+ \dfrac{135}{15}$ (time difference between GCT and time at 135° E) $=$
31^h. $31^h - 24^h = 7^h$ Thursday. (If the sum exceeds 24 hours, a new day
has started for that longitude.)

As a check, going westward from the 75° meridian, $17 - \dfrac{105}{15}$ (time difference between EST and time at 180° meridian) $- \frac{45}{15}$ (time difference between times at 180° meridian and 135° E meridian) $= 7^{\text{h}}$ *Thursday* (because the 180° meridian was crossed).

Note on Time-Longitude Problem Solutions. It is re-emphasized at this point that the student will find it helpful to draw a series of vertical lines to represent meridians, and place their corresponding longitudes and times on them. This is especially helpful when a change in date occurs between longitudes. It is strongly recommended in studying time-longitude relationships involving the International Date Line that the student, at first at least, take the little time necessary to sketch 24 vertical lines to represent the 24 multiple-of-15° lines of longitude around the world. The corresponding times should then be marked on these lines of longitude. *The purely mathematical solutions of problems should be worked out in conjunction with such sketches until the student can actually visualize the correct relationships in his mind's eye.*

REVIEW

1. Explain why the mean solar day is exactly 24 hours in duration.

2. What is apparent solar time? What is mean solar time? What is the equation of time?

3. Explain the construction of the analemma in terms of what is plotted and how it is plotted.

4. Do watches and clocks keep apparent solar time or mean solar time? Why?

5. State the general relationship of degrees of longitude to time.

6. What is standard time? What is the relationship of standard time to daylight saving time?

7. Where is the International Date Line? What is its significance in terms of dates?

8. Explain the difference between civil time and local civil time. How does local civil time differ from local apparent time?

EXERCISES

(Answers are given in the answer section at the back of the book.)

1. In changing from a standard time to daylight saving time is a clock set back one hour from, say, 2:00 to 1:00 or is it set ahead one hour to read 3:00?

2. When it is 14^h 26^m 25^s Greenwich Civil Time, it is 9^h 20^m 20^s local civil time at a given place. What is the longitude of the place?

3. On a certain day the true sun crosses a certain meridian at 11^h 45^m 20^s local civil time. What is the equation of time?

4. It is 10:00 P.M. Central Standard Time, Tuesday. What time is it in a place whose longitude is 120° E. What day?

5. What will be the watch time (Pacific Standard Time) on October 20 when the true sun crosses the meridian of a place whose longitude is 115° 20′ 25″ W? Use the information from the analemma printed in this chapter.

6. A navigator in the northern hemisphere "shoots" the sun at true noon and observes that the angle of the sun above the horizon is 40° 23′. The declination of the sun at that instant was −10° 16′. The Greenwich Civil Time at that instant was 16^h 45^m and the equation of time was −10^m. What is the navigator's latitude? His longitude?

7. On a certain day the mean sun is behind the true sun by 5^m 23^s. State the value of the equation of time, with proper sign.

8. The crew of Ship A experienced no Christmas Day last year. The crew of Ship B experienced two Christmases last year. Explain what happened.

9. The answer to this exercise will not be found in this book, and the question itself is asked only as a thought stimulator: It takes approximately 8 minutes for the light from the sun to reach the earth; therefore by the time the sun appears to us to be on a certain meridian it has really passed that meridian 8 minutes before. How can we say, then, that this is the time of true noon, and thus base our entire system of time upon meridional observations which apparently are always in error by 8 minutes?

CHAPTER 8

The Atmosphere and Its Temperature

Radiation from the sun travels through space at 186,000 miles per second, the speed of light. The radiation reaches the earth's magnetic field in about 8½ minutes. Then, in less than ⅓ of a second, the earth's magnetic field and atmosphere sort out, process, and distribute the solar radiation on and about the planet. This is the primary step toward the heating of the earth's atmosphere. At any one instant, and for several reasons, the heating is done unequally from equator to pole. The cumulative effects of this unequal heating are directly responsible for the major phenomena of weather and climate.

Weather, Climate, and the Atmosphere

Weather and Climate. The study of weather is called *meteorology*. The study of climate is called *climatology*. *Weather* refers to the condition of the earth's atmosphere in a locality or region at a specific time. *Climate* refers to the general condition of the earth's atmosphere in a locality or region over an appreciable period of time. For example, a "fair day," a *weather* observation, could describe one particular day in a region whose *climate* is described as "rainy."

The Atmosphere and Weather. The *atmosphere* consists of the gases surrounding the earth. These gases are held around the earth by the gravitational attraction between the earth and each particle of gas. *Dry* air, "air" being a mixture of gases, consists of about 78 percent nitrogen, 21 percent oxygen, 0.93 percent argon, and about .03 percent carbon dioxide, all by volume. Krypton, xenon, neon, helium, ozone, hydrogen, and some other gases exist in the atmosphere in very small amounts. The gases in air occur in almost precisely the same proportions in any usual sample of air, whereas the moisture content of air may vary considerably. For example, tropical air can contain up to about 5 percent water vapor by volume, a very important fact which will be referred to later when heat transfer and storm generation are discussed.

Many kinds of particles are scattered throughout the gases of the atmosphere. These include dust, salt, and ice particles, all of which act as nuclei for precipitation in the lower atmosphere and thus play an all-important role in weather and climate. Most of these particles and most of the water vapor in the atmosphere occur in the *troposphere,* the lowest layer of the atmosphere. Our directly experienced weather is therefore confined to the troposphere whose thickness above the earth's surface varies from about 4 miles above the poles to about 11 miles above the equator. It would be incorrect, however, to state that all of our weather originates in the troposphere. More and more evidence indicates that disturbances in the upper atmospheric layers have strong influence upon our weather and climate.

The Constitution of Weather and Climate. What constitutes weather and climate? Imagine that we are to describe the condition of the atmosphere at a certain time at a certain locality. So we are to describe the weather. As a start, *air temperature* would be part of our report. Then, perhaps, it is cloudy or humid or even raining, or perhaps the air is extremely dry at that time. *Atmospheric moisture* would be a second part of the description. Perhaps it is very windy, or there may be a dead calm. *Winds,* or the lack of them, would be included in the description. If the locality is experiencing, or about to experience, rainy weather, the barometer is probably reading lower than average; if it is experiencing, or about to experience, good weather the barometer readings are probably getting higher. *Atmospheric pressure* would also be part of our description of the condition of the earth's atmosphere at that place and at that time.

Most weather measurements will therefore fall into one or more of these four major categories: *air temperature; atmospheric moisture; winds;* and *atmospheric pressure.* As climate patterns result from weather patterns, the above four groups also constitute the four major areas in the study and analysis of climate.

Solar Radiation and Our Atmosphere. If all the radiant energy which starts out from the sun suddenly got through to the earth's surface, virtually all animal life on this planet would be destroyed in a matter of minutes. Within these same minutes great storms all over the world would reflect the birth of almost unimaginably violent weather and climate.

As previously stated, it takes about 8½ minutes for radiation from the sun to reach the outer limits of the earth's magnetic field 60,000 miles or so above the earth's surface. Then, the solar radiation, consisting of great waves of particles and rays ranging from the short-wave X rays to invisible, long-wave heat rays, hurtles through the magnetic field, toward the earth. (See Figure 45.)

At an elevation of approximately 20,000 miles above the earth's surface the sun's radiation streams into the outer layer of the earth's atmosphere, the *exosphere*. This is a fantastic region of charged atomic particles of nitrogen and oxygen, some of which are at temperatures of more than 3000° Centigrade, yet are so thinly distributed that the spaces between them are regions of bitter cold when the sun is on the opposite side of the earth. It is in the exosphere that some of the particles from the sun are abruptly trapped by the earth's magnetic field in a huge doughnut-shaped ring whose center is about 10,000 miles above the earth's surface. This is the outer Van Allen radiation belt.

Sweeping through the exosphere, the solar radiation now passes the inner Van Allen radiation belt, centered about 2500 miles above the earth's surface, and enters the *ionosphere* at approximately 500 miles above the surface of the earth. As rare as the atmosphere of the exosphere is, a little of the solar radiation has already been reflected and deflected back into space, through collision. It has taken about $\frac{1}{10}$ of a second for the bulk of the remaining radiation, if not trapped in the Van Allen belts, to travel through the exosphere.

Into the ionosphere now pour X rays, infrared rays, ultraviolet rays, charged particles, radio waves, and light waves. Due largely to the ultraviolet radiation, molecules are split, electrons are torn away from atoms to make ions, and huge charged, or *ionized,* layers are thus constantly replenished throughout the ionosphere. More particle collisions take place with tremendous combined velocities and more particles are hurled back into space. Light, also now colliding with particles in the lower ionosphere, begins to break up into its component colors. Blue light scatters from particle to particle, making the first of a blue "sky" as seen from the lower portion of the atmosphere. Within $\frac{2}{1000}$ of a second from the time it entered the ionosphere the radiation, depleted by the ionosphere of X rays,

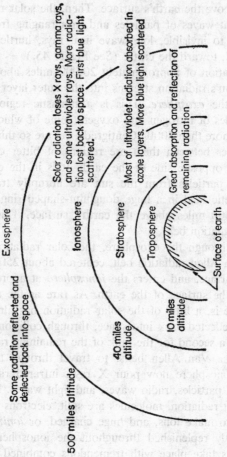

Fig. 45. Diagrammatic representation of depletion of solar energy in the atmospheric shells. Read diagram from top to bottom. Not to scale.

gamma rays, and some ultraviolet rays, is bombarding the upper limit of the stratosphere, 40 miles above the surface of the earth.

As the remaining solar radiation plunges into the thin air of the stratosphere, the radiation is now composed mainly of visible light rays, infrared rays, and ultraviolet rays. More blue light is scattered. The ultraviolet rays constitute a potentially lethal packet of energy in that if most of them got through to the earth, surface animal life would be blinded and killed within a few minutes, by radiation. Only 20 miles above our heads, however, most of the incoming ultraviolet radiation is absorbed in ozone layers in the stratosphere. As the remaining solar radiation comes into the troposphere, it is largely made up of visible light rays and infrared rays, with relatively little ultraviolet. In approximately $\frac{1}{4000}$ of a second what is left of the traveling solar radiation will reach the earth's surface. The troposphere will do the final screening and distributing of the radiant energy.

In the troposphere, the solar energy is suddenly confronted by what, compared to its former travels, is almost a solid wall of dust particles, ice particles, molecules, pollen, salt particles, clouds, and invisible water vapor. Wholesale absorption of energy and reflecting of energy is done in the troposphere and the sun's radiant energy finally reaching the earth's surface is just about 50 percent of that originally leaving the sun. About 35 percent of the energy has been reflected or deflected back into "space" and about 15 percent has been absorbed in the earth's atmosphere. In $\frac{1}{3}$ of a second, the amount of incoming radiation has been cut in half before reaching the earth and its originally deadly constitution altered to that which makes present life possible on this planet.

(NOTE: In actual scientific practice today, the atmosphere is commonly considered to consist of 9 shells, based upon temperature differences, molecular weight differences, ionization, chemical reaction, etc. For purposes of clarity, however, the above description was given in terms of four major divisions.)

How the Atmosphere Is Heated

Heat and Temperature. An understanding of the meanings of "heat" and "temperature" is basic to an understanding of atmospheric heating. *Heat* is the total energy possessed by something due to the motion of its molecules. *Temperature* is merely an *indication* of heat.

To illustrate, consider a pool of rain water, and an ocean. Both may be at the same average temperature but the ocean contains almost infinitely more heat because of the relative sizes of the two bodies of water. The little heat contained in the pool of water will, by itself, do virtually nothing to warm the atmosphere. On the other hand, as will be seen later, the heat energy absorbed and reradiated by the oceans is at the very basis of climate control.

Measuring Temperature. The three temperature scales commonly used are *Centigrade, Fahrenheit,* and *Kelvin.* At standard atmospheric pressure, pure water freezes at 0° on the Centigrade scale and boils at 100°. On the Fahrenheit scale, water freezes at 32° and boils at 212°. As 100 Centigrade degrees equal 180 Fahrenheit degrees, the length of one Fahrenheit degree equals ⅝ of the length of a Centigrade degree if both scales are placed on the same thermometer. The Kelvin degree is the same as the Centigrade degree in value but begins at the temperature of no molecular motion, or *absolute zero.* Therefore, 0° K is equivalent to −273° C, while 0° Centigrade is equivalent to 273° K. Kelvin temperature is often referred to as *absolute* temperature; for example, "296°, absolute."

Readings on any one of the three scales may be converted to equivalent readings in the others by use of the following listed formulas:

$$C = \frac{5}{9}(F + 32)$$

$$F = \frac{9}{5} C - 32$$

$$K = \quad C + 273$$

$$C = \quad K - 273$$

Insolation. The net solar energy received by the earth and its atmosphere is called *insolation* and, as indicated before, amounts to about 65 percent of the total energy originally emanating from the sun. It will be recalled that 15 percent of the total radiant energy has been absorbed by the atmosphere and that only 50 percent of the energy reaches the earth's surface. These figures are, of course, averages.

The 15 percent of the radiant energy originally absorbed by the atmosphere consists mainly of some infrared and ultraviolet whose wavelengths were long enough to enable water vapor and carbon dioxide to absorb them and convert their energy to heat energy, thus helping to warm the atmosphere.

About 10 percent of the energy reaching the surface bounces off the surface and back into the atmosphere where it is also largely converted to heat energy. Again this is an average figure and it can vary greatly according to what and how the radiant energy hits.

The amount of radiant energy so reflected from a surface is called the surface's *albedo*. The albedo is expressed in percent and just as the albedo for the earth as a whole varies, the albedo for a certain substance can also vary widely. For example, water being heated in the vertical rays of the sun, such as ocean water near the Tropic of Cancer on June 21, will reflect only about 2 percent of the energy. At the same time, however, due to the angle of the sun's rays, water toward the south pole may be reflecting about half of the energy. The albedos for ground and rock surfaces vary from about 2 percent to 30 percent. Snow and ice reflect from about 50 to 90 percent of the impinging visible light, infrared, and ultraviolet, a fact which explains why snow does not melt much under the action of a blazing sun if the air is cold, and why snow blindness occurs.

The amount of solar radiation finally received by a particular locality on a particular day as insolation is controlled by two things: the angle of the sun's rays at that locality, and the number of hours of full exposure to the sun on that day. Both of these factors depend upon the latitude and the time of the year, as discussed in Chapter 6.

The relationship between the number of hours of exposure to the sun, and the amount of insolation is obvious. As for the effect of the angle of the sun's rays upon the amount of insolation, this can easily be demonstrated by holding a hand horizontally over a lighted electric lamp, and about 4 inches above it until the hand becomes almost uncomfortably warm. Then, with the center of the hand at the same elevation as before but with the hand at an angle of about 45°, repeat the procedure. It will be found that with the hand at an angle, it takes appreciably longer for even the lower part of the hand to attain the same intensity of sensation of warmth as before.

In the above experiment the average intensity of the heat per unit area of hand surface was diminished by about 30 percent by rotating the hand through 45 degrees. The general relationship between the angle of the sun's rays and the amount of energy per unit area received by the earth's surface is shown in Figure 46.

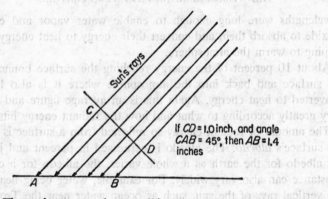

If CD = 1.0 inch, and angle
CAB = 45°, then AB = 1.4
inches

Fig. 46. The sun's rays are shown striking AB, an earth surface, at an angle of 45°. The surface CD represents a surface at right angles to the sun's rays. Each surface receives the same amount of energy (E); however, if the concentration on CD is $\frac{E}{1}$, then that on AB is $\frac{E}{1.4} = .70\ E$. Therefore, the *intensity* of heat is about 30 percent less on AB than on CD.

From what has been said already, it will be apparent that, as the sun's rays are always vertical somewhere between the Tropics of Cancer and Capricorn, maximum yearly insolation will occur in the approximately 3000-mile-wide "tropics" belt whose center is the equator. At the other extreme, each polar region receives only the sun's most slanting rays, and then for only one half of the year. The polar regions are therefore regions of minimum insolation throughout the year. The yearly total of insolation, then, is a maximum at the equator and decreases toward a minimum at the poles.

It is informative to note the insolation pattern at the time of a solstice, say the winter solstice in the northern hemisphere. The sun's noon rays are vertical at the Tropic of Capricorn, at 23½° S latitude. The date is December 22. For the past three months the sun's vertical noon rays have been sweeping southward from the equator. Now they are moving toward the equator and they will be there in three months, on March 21. Therefore December 22 represents the halfway mark in the six months that the entire southern hemisphere is exposed to the most direct solar radiation it ever experiences.

There is another consideration. As it is during these six months that the sun's average altitude also reaches a maximum in the southern hemisphere, the average length of daylight in the southern hemisphere also reaches a maximum. (See Chapter 6.) During these six months, then, the southern hemisphere experiences insolation of both maximum intensity and maximum duration. During those same six months from September 21 to March 21, the northern hemisphere is experiencing its minimum amount of insolation. Then, from March 21 to September 21, the northern hemisphere experiences its maximum amount of insolation while the southern hemisphere experiences its minimum.

Reradiation. Insolation in itself does not heat the earth's atmosphere. The bulk of the solar radiation coming into the troposphere, especially the lower troposphere, is composed of short-wave infrared or near-infrared which has little difficulty in passing through the atmosphere and reaching the earth's surface. There, it is absorbed and converted to heat in widely varying degree in rock, soil, fresh and ocean water, snow, and ice. These receiving mediums are warmed to different depths and intensities depending upon the substance and the angle of impact of the radiation.

Any heated material will give off infrared radiation and hence the earth *reradiates* infrared back into the atmosphere. There is an all-important distinction, though, between this reradiated infrared and the original infrared, and the difference is due to the fact that the greater the temperature of a body, the shorter are the wavelengths of the heat or infrared waves emitted. The short-wave infrared from the sun passes easily through the atmosphere because it *is* short wave and is absorbed at the earth's surface where it is converted into heat energy. The temperature of the earth's surface, although raised, is of course nowhere near the temperature of the sun, so the earth's surface reradiates relatively long-wave heat or infrared rays. Where the shorter rays could pass through the atmosphere almost at will, the longer rays emanating from the ground are trapped and absorbed by water vapor and carbon dioxide and converted into heat energy. *It is by this process of reradiation from the earth's surface that the atmosphere receives more than ⅔ of its heat.* The remaining atmospheric heat results chiefly from the radiation that is trapped in the atmosphere before reaching the earth's surface.

The "Greenhouse" Effect. The heating of the atmosphere by reradiation is often referred to as the "greenhouse effect." Short-wave infrared streams through the glass of a greenhouse and is absorbed by the soil and other material in the greenhouse, and is converted into heat energy. This energy is now reradiated as relatively long-wave infrared which cannot pass through the transparent glass. Thus the infrared, trapped, is absorbed by the atmosphere within the greenhouse and again converted into heat energy, keeping the greenhouse at a temperature which, even during freezing weather outside, is usually well into the 70s or 80s. Similarly, the atmosphere acts as a mammoth greenhouse roof surrounding the earth.

The Horizontal Distribution of Temperature

Isotherms. Lines connecting points of equal temperature are called isotherms. Figure 47 and Figure 48 are isothermal maps of surface temperatures for the months of July and January, respectively. Notice that the isotherms tend to parallel lines of latitude and that this tend-

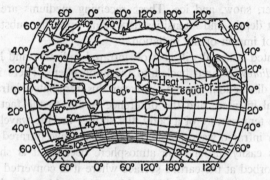

Fig. 47. Average sea level temperature, July. (Adapted from the U. S. Navy Department)

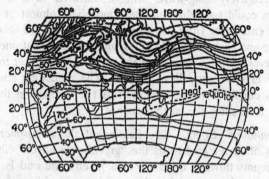

Fig. 48. Average sea level temperature, January. (Adapted from the U. S. Navy Department)

ency is especially strong in the southern hemisphere where there are fewer and smaller land masses.

Heating of Land and Water.   If the earth's surface were all water, the isotherms would directly reflect the earth's insolation pattern and they would all, except for minor variations, be east-west lines. The land masses deflect the isotherms from this trend because the temperatures of land masses generally differ from the temperatures of the ocean surface at the same latitudes. One reason for these differences in temperature is due to the *specific heats* of water and soil.

Specific heat was defined in Chapter 2 as being the amount of heat necessary to raise a unit mass one degree in temperature. The specific heat of water is about 5 times that of rock and soil, which means that rock and soil will heat up to the same temperature 5 times as rapidly as will water. Conversely, rock and soil will lose heat 5 times as rapidly as will water. Compared with land, then, it is relatively difficult to heat water and it is also relatively difficult to cool water.

In addition, solar radiation can enter the transparent ocean to considerable depth before being absorbed and reradiated to warm the water. Ocean currents of various kinds perform a wholesale mixing service and the net result of reradiation at depth and mixing is that an average cubic foot of sea water is heated slowly. Conversely, and for the same general reasons, ocean water will lose its heat slowly. Also, the air over the ocean is almost supercharged with water vapor which holds the heat in, above the oceans. All in all, therefore, the temperature of ocean water exhibits a relatively small range between summer and winter. As would be expected, the air directly above the oceans in general has the same temperature patterns as the surface ocean waters.

On the other hand, land heats up much more rapidly than does water and it also loses its heat much more rapidly. Next, land surfaces are opaque. Much of the solar radiation is reflected back toward space but that which is absorbed by the land penetrates only skin-deep and thus rapidly and intensely heats the very surface. (As a matter of fact solar radiation penetrates much deeper into snow and ice than into a typical land surface.) All of the above helps to explain why the highest and lowest temperatures recorded on the earth's surface are land and not ocean temperatures. Again, the temperature of the air directly over land surfaces is mainly determined by the temperature of the land surface, just as the temperature of air over the ocean is largely governed by the temperature of the ocean water.

Displacement of Isotherms. Now to understand what happens to isotherms because of the differences in temperature between land masses and the oceans, refer to Figure 49, which shows a hypothetical

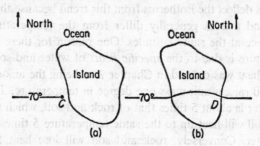

Fig. 49. Influence of land mass upon isotherms. For the conditions stated in the text the 70° isotherm shown in (a) will be displaced as in (b).

island in the northern hemisphere in July. The 70° isotherm approaches the west coast of the island at point *C.* Which way will it turn?

First of all, it is July, summer in the northern hemisphere. From what has been said before, the land surface at a particular latitude will be at a higher summer temperature than ocean water at the same latitude. The land temperature at point *C* will be higher than the ocean temperature at point *C.*

Second, temperature in general must decrease from the equator toward the poles, therefore the 70° temperature on land will be found to the *north* of point *C,* and the isotherm is drawn as shown across the continent to point *D.* From *D* the isotherm swings back south as the water directly offshore is colder than water to the south.

Two things should be pointed out at this time: first, *if the student will take the few minutes necessary to understand thoroughly why isotherms shift as in the above simple example, an extremely good start toward the grasp of weather and climate fundamentals will have been made.*

Second, some readers may wonder why the isothermal maps are drawn for the months of July and January, rather than for the months of June and December, the months of the solstices, when the difference in insolation between the northern and southern hemispheres is at a maximum. The reason for this is that there is about a six-week lag between the receipt of insolation and the total distribution of the resulting heat. So, although the difference in *insolation* is a maximum in June and December, the differences in *temperature* are at a maximum in July and January. The same effect can be seen on a minor scale during any day. The sun's noon rays are vertical at noon but the highest temperature in a certain locality on a still day usually occurs at about 3:00 P.M.

Air Temperature throughout the Day

It is seen from the above that by the time of maximum temperature at about 3:00 P.M., insolation has been decreasing from its maximum value for about three hours. After about 3:00 P.M., therefore, the ground and the air above it are losing more heat than they are gaining from solar radiation and this will of course continue through the night although at a continuing lesser pace.

At sunrise the ground and the air above it are still losing heat, and the sun's radiation is just starting to strike a given locality. Again it will take time for the ground to convert this radiation and heat the air. In the meantime the ground is still losing heat. With the sun becoming higher, the amount of heat furnished by insolation will, however, eventually surpass the amount of heat being lost by the ground, and at that point the temperature of the ground and of the air above the ground will start to rise. Up to this point the ground and the air above the ground have been steadily getting colder, so this point represents the time of minimum daily temperature, usually twenty minutes or so after sunrise.

The student may have wondered during the first part of the above explanation, why the ground radiates heat throughout the night at a "continuing lesser pace." This introduces a relationship between heat and temperature whose presentation, for the purpose of clarity, has been reserved for now: the quantity of heat emitted by a body varies directly as the 4th power of the absolute temperature of that body. As an example, a body radiating a certain amount of heat at a certain absolute temperature will radiate only $\frac{1}{2^4}$, or $\frac{1}{16}$ of that amount of heat at an absolute temperature half that of the original. For all (natural) temperatures expressed in °F or °C on earth, however, the corresponding absolute temperatures are not materially different from each other, hence losses of heat at the surface of the earth are not nearly as dramatic as they might first appear to be.

In accordance with the above, a desert which cools from 100° F to 40° F at night will still be radiating two thirds of the energy that it did at the higher temperature. The energy is still in the form of long-wave infrared, though, and as there is relatively less carbon dioxide or water vapor over deserts, much of the reradiation escapes without being converted into heat. Thus, with practically "everything going out and nothing coming in" the desert may reach an extremely low temperature just after sunrise. Land with appreciable vegetation on it has relatively greater amounts of carbon dioxide and water vapor in the air above it. Much of the reradiation from the ground will be absorbed by the water vapor and the carbon dioxide to heat the air, giving a higher minimum temperature after sunrise than that for a desert at the same latitude.

Air Temperature and Altitude

No one who has ever walked barefooted over a pavement, or beach sand, on a hot day can doubt that the most intense heating of the air is done at ground surface. This fact, which is of vital importance in the growing of many crops, is also of great importance in the vertical distribution of air temperature.

The heat from the air layer near the surface, and the heat already trapped in the atmosphere is distributed only slightly by conduction. *Convection* is the great distributor of heat vertically throughout the troposphere. Even so, the temperature of the air will generally decrease with altitude, the average rate in still air being about 3½° Fahrenheit per 1000 feet difference in elevation. This rate is called the *normal lapse rate* and it should be noted that the normal lapse rate applies only to air which is still and not rising. The temperature keeps dropping at this rate until the troposphere meets the stratosphere at the *tropopause* and there the lapse rate virtually ceases in the thin air of the stratosphere. The temperature in the stratosphere remains fairly constant at various "latitudes," averaging about −60° F over polar regions and around −90° F over equatorial regions.

As the height of the troposphere over the polar regions is approximately 4 miles versus a height of about 11 miles over the equator, the troposphere also has an "equatorial bulge." Although contributed to by a maximum centrifuging action at the equator, the bulging of the tropopause is also caused by the increase in air temperature as the equator is approached, which brings about a corresponding increase in the height to which the lighter air will rise. Stratospheric flight is thus simpler to attain the nearer the poles are approached because the stratosphere is at a lower altitude. Also, over equatorial regions, the stratosphere becomes very thin and may apparently not even exist over some areas.

A curious fact which has only fairly recently come to light is that the tropopause has, in places, an overlapping or shingled structure instead of being an unbroken surface. As will be seen in Chapter 10, this feature may have great influence upon certain wind systems and storm patterns.

Temperature Inversions; Frost; Fog; Smog

As the temperature of the atmosphere normally decreases with the altitude, the reverse of this situation is called an *inversion*. What causes colder air to underlie warmer air?

First, an inversion could be caused by a relatively cold air mass moving in and bodily displacing the warmer air to a position above it. This is a *frontal inversion* and this can happen between air layers at any place in the troposphere. Next, *ground inversions* result when the air near the ground is losing heat so rapidly that the lower layers of air finally become colder than the upper layers. In this type of inversion, the air may lose enough heat to precipitate moisture, in which case a *ground radiation fog* may form. As has been noticed by many readers of this chapter who drive to work in the early morning, this type of inversion is usually a night phenomenon and, unfortunately for early morning driving, it usually keeps forming with increasing intensity until minimum temperature, just after sunrise. There is the consolation, however, that the conditions which make the rapid re-radiation possible in the first place, clear sky and stable air, are usually associated with generally good weather for at least a few days. In cold dry weather, however, a ground inversion can bring about a killing frost.

All in all, inversions may be caused in five major ways, two of which are outlined above. The three remaining types of inversion are:

Air drainage inversions. Example: cold air slides down a hill slope into a valley and stays there.

Advection inversion. Example: relatively warm ocean air passes over a cold ocean current.

Subsidence inversion. Example: a large air mass high in the troposphere suddenly "collapses" and spreads itself out. In so doing it becomes warmer than the air below it.

If the inversion is of the type that can form at high altitudes as well as near the ground, it may go unheeded by all except airlines and their passengers. If the inversion occurs near the ground surface its presence may be signified by a radiation fog, by smoke moving lazily to a certain level and then seeming to drift horizontally, or by thick haze near the ground. In many cities inversions of varying degree and duration cause a poisonous blanket of *smog* to hang over an area rather than allowing the particles from incomplete combustion of gasoline in motor vehicles, and particles of industrial waste, to escape into the higher atmosphere and be dissipated by the upper winds. As it is, water vapor condenses around the particles, thus giving the effect of a combination of smoke and fog, hence the word "smog." Unfortunately, the action of sunlight upon smog particles often converts the particles to new substances which are far more poisonous than the original particles, and brings about the acrid smell and eye-watering characteristics so familiar to residents of many large cities.

REVIEW

1. Distinguish between "weather" and "climate."
2. What is the earth's atmosphere? How thick is it? Name its four major divisions as given in this chapter and state their characteristics.
3. Distinguish between "insolation" and "heat."
4. Distinguish between "temperature" and "heat."
5. Other than the screening function of the atmosphere, what two things determine the amount of insolation received in a locality at a particular instant?
6. Explain fully how the earth's atmosphere is heated.
7. What is the "albedo" of a substance?
8. Explain the influence of land masses upon isotherms, including the directions in which the isotherms swing in each hemisphere over land masses in both summer and winter.
9. Why are isothermal maps usually drawn for the months of July and January?

10. When is the coldest time of the day? Why?
11. What is a temperature "inversion"? List two possible causes.
12. What is the "normal lapse rate"?

EXERCISES

(Answers are given in the answer section at the back of the book.)

1. When an electric heater or stove is turned on, a hand close to the coil senses increasing warmth before the coil glows visibly. What is the hand feeling, in terms of radiation? That is, what kind of radiation is being emitted—X-ray, infrared, or ultraviolet?

2. It was stated in this chapter that the higher the temperature of a radiating body, the shorter the wavelength of the radiation. What does the glowing of a heater coil indicate about the wavelengths of visible light versus the wavelengths of the invisible radiation first felt after the switch is turned on?

3. Change $-20°$ F to °C.

4. Change $60°$ C to °K.

5. The temperature in the stratosphere over polar regions is about $-60°$ F; over equatorial regions about $-90°$ F. Assuming that the stratosphere begins at 4 miles above polar regions and at 10 miles above an average equatorial region, and that the lapse rate is $3\frac{1}{2}°$ F for every 1000 feet, vertically, what would be the ground temperatures in the polar regions and in the equatorial regions? Contrast these values with averages for these areas from the isothermal maps of Figures 47 and 48.

4. Change ...

CHAPTER 9

Atmospheric Moisture

Water exists in the air as solid, liquid, and gas. The solid phases such as ice and snow, and liquid forms such as rain and dew, result from the condensation of water vapor. Water vapor, the gaseous form of water, results from vaporization over oceans, lakes, rivers, glaciers, snowfields, swamps, or moist ground, and vegetation. This *vaporization,* the change from a solid or liquid state to the gaseous state, is the process which feeds virtually all of the moisture for rain, snow, sleet, hail, and dew into the atmospheric machinery.

Vaporization

Evaporation; Boiling; Sublimation. Vaporization can be accomplished by evaporation, by boiling, or by sublimation. *Evaporation* is the vaporization of a liquid at its surface only. Evaporation can occur at any temperature and should not be confused with boiling. During *boiling,* vaporization is occurring in bubbles throughout the liquid as well as occurring on the surface. The expanding bubbles rise to the surface and then break, releasing vapor into the air. *Sublimation* occurs when a solid changes directly into the gaseous state, bypassing the liquid state. The vaporization of "dry ice" is an example of sublimation.

Of the three methods, evaporation is by far the most important in furnishing water vapor to the atmosphere. This can easily be appreciated by glancing at a globe or world map. About three fourths of the earth's surface is covered by water, and evaporation is constantly taking place over the approximately 150 million square miles of water surface, over moist ground, and over vegetation by transpiration. The latter source of water vapor is by no means insignificant. Some trees are capable of individually transferring up to 2 tons of water annually into the atmosphere.

Ice covers more than 10 percent of the earth's surface, hence vaporization by sublimation of ice and snow contributes appreciable water vapor to the atmosphere.

Boiling furnishes the least amount of atmospheric moisture, from steam from volcanic eruptions, geysers, etc. It should be remarked, however, that our atmosphere originated from precisely such volcanic eruptions all over the world when the earth was in its infancy.

Vaporization and Heat. The interrelationship of vaporization and heat is extremely important in meteorology. Water vapor contains *latent heat,* heat whose presence is not felt or sensed until the vapor condenses to water again and releases the heat. In addition to the fact that water vapor helps distribute heat all over the world (Chapter 10), water vapor is also the fuel which powers major rainstorms and the great hurricanes or typhoons.

The energy of the water vapor in the atmosphere is tremendous. In 10 days, for example, an average hurricane, by condensing water vapor, releases heat equal to 10 million atom bombs and it is this heat which keeps the great storms going and which intensifies their fury. Even a gentle convectional rain shower covering only about 4 square miles releases heat equivalent to an early type atom bomb and it is this heat which sustains the storm action.

As to where the heat in water vapor comes from, consider the surface of an ocean, lake, pond, or river. As outlined in Chapter 8, the *temperature* of the water may be fairly low, but these bodies of water possess tremendous *heat* due to the activity of their countless numbers of molecules.

These molecules are rapidly moving around in all directions and every now and then, one of the most active molecules at the surface will hurl itself into the air and stay there, between the air molecules. The water molecules which do this are literally few and far apart, so far apart in fact that they no longer form a liquid; they form water vapor, a gas.

As the molecules which escape from the liquid are the most energetic, they take considerable heat with them in the form of energy of motion. Evaporation is therefore a cooling process for the surface of a liquid. For every gram of water evaporated, surface water gives up about 600 calories. These calories are now in one gram of water vapor, as *latent heat of vaporization,* which represents the extra energy possessed by one gram of these more energetic molecules, over and above the energy possessed by one gram of average molecules of water.

Air Temperature and Moisture. A molecule of water which has enough energy to leave the surface of the water has an excellent chance of staying in the air as water vapor. Once in the air, the molecule of water vapor is surrounded by air molecules moving at an average speed which depends upon the temperature of the air. The warmer the air the more rapidly will the air molecules move, and the more often will they collide. Thus the relatively few molecules of water vapor are more effectively partitioned off from each other and more effectively trapped within an air mass if the air is warm. In a cooler air mass, molecular activity decreases and this results in a decrease in the efficiency of the "trap." Fewer water vapor molecules can therefore be held in cooler air.

The above, although extremely simplified, is basically what happens when an air mass at a given temperature is absorbing water vapor. *The fact that warm air can hold more moisture than cooler air is a fundamental of weather and climate.* Knowing why warm air can hold more moisture is basic to a complete understanding of major weather and climate phenomena.

Humidity

Absolute Humidity; Relative Humidity. *Absolute humidity* is the weight of water vapor in a specified volume of air. The weight of the water vapor is commonly expressed in *grains,* one grain being equal to about $\frac{1}{7000}$ of a pound. The volume is commonly expressed in cubic feet. The absolute humidity is dependent upon temperature as has previously been explained. This is represented graphically in Figure 50. It should be emphasized here that these values represent the amounts of water vapor that *can* be contained in one cubic foot of air, not what *have* to be contained at the corresponding temperatures.

Relative humidity is the ratio of the actual number of grains of water vapor in one cubic foot of air to the maximum number of grains which one cubic foot of air can hold at that temperature. Relative humidity is usually expressed in percent. For example, suppose that a cubic foot of air at 90° F holds 9 grains of water vapor. From Figure 50, one cubic foot of air at that temperature can hold 15 grains of water vapor. The relative humidity is therefore $\frac{9}{15} \times 100 = 60$ per-

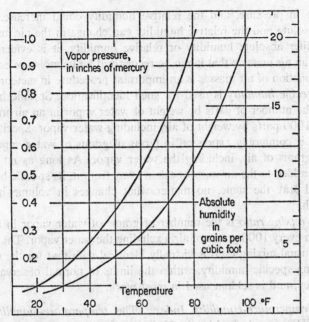

Fig. 50. Absolute humidity, vapor pressure, and temperature. (Courtesy of John Wiley & Sons, Inc. Adapted from A. Strahler's *Physical Geography*, 2d edition, 1960)

cent relative humidity. Relative humidity is changed by an actual change in moisture content or by a change in temperature. The latter method is by far the easier method of changing relative humidity. For instance, in the above example, if the temperature were 80° F, the cubic foot of air would have a relative humidity of $\frac{9}{11} \times 100 = 82$ percent. (See Figure 50.)

Specific Humidity; Mixing Ratio. The volume of a given air mass will change with pressure and therefore with elevation. What is one cubic foot of air at sea level will expand to successively larger volumes as the air mass rises. If the absolute humidity was, for example, 8 grains per cubic foot of air at sea level, its absolute humidity at a higher elevation, assuming no precipitation, will be 8 grains per some volume which is larger than one cubic foot. In other words the absolute humidity has been reduced, perhaps to 6 grains per cubic foot of air. At a higher elevation the air mass could be cooled due to change in pressure, and the relative humidity could increase. Both the absolute and the relative humidity can change in the air mass.

Neither absolute humidity or relative humidity, it is evident, describe an air mass so that it can be recognized by its moisture content. Identification of air masses is an important procedure in meteorology, and *specific humidity* is used for such identification. Specific humidity is the number of parts by weight of water vapor in an air mass in every 1000 parts by weight of air, including water vapor. Specific humidity is commonly expressed in terms of grams of water vapor per 1000 grams of air, including the water vapor. As long as no moisture is added to the air mass or taken away from it, its specific humidity will stay the same, no matter what changes in volume it goes through.

The *mixing ratio* is the number of grams of water vapor in an air mass in every 1000 grams of air, excluding the water vapor. The value of the usual mixing ratio is virtually identical with that for the corresponding specific humidity, within the limits of normal observational accuracy, and is seldom used in most work.

The Temperature-Humidity Index. The *temperature-humidity index* (THI) was devised by the U. S. Weather Bureau as an advisory "discomfort" index for indoor work. Most people feel comfortable indoors at a THI of about 60 while a THI of about 75 in a particular indoors situation may indicate the advisability of dismissing workers, school children, etc. The mathematical value of THI is based mainly upon temperature and relative humidity. The "discomfort" correlations with the mathematical values were obtained by an extensive nation-wide survey of opinion.

Vapor Pressure. Atmospheric or barometric pressure varies with the density of air which in turn varies with the amount of contained water vapor. *Vapor pressure* is that portion of the barometric pressure which is due to the water vapor. Vapor pressure is expressed in inches of mercury. Like absolute humidity, vapor pressure also increases with temperature, as shown in Figure 50.

Measuring Humidity

Hygrometer. A *hygrometer* is an instrument which measures relative humidity by means of a human hair or some other filament which shortens and lengthens with varying humidities. A hygrograph is based upon the same principle and it automatically charts the humidity over a period of time.

Sling Psychrometer. A *sling psychrometer* consists essentially of two thermometers which are fastened onto a small base so that the thermometers can be whirled around together by means of a handle. The bulb of one thermometer is covered by wet cloth. As the psychrometer is whirled around, evaporation will cool the wet bulb thermometer to a lower temperature than that registered by the other thermometer: The difference in the temperature readings depends upon the amount of evaporation from the cloth which in turn depends upon the actual moisture content of the air. Tables and graphs make it possible to determine relative humidity, absolute and specific humidity, and dew point from psychrometer readings.

Dew Point

Condensation. The *dew point* is the temperature below which condensation would usually be expected to occur in a given air mass. The dew point is therefore the temperature at which there is 100 percent relative humidity.

At this point an example would probably be helpful. Suppose that a given volume of air is at a temperature of 78° F and that its absolute humidity is 6 grains per cubic foot. From Figure 50, a cubic foot of air at 78° F can hold 10 grains of water vapor, therefore the relative humidity is $\frac{6}{10} \times 100 = 60$ percent. Now, if the air is cooled to 62° F, its relative humidity (see Figure 50) will be $\frac{6}{6} \times 100 = 100$ percent. Below 62° F, then, the air must be either *supersaturated* with water vapor, or water must start to condense out of the air. If potential nuclei such as ionized dust particles, salt particles, etc. are present, condensation as small droplets of water normally occurs. If nuclei are not present the air may become supersaturated and the relative humidity may exceed 100 percent.

The normal procedure of course is for condensation to occur around nuclei. The condensation may take the form of ice particles or of water, and a *cloud* consisting of ice or water particles, or both, may be formed. If condensation is taking place near the surface of the earth, *fog* may occur. On the ground itself, or on objects on the ground, condensation will take place on leaves, grass, house tops, and anything whose colder temperature will bring the adjacent air to and above the saturation point, or 100 percent relative humidity. In this manner a warm day, followed by a cool night, may result in heavy *dew,* and a moderately cool day followed by a night of freezing temperatures may result in *white frost* being precipitated on the cooler surfaces. The commonly held belief that dew "falls" out of the air onto grass, etc. is a misconception. Dew does not fall; it forms by condensation around an object, much as beads of moisture form on the outside of a glass holding a cool drink, on a warm day.

Precipitation Fundamentals

Forms of Precipitation. As seen from the above, condensation is a common, everyday occurrence as evidenced by dew, fog, white frost, and clouds. These are all forms of condensation, yet they do not in themselves, in those forms, contribute much moisture to the surface of the earth as *precipitation.* The usually recognized forms of precipitation are *rain, snow,* and *hail,* separately or in some combination as *sleet.*

Why Precipitation Occurs. As has been brought out, condensation occurs when the relative humidity is greater than 100 percent, and this occurs if the temperature of the air is lowered to the proper temperature, or *dew point.* The question may well be raised at this point as to why a great mass of fog does not produce rain as such. As fog may be considered as being a cloud close to the ground, the question could also be put in these terms: What causes rain to fall?

First of all, one single definite answer to the above question, which would apply under all conditions, will bring fame and possibly fortune to its author. In other words, the "why" of precipitation is not known with any certainty, mainly because it is not known "what" is going on, in entirety, during precipitation. Some "whats" are known. For one thing, for appreciable precipitation, the air mass containing the water vapor must be rising. As the air rises it expands, and this cools the air. This means that the air molecules are now farther apart and are colliding less frequently. This being the case, if the dew point has been reached, molecules of water vapor can now meet to coalesce, forming droplets of water around nuclei. The air mass keeps rising, the dew point is reached time after time as the temperature drops, and the cloud cover becomes thicker and thicker. When enough water condenses around each nucleus, the drops fall as rain, due to their weight.

But the foregoing sentence contains the big mystery: What causes that much water to form around a nucleus? Fog particles near the ground are certainly very close together and yet fog does not produce raindrops as such. Recent research indicates that electricity probably plays a major role in precipitation; that the particles of water vapor coalescing around a nucleus in a potential rain cloud are in an electrical field formed by the incipient storm system. The droplets of water are therefore attracted to each other electrically and, when many meet at one nucleus, a raindrop heavy enough to fall is formed. As promising as this attack is, it still leaves some questions unanswered and may pose several new ones as time goes on.

What Happens When Air Rises?   When an air mass rises it expands, its temperature is decreased as stated above, and condensation continually occurs as various dew points are reached and passed. Before condensation, the air mass, due to continuing expansion, will experience a temperature decrease at the rate of about 5½° F for every 1000 feet that the air mass rises. This value is called the *dry adiabatic rate*. In the adiabatic process, little heat is released to the surrounding air, due to the rapidity of the volume change and to the fact that air is a poor conductor of heat. When water vapor starts to condense, the already mentioned latent heat of vaporization (about 600 calories per gram) is now returned to the air mass as *heat of condensation* which serves to warm the air mass. This decreases the rate of change in temperature to a *wet adiabatic rate* of about 3° F per 1000 feet of elevation. The wet adiabatic rate is subject to far more fluctuation than is the dry adiabatic rate for several reasons including dependence upon temperature, pressure, and actual moisture motion. Care should be taken to distinguish between the adiabatic rates and the *lapse rate* described in Chapter 8. The adiabatic rates refer to rising air while the lapse rate of 3½° F per 1000 feet applies to still air. An example involving adiabatic and lapse rates follows:

Problem: The temperature of air at the surface of a plowed field adjacent to a large lake is 90° F. The temperature of the air at the surface of the lake is 80° F. Below what height would an airplane probably encounter turbulence due to the warm air current rising from the plowed field? Assume that the air over the lake is essentially stable and not rising, and that there is no condensation in the air current.

Solution: The air current from the field will rise until its temperature (and therefore its density) is the same as that of the still air. This will occur at the same altitude, h.

The still air cools at the rate of $3\frac{1}{2}°$ F per 1000'. Its temperature at altitude h will be: $80° - 3\frac{1}{2}° \times \dfrac{h}{1000} = 80° - \dfrac{3.5°h}{1000}$.

The rising air cools at the rate of $5\frac{1}{2}°$ F per 1000'. Its temperature at altitude h will be: $90° - \dfrac{5.5h}{1000}$.

Equating the two temperatures, $80 - \dfrac{3.5h}{1000} = 90 - \dfrac{5.5h}{1000}$, from which $h = 5000$ feet. (This answer advances one reason why considerable turbulence is often encountered by airplanes as various types of ground surface are flown over at fairly low altitudes.)

Why Air Rises; Resulting Types of Precipitation

As appreciable precipitation occurs only when large masses of air are rising, the next logical consideration would be that of why air rises in the first place. There are three general ways in which large air masses can be made to rise and the descriptive names of these ways are applied to any resulting precipitation, describing it as *convectional, orographic,* or *cyclonic.*

Convectional Precipitation; Thunderstorms. The foregoing problem involving the current of rising warm air is an example of *convectional* action. Unlike the example, however, suppose that the dew point is reached before the top of the air current reaches the altitude of 5000 feet.

As soon as condensation begins the air is no longer being cooled at the rate of $5\frac{1}{2}°$ F per 1000 feet; it is being cooled at the lesser rate of $3°$ F per 1000 feet. By the time the top of the air current reaches the altitude of 5000 feet, it will still be warmer and lighter than the surrounding air and must therefore keep climbing, cooling, and precipitating moisture before it is stabilized at an elevation where its temperature and that of the surrounding air are equal.

This may seem like a rather gentle, uniform procedure but the above description is only what basically happens. Actually, as precipitation increases, more and more heat is added to the storm system and great quantities of moisture-laden air are sucked into the storm in much the same manner as a forest fire creates its own drafts, and for the same reason—in each case a gigantic, growing heat exchange system has been born. Several convection cells may form, each with its own updraft and downdraft system to process and extract the heat from many thousands of tons of water. By this time the original lazily rising cloud form may have grown into a gigantic mushrooming thunderstorm cloud.

In effect, any convectional precipitation is caused by an air mass which almost literally "kicks itself upstairs" until it runs out of its fuel, water, and thus loses its energy, usually before the top of the cloud mass reaches an altitude of 40,000 feet, although some thunderstorm clouds over the tropics often reach to just below the stratosphere.

Although convectional precipitation commonly results in thunderstorm activity of varying degree, it must not be assumed that all thunderstorms are convectional, or "thermal" or that convectional precipitation automatically brings about thunderstorms. The basic ingredients, however, are all there, on a yearlong basis over the warm, tropical ocean areas and during the summer in many other regions.

Orographic Precipitation. When an air mass being carried along on some wind system is forced up and over mountains, the precipitation which may result is called *orographic*. As the air mass is forced up one side of the mountain it expands adiabatically and may thus produce considerable rain. On the other side of the mountain the air mass will descend and, as it descends, its volume will decrease due to the increasing pressure about it. This decrease in volume brings the air molecules closer together and they will collide more frequently, thus raising the temperature of the air mass. This change in temperature is also adiabatic, little heat being taken from the surrounding air. (As commonly expressed, "a compressing gas will warm itself," a common illustration being that of a bicycle or automobile tire pump becoming warmer as the air inside is compressed.)

It is very likely that the air mass has lost much of its moisture on the windward side of the mountains, if the mountains are of any appreciable height, and the air mass will be fairly dry as it starts down the lee side. Furthermore, it ascended the windward side at the wet adiabatic rate which means that its temperature at the summit was higher than if no precipitation had occurred. So, it was relatively warm at the summit and it becomes much warmer as it descends.

The result is that these warm winds may melt snow in winter, and be very hot in summer. These winds are the *foehn* winds of some European countries, the *chinooks* of the northwestern United States, the *Santa Ana* or *Santana* winds of southern California, and are sometimes the *sirocco* winds of the Mediterranean area.

As an example of adiabatic cooling and warming, imagine that air is being forced over a 10,000 foot high mountain range and that the temperature of the air at an elevation of 1000 feet above sea level is 70° F. Assume that condensation starts at about the 3000 foot level. Cooling itself at the dry adiabatic rate, the change in temperature of the air will be $5\frac{1}{2} \times \left(\dfrac{3000 - 1000}{1000} \right) = 11°$ F. The air temperature at the 3000 foot level will be $70° - 11° = 59°$ F.

The air will then cool at the wet adiabatic rate of 3° F per 1000 feet, to the top of the range. The air temperature at the top of the mountain range will be: $59°$ F $- \left(\dfrac{10,000 - 3000}{1000} \right) \times 3° = 38°$ F.

The air now descends. As whatever water vapor left will not condense due to increase in temperature as the air goes down the lee side, the air will warm up at the dry adiabatic rate of $5\frac{1}{2}°$ F per 1000 feet. Thus at an elevation of 1000 feet above sea level, on the lee side of the mountain, the air temperature will be $38°$ F $+ \left(\dfrac{10,000 - 1000}{1000} \right) \times 5\frac{1}{2}°$ F, or about $88°$ F. Contrast this temperature with the 70° F temperature of the same air on the other side of the mountain range, at the same elevation of 1000 feet.

As has probably already been correctly deduced by the reader, the windward sides of many mountain ranges around the world have luxuriant foliage due to orographic precipitation while the leeward sides of the same mountain ranges may be very dry, with sparse vegetation. These dry regions are called *rainshadows,* and they may be very extensive. A common occurrence is to find deserts bordering mountains whose opposite slopes are green and moist, an example in the United States being the Sierra Nevada, whose forested, gradual west slopes abruptly give way at the summit to the sparsely vegetated east slopes which plunge steeply into the great California-Nevada desert area.

It should be pointed out at this time that considerable thunderstorm activity is often caused when unstable air masses are made to ascend mountain ranges. These storms are called *orographic thunderstorms*.

Cyclonic Precipitation. *Cyclonic,* or *frontal* precipitation results, in general, when large masses of warm air are cooled to below the dew point by gradual or strongly forced ascension over large masses of cold air. This type of precipitation, of world-wide scope and major importance, is discussed in Chapter 11.

Clouds

Clouds. Clouds are aggregates of minute particles of water or ice, or both, and represent the *condensation* phase. As already explained, condensation is prerequisite to precipitation, hence the type of cloud cover over a region is an index to the form and quantity of possible precipitation. The form of precipitation—rain, snow, sleet, or hail—is usually closely associated with the type of cloud and its temperature, both of which are usually reflected by the cloud's altitude. An elementary knowledge of clouds is a distinct aid in understanding weather.

There are three major cloud types: *cirroform, stratiform,* and *cumuliform.* The cirroform clouds are the feathery or wisp-like clouds at high altitudes, an example being the "mares' tails" commonly spread across the sky. Cirroform clouds are at times seen even in the stratosphere. The cirroform clouds, due to their great height, are usually composed of ice crystals. It is possible, however, for supercooled water to exist as water in these clouds at temperatures ranging down to $-40°$ F.

The stratiform clouds are usually low clouds and it is often impossible to distinguish individual cloud forms in the dull, gray, stratiform "blanket."

Cumuliform clouds are typically rounded and, in good weather, are the *cumulus* or "fleecy, white clouds" so often described as such in summer. It is the same cumulus, however, which can mushroom into the gigantic, towering cumulonimbus or "thunderhead" with its violent updraft and downdraft systems. Major cloud types and their physical characteristics and ranges of elevation are illustrated in Figure 51.

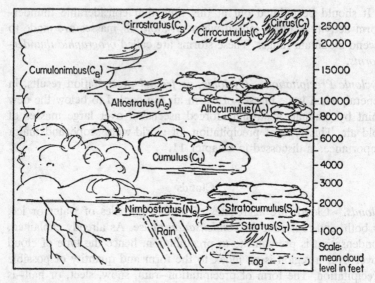

Fig. 51. Families of Clouds. (Adapted from the U. S. Navy Department)

Forms of Precipitation

Rain and Snow. Rain and snow supply most of the moisture precipitated onto the earth's surface. *Rain* is formed when, for some reason as previously discussed, minute cloud particles of water coalesce until the weight is sufficient to make a small mass of water fall as a "drop." Up until that time, surges and drafts in the air have kept the potential drop suspended in the cloud.

Snow is formed when water vapor changes into solid form at a temperature below that of freezing, usually around 0° F. The formation of snow is therefore a *sublimation* process, a reversal of the formation of water vapor by sublimation over glaciers, etc. Snowflakes are primarily hexagonal in shape, although they may be intricately modified from the basic pattern. Snowflakes formed at very low temperatures are of generally small size. Those formed at higher temperatures are generally large in size.

Sleet. In the United States, *sleet* is described by meteorologists as being rain which freezes as it falls through the air and becomes ice before it reaches the ground. In much of the English-speaking world, sleet is the popular term for a mixture of rain and snow, or rain, snow, and hail, etc.

Hail.   *Hail* is composed of rounded pellets of ice, or snow and ice. Hail is formed during thunderstorm activity. One theory as to its formation is that the original falling ice pellets are coated by rain and then are swept upward in an updraft in a cumulonimbus cloud until an enveloping layer of ice is formed at higher altitude. The stone then drops, is coated by more rain, and is swept up again until another layer is frozen. The process is repeated until the stone is heavy enough to fall to earth. By counting the concentric layers commonly seen in hailstones it would be possible to determine about how many times the stone went up and down in the thunderstorm cloud before finally falling to earth.

A more recent theory is that the original pellet of ice, in falling, is coated by supercooled water which then immediately freezes around the pellet. If supercooled water exists at varying elevations, this would also lead to the onionskin layering evident in many hailstones. It seems probable that many hailstones may be formed by a combination of the "up-and-down" and the strictly "down" mechanisms.

Maps of Precipitation

A convenient way of showing the seasonal or annual precipitation for an area is by means of maps. On these maps which show precipitation, lines connecting points of equal precipitation are called *isohyets*.

In addition to maps indicating the amounts of area rainfall, there are maps showing the world distribution of precipitation. As any definite precipitation pattern over a large area depends largely upon the world's pressure and wind belts, detailed discussion of the world distribution of precipitation is left until the next chapter.

REVIEW

1. Distinguish between evaporation and boiling.
2. Discuss "latent heat of vaporization."
3. Distinguish between temperature and heat.
4. Explain why warm air can contain more moisture than cooler air.

5. What is absolute humidity? Relative humidity?

6. Define "specific humidity." Does the specific humidity of a given air mass change with only a change in volume?

7. Define "dew point."

8. What is the major requisite for large-scale precipitation in addition to the fact that a given air mass must have a sufficient amount of moisture?

9. Distinguish between lapse rate, dry adiabatic rate, and wet adiabatic rate. Give the values for each.

10. Discuss the three main types of precipitation.

11. Explain the occurrence of "foehn" or "chinook" winds.

12. What is an isohyet?

EXERCISES

(Answers are given in the answer section at the back of the book.)

1. If 1000 tons of air hold 35 tons of water vapor, what is the specific humidity expressed in terms of grams of water vapor per 1000 grams of air, including the water vapor?

2. In (1) above, what part of the barometric pressure is due to the vapor pressure?

3. A large volume of air is at a temperature of 70° F and its relative humidity is 70 percent. At what temperature, assuming no change in pressure such as occurs in the adiabatic process, will condensation occur? Hint: refer to Figure 50. At 70° F, how many grains of water can one cubic foot of air hold? Then, how many grains per cubic foot does the particular volume of air hold? Again from Figure 50, at what temperature will the volume of air reach 100 percent relative humidity?

4. Assume that a mass of air is warming itself adiabatically as it descends a mountain. It is compressed in such a manner that one cubic foot of air at the top of the mountain is compressed into ¾ of a cubic foot at the bottom.

The air held 2 grains of water per cubic foot of air at the top of the mountain where the temperature of the air was 40° F. The temperature of the air at the base of the mountain is 80° F.

(a) What was the relative humidity of the air on top of the mountain?

(b) Does the air become lighter or heavier as it goes downhill?

(c) What is the relative humidity of the air at the base of the mountain?

CHAPTER 10

Atmospheric Pressure and Winds: World Precipitation Patterns

How Atmospheric Pressure Is Measured

What Atmospheric Pressure Is. Atmospheric pressure is the weight of a column of air extending from the earth's surface to the outer limits of the atmosphere. Although we tend to think of air as being weightless, the atmosphere exerts a force of about 28 million tons on every square mile of ground surface. This is equal to about one ton per square foot, or about 15 pounds per square inch. Air, being composed of molecules of gases, has mass and is held around the earth by gravitation, as a shell. Thus the atmosphere has weight (about 5 quadrillion tons, altogether) and atmospheric pressure is the weight of a sample column through this gigantic shell at a particular instant.

Units of Atmospheric Pressure. Atmospheric pressure could be expressed in an unlimited number of ways but three methods are commonly used:

1. *Pounds per square inch.* An example is in stating that "the average atmospheric pressure at sea level is 14.7 pounds per square inch." This means that a column of air, having a cross section of one square inch and extending from sea level to the outer limits of the atmosphere, weighs 14.7 pounds.

2. *Inches of mercury.* Suppose that we wish to express atmospheric pressure at sea level in terms of inches of mercury. Another way of stating the problem is that we want to know how many cubic inches of mercury weigh 14.7 pounds. As one cubic inch of mercury weighs about .49 pounds, this proportion can be made: $\dfrac{1}{.49} = \dfrac{x}{14.7}$, from which x, the cubic inches of mercury, is about 30. The actual value

is 29.92, so normal sea level pressure is commonly expressed as "29.92 inches of mercury."

3. *Millibars*. Unlike the inches of mercury notation, the *millibar* is in terms of actual pressure in that it is a force divided by an area. (For those readers who may have studied physics, the millibar equals 1000 dynes per square centimeter.) A pressure of 1013.2 millibars = 14.7 pounds per square inch = 29.92 inches (or 760 millimeters) of mercury. Pressures above or below this are *high* and *low* pressures respectively.

The millibar currently is almost universally used by professional meteorologists; the inches of mercury method of expressing atmospheric pressure is still much used by and for the public; expressing pressure in millimeters of mercury is still widely used in many countries for certain scientific work, while expressing atmospheric pressure in pounds per square inch is common among engineers of the English-speaking countries.

Barometers. Instruments which measure atmospheric pressure are called *barometers*. There are two types of barometers.

The *mercurial barometer* is, essentially, a long glass tube which is sealed at one end, open at the other, and almost filled with mercury. The tube is vertical, the open end being in a cup or "cistern" holding mercury. Atmospheric pressure presses down upon the mercury near the open end and, as indicated in the section "Units of Atmospheric Pressure," the column of mercury will rise or fall until its weight per unit area equals the atmospheric pressure. Mercury is used because it is heavy and acts like a liquid. Its main advantage over water for measuring atmospheric pressure is obvious when the necessary length of a water barometer is calculated against the 30-inch mercury column: 30×13.5 (specific gravity of mercury) = 405 inches, or about 34 feet of water.

The *aneroid barometer* is based upon the fact that a thin-walled container, most of the air evacuated from it, is very sensitive to changes in pressure. The change in the shape of the container, due to a pressure change, activates a series of links, gears, and levers, to indicate the atmospheric pressure value on a calibrated dial. The container is prevented from entirely collapsing due to atmospheric pressure by its corrugated design and supporting springs. The aneroid barometer is less accurate than the mercurial barometer. An example of aneroid action is that of the human eardrum as it reacts to changes in elevation by pulling in or pushing out, and then "popping." An aneroid barometer which records its data upon a revolving drum is called a *barograph*.

Pressure and Isobaric Maps

Atmospheric pressure will normally become lower the higher one goes in elevation for the simple reason that the weight of a successively shorter column of air is being measured. In addition to differences in atmospheric pressure due to altitude, differences in atmospheric pressure at sea level occur due to various other factors. In order to study atmospheric pressure data in terms of a common reference plane, readings taken in the mountains or any other place above or below sea level are commonly "reduced" to sea level readings. Mathematically the "reduction" is really an addition as the estimated weight of the column of air between the recording station and

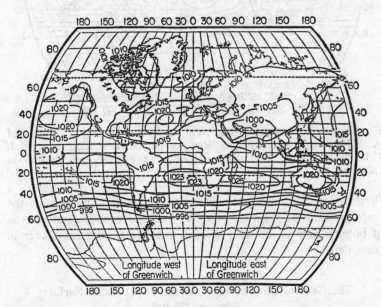

Fig. 52. World pressure distribution at sea level in July. (Courtesy of A. J. Nystrom & Co., Chicago, Van der Grinten projection. Howard J. Critchfield, *General Climatology*. © 1960. Prentice-Hall, Inc., Englewood Cliffs, N. J.)

sea level is of course added to the atmospheric pressure reading obtained at the recording station.

Figures 52 and 53 are maps showing world-wide barometric pressures for the months of July and January. As explained in Chapter 8, it is during these months that temperature extremes are reached.

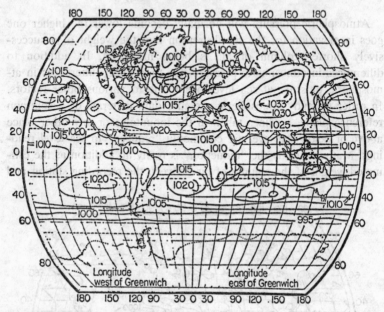

Fig. 53. World pressure distribution at sea level in January. (Courtesy of A. J. Nystrom & Co., Chicago, Van der Grinten projection. Howard J. Critchfield, *General Climatology.* © 1960. Prentice-Hall, Inc., Englewood Cliffs, N. J.)

Pressure extremes also occur during these months. The lines on the maps are *isobars,* connecting points of equal pressure. Another type of isobaric map is the daily weather map, to be discussed later in some detail.

The General Circulation of Air near the Earth's Surface; Pressure "Belts"

Heated air from the tropics rises and moves toward the poles, aloft. If the earth were not rotating, the cooled air would sink in the polar regions, move back along the surface toward the equator and lift again, to complete two giant convectional heat exchange systems, one in each hemisphere. What actually happens is quite different.

Winds near the Earth's Surface. Moving air is called *wind*. A wind *coming* from the northeast is a northeast wind, one *coming* from the south is a south wind, etc. The horizontal movement of all air on the surface of the earth is induced, governed, or modified by one major factor: a difference in atmospheric pressure between regions. A difference in atmospheric pressure can be caused by a difference in temperature. Atmospheric circulation depends, first of all, upon the fact that the equatorial and polar regions receive maximum and minimum insolation, respectively, and are therefore areas of low and high pressure, respectively. As will be seen, however, other regions of high and low pressure on the earth are due to factors other than temperature difference.

We will begin by considering air which has just risen above the equatorial zone and, aloft, is now moving toward a pole. For purposes of clarity, we will restrict the discussion for the time being to the northern hemisphere. As the air moves north, it will be deflected by the earth's rotation.

To visualize what happens to north-moving winds in the northern hemisphere, place a sheet of paper in front of you on a desk. Draw a line across the paper, about in the middle, to represent the equator. On the top of the sheet place an "N" for "north." Place the point of your pencil (the softer the lead the better) on the "equator" and grasp a lower corner of the paper. Now, move the pencil point toward the "N" and at the same time quickly revolve the paper in a counterclockwise direction. It will be found that the pencil line veers off toward the "east."

Exactly the same thing happens to the high winds going north from the equatorial zone. They deflect to the right, and at about latitudes 30° N they are all going appreciably eastward. And so the air piles up. The result is that a region or giant ridge of high pressure is formed and some of the air is forced down onto the earth's surface. (See Figure 54.)

Streams of some of this air near the surface move north and are also deflected to the east. These are the surface *"prevailing westerlies"* of the northern hemisphere. Other streams of the air forced down around the 30° N latitude move back toward the equator. As

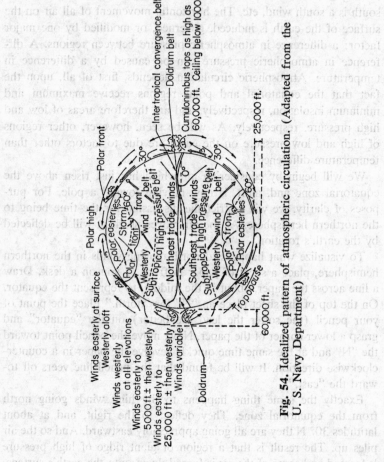

Fig. 54. Idealized pattern of atmospheric circulation. (Adapted from U. S. Navy Department)

can be determined by the simple experiment outlined above, but moving the pencil toward the "south" this time, these winds deflect toward the west. These are the surface *trade winds* of the northern hemisphere.

In the meantime that air which came from the tropics and was not forced down around 30° N latitude will eventually reach the polar region where it cools and descends. As it comes down in the Arctic there is only one major direction in which most of it can now go—south—and as it does so it deflects to the left, or west, and thus becomes the *"polar easterlies."* At about 60° N latitude these strong surface winds meet the strong westerlies and a turbulent *"polar front"* is formed as the moist, warm air from the south is forced up and over the colder dense air from the north.

The southern hemisphere has similar wind systems with the same names of "westerlies," "trades," and "easterlies." These winds, however, deflect in directions opposite to those of their counterparts in the northern hemisphere as may be visualized by recalling the "rotation" experiment with pencil and paper. The polar easterlies do exist more or less as a belt in the Antarctic but in the Arctic are spotty, being continuous only around Greenland, and occurring around Siberia and Canada in winter.

Pressure "Belts." It has already been mentioned that the general latitude of 30° N is a region of high pressure and, of course, the same thing is true concerning the region of 30° S. These regions, the *subtropical highs,* are places of descending, fairly dry air which warms and dries itself as it descends. These general latitudes between the trade winds and the westerlies, are therefore regions of general good weather and of not too much wind during most of the year. The latter point had its drawbacks in the days of sailing vessels, in the northern hemisphere. Ships which had come to a coast via the trade winds had to cross this "belt of calms," sometimes 500 or so miles wide, to get to colonies and trading ports to the north. Many ships became becalmed for long periods of time and horses, etc., were often thrown overboard to lighten ship and to conserve the water supply, hence the term "horse latitudes."

The polar regions are also considered to be general regions of high pressure due to a general pattern of descending winds. Contributing to the high pressure, of course, are the low temperatures of the polar regions.

On the other hand, the equatorial zone is a region of low pressure. Heated air is further forced to rise by convergence and the pressure is made even lower by the fact that, aloft, the equatorial air diverges, about one half going toward either pole. (The effect which a horizontal movement of air aloft has upon the already low pressure associated with rising warm air has been witnessed by anyone who has ever watched the sudden updrafts of smoke and flame in a fireplace as strong, horizontal wind gusts blow above the house.) The zone between about latitudes 5° N and 5° S is sometimes called the "doldrums," or the "belt of variable winds and calms." As it is actually a zone of convergence, it is also called the *Intertropical Convergence Zone* (ITCZ).

The other belts of low pressure are in the general latitudes of 60° N and S. In the northern hemisphere, this is the zone of convergence of the prevailing westerlies and the polar easterlies, the *polar front*. Convergence forces the air aloft, hence low pressure results. Here, also, prevailing westerlies may be forcibly and quickly lifted over the cold polar easterlies. As already explained in Chapter 9, major precipitation can only occur when air is being made to ascend, hence the equatorial zone and the very general regions of 60° N and S are regions of major world-wide precipitation and major storm activity.

The approximate boundaries of the world's idealized pressure and wind belts are again presented in Chapter 13. The seasonal shifts of the "belts" and the effects of this shifting are also presented in some detail in that chapter.

Effects of Land Masses and Seasons
upon Wind and Pressure Belts

If the earth were entirely covered with water and were permanently in one of the equinoctial positions, the sun always on the equator, the earth would have sharply defined pressure and wind belts as shown in Figure 54. These unmoving belts would girdle the earth and a given belt in the northern hemisphere would have its counterpart in the southern hemisphere at the same distance from the equator.

Land Mass Effects.   As it is, however, about 30 percent of the earth's surface is land. Land heats up much more rapidly than does water and also loses its heat more rapidly (Chapters 2 and 8). As also brought out in Chapter 8, land surfaces in summer are in general warmer than the ocean, and are colder than the ocean in winter. In summer, therefore, areas of relatively low pressure would be expected to form over large land areas and in winter be replaced by areas of high pressure. The idealized wind and pressure "belts" of Figure 54 are in reality considerably modified in this manner.

Seasonal Effects. A second consideration is that, as the earth revolves, bringing seasonal change, one hemisphere is always receiving more heat than the other except at the instances of the equinoxes. The result is that pressure and thus wind "belts" migrate north or south as the sun goes north and south, a fact of major importance to be discussed more fully under the subject of climate.

Highs and Lows. Due to seasonal and land mass influences, therefore, the pressure "belts" of Figure 54 are really, in a number of instances, separated areas of high and low pressure, *highs* and *lows,* which migrate north and south during the year. The pressure belts are better preserved as true belts in the southern hemisphere where the ocean-land ratio is much higher than in the northern hemisphere. This is especially true between about latitudes 40° to 60° S.

In July, as shown in Figure 52, North America lies between two highs. These are the *Pacific high* and the *Azores high,* both of which play major roles in weather in the northern hemisphere. In winter, as Figure 53 shows, the principal cells in the northern hemisphere are the *Aleutian low* and the *Iceland low* which more or less dominate winter weather in North America and much of Europe.

Pressure Gradients and Wind Flow

As air flows from regions of higher pressure to regions of lower pressure, the greater the difference between pressures the faster will the wind flow. The situation schematically is much like water flowing down slopes of varying grades, hence the term *pressure gradient* is often used to describe the "slope" between isobars. Isobars which on maps are close to each other indicate steeper slopes and thus indicate strong winds. Isobars spaced some distance apart indicate weaker winds. These relationships may easily be seen by drawing parallel lines about two inches apart on a sheet of paper and then noting how the apparent distance between the isobars successively decreases as the paper is tilted and viewed from the same point. The student should remember, however, that this is a schematic representation in that, usually, isobars on maps are drawn on a common datum such as sea level. Therefore, for the present we will consider winds flowing "down a pressure gradient" as winds which are flowing at the same general elevation above sea level.

The Coriolis Effect

It has already been developed that north-moving winds in the northern hemisphere are deflected toward the east while south-moving winds in the northern hemisphere are deflected toward the west. From this, and from what has also been said about winds in the southern hemisphere, it may already have occurred to the reader that the deflection of winds follows a simple rule. One way of stating this rule is this: *Winds deflect to their right in the northern hemisphere, and to their left in the southern hemisphere*. In using these rules one should always imagine the observer standing with his back to the wind.

This deflection is often attributed to the Coriolis "force" but the deflection is really an effect of the earth's rotation rather than being the result of a force. As a matter of fact, the deflection due to the Coriolis *effect* is a relative deflection.

This may be demonstrated by slightly altering the experiment with the rotating paper. This time, after placing the paper flat on the desk or table, turn back the cover of a hard-cover book and then, the binding up, place the book so that the book's cover is over about one third of the paper. The left edge of the cover represents a north-south line. The pages of the book should be entirely off the sheet of paper and to the right of it. In this manner the sheet of paper can be easily rotated for a distance, and the book cover will stay in the same position. Now quickly rotate the paper as before, but this time draw toward the "north" of the paper by keeping the pencil along the edge of the book cover. The pencil line will again veer to the right on the paper, but the pencil point itself has actually traveled a straight line.

The results of this "illusion," as it is sometimes misleadingly called, are very real. As already outlined, air traveling aloft and poleward from the equator does pile up at about the 30° latitudes due to the Coriolis effect and thus creates the zone called the "horse latitudes." Also, as will now be seen, it is the Coriolis effect which brings about the directions of rotation in weather structures such as cyclones, hurricanes, and tornadoes.

Gradient Winds and Geostrophic Winds

It has already been explained that air will tend to move, as wind, at right angles to the isobars and that, in the northern hemisphere, winds will be deflected to the right by the Coriolis effect. If the isobars are curved this means that the winds will also be acted upon by a centrifugal reaction. To simplify the situation, it may be stated that the winds are trying to cross the isobars at right angles but that the resultant combination of the Coriolis and centrifugal reactions in the northern hemisphere is deflecting the wind to the right. If this combination is strong enough, the wind will be deflected so that it parallels the isobars. In the case of curved isobars, these winds which parallel isobars are called *gradient winds*.

Where the isobars are straight, the winds are deflected by the Coriolis effect alone, centrifugal reaction being absent because of a lack of circular motion. These winds are called *geostrophic* winds. Winds about 2000 or 3000 feet above the earth's surface and higher, tend to follow the isobars and are in general either gradient or geostrophic winds.

Wind Direction in Highs and Lows

Wind Direction in Highs. Due to the Coriolis effect winds leaving a high pressure area will veer to the right. Part of the resultant motion is due to centrifugal reaction but more important is the fact that the velocities of the surface winds are retarded by friction with the ground. The winds do not therefore attain enough velocity to offset the pull of the pressure gradient and to become gradient winds following the isobars. Rather, tending to move straight across the isobars due to the pressure gradient, and to the right because of the Coriolis effect, surface winds emanating from a high pressure center end up by spiraling out to the right, crossing the isobars at angles which vary with the roughness of the surface. (See Figures 55 and 56.) As seen from a position above, the winds spiral out of a high pressure center in a clockwise direction in the northern hemisphere, and in a counterclockwise direction in the southern hemisphere. Large masses of air whirling in this particular manner are called *anticyclones* or *highs*.

Wind Direction in Lows. Air moving toward a center of low pressure in the northern hemisphere will also be deflected to the right. At

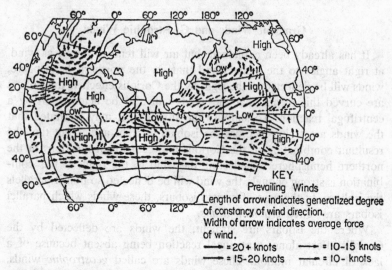

Fig. 55. Generalized pattern of prevailing winds, January and February. (Adapted from the U. S. Navy Department)

elevations of 2000 or 3000 feet above the surface, as previously stated, the winds generally will attain enough velocity to become gradient winds and will follow the isobars. Near the ground, however, the velocity of the wind drops sharply because of friction with the ground. The result is that what would otherwise be gradient winds are pulled across the isobars at angles, toward the center of low pressure. The general action is very similar to that of what would happen to our moon if, for some reason, its velocity of revolution were suddenly decreased. The moon would, of course, be pulled into the earth, not directly but in a spiral due to its remaining velocity. In a similar manner the winds, coming into a center of low pressure, spiral into the center. (See Figures 55 and 56.) In the northern hemisphere winds spiral counterclockwise into a low pressure area, while in the southern hemisphere winds spiral into a low pressure center in a clockwise direction. Large masses of air whirling in this manner are called *cyclones,* or *lows.*

Determining the Positions of Highs and Lows. The surface winds associated with highs and lows make an angle of about 45° with the isobars on land surfaces. If an observer stands with his back to the wind and then turns through 45° (right in the northern hemisphere,

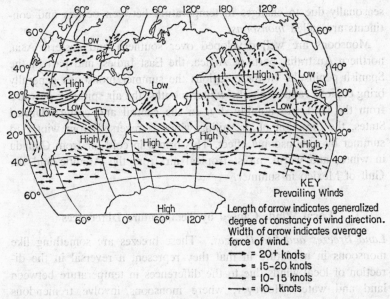

Fig. 56. Generalized pattern of prevailing winds, July and August. (Adapted from the U. S. Navy Department)

left in the southern hemisphere) low pressure will be on his left, high pressure to his right.

Winds Aloft. In general, due to decreased friction, the winds aloft in high and low pressure systems are moving with about twice the velocity of the winds on the ground although this ratio can vary considerably with the roughness of the surface. As these higher winds in general follow the isobars, photographs of the clouds aloft in these wind systems often show, almost perfectly, the extent of the cyclonic or anticyclonic whirl which has developed.

Monsoons

As already explained, land surfaces are relatively warmer than the ocean in summer, and colder in winter. Some parts of some continents would be expected, therefore, to develop centers of low pressure in summer and centers of high pressure in winter. This in turn would bring about ocean-to-continent winds in summer, and continent-to-ocean winds in winter. Winds which reverse their direction seasonally due to changes in temperature between oceans and continents are called *monsoons*.

Monsoons are well developed over southern and eastern Asia, northern Australia, parts of Africa, the East Indies, and part of the Spanish peninsula. In these regions the summer monsoons generally bring copious rains while the winter months, the air spiraling outward from the land, are notably dry. In the central and eastern United States, the direction of prevailing winds is reversed from winter to summer by a monsoonal effect. This brings in cold air from Canada in winter and warm, moist tropical air from the Atlantic and the Gulf of Mexico in summer.

Local Winds Caused by Temperature Differences

Land Breezes and Sea Breezes. These breezes are something like monsoons in miniature in that they represent a reversal in the direction of local winds due to the differences in temperature between land and water. However, where monsoons involve tremendous masses of air traveling thousands of miles, land and sea breezes are confined to a relatively thin layer anywhere from 1 to 25 miles long.

As the land warms up after sunrise, the heated air rises and expands, and then flows toward the ocean. This decreases the pressure on land, and the cooler ocean air moves into this area of low pressure as a breeze.

At night, the land cools off rapidly and the air becomes dense and contracts. Ocean air flows down onto the contracted air over the land and increases the pressure on land. The air on land then moves toward the ocean, toward the region of lower pressure. Land breezes and sea breezes constitute only partially-complete convectional systems as much of the air spreads out and is lost to the system.

Valley Breezes and Mountain Breezes. During the day the air in a valley may become so warm that in expanding, some of the air is forced up the valley side as a *valley breeze*.

During the night, air near the tops of mountains becomes colder than the air in the nearby valleys and, being denser, will descend the mountainside under the pull of gravity, creating a *mountain breeze*. As it descends, the air will tend to be slightly warmed by compression but it will be much more cooled by radiation than it is warmed by compression. By the time the air arrives at the base of the mountain, it may be considerably colder than when it started out, and thus result in a temperature inversion on the valley floor.

Katabatic Winds. *Katabatic winds* are much like mountain breezes except that they involve much larger areas, and are generated differently. The air of a katabatic wind is made denser by radiation at any time instead of strictly by cooling at night, and then the air drains down slopes by gravity. Thus katabatic winds are rather common phenomena which may happen at any time of the day in large areas adjacent to and lower than snowfields and glaciers, such as regions in Scandinavia, Greenland, and Antarctica.

Other Local Winds

Perhaps every region in the world has local winds to which local names have been assigned. These winds generally occur at more or less specific times of the year when local meteorological conditions reach a seasonal imbalance, or when meteorological conditions on a wide scale bring about unusual wind conditions locally. Winds of the *foehn* or *chinook* type were described in Chapter 9.

High Altitude Winds; Jet Streams

It has been only in recent years that we even started to suspect that gigantic streams of air, tier upon tier, hurtled around the earth, and past each other, far above our heads. The general pattern of high altitude winds is so intricate and varied that it is largely a pattern of bewildering change. For example, winds at about 40,000 feet blow in a general easterly direction all year while, above them, winds in another tier blow in the opposite direction. Far above both tiers are other wind systems which reverse their direction with a change in seasons, and sometimes do so for no apparent reason at all.

An important development made only since World War II was the advancement of the idea that high altitude winds strongly affect and even govern surface weather. In the northern hemisphere, the high altitude westerlies seem to be the most important in this respect.

These westerlies, just below the stratosphere, at an altitude of from about 30,000 to 40,000 feet, are some of the most erratic winds known. Only roughly confining themselves to the belt of the surface westerlies, the high altitude westerlies swing in meandering paths as they go eastward. The wave motion related to these winds, known as the "planetary wave," distributes high altitude westerly winds to within 1000 miles of the equator and the pole over a period of a year. It is in these high altitude westerlies that the high altitude *jet streams* occur, also going from west to east.

A jet stream is, as defined by the Technical Commission for Aerology of the World Meteorological Organization: ". . . a more or less horizontal, flattened tubular current, in the vicinity of the tropopause . . . characterized by high wind speeds. . . ." A typical jet stream is about 300 miles wide, 3 miles deep, and several thousand miles long. The winds in its core are the fastest winds in the jet stream. (See Figure 57.)

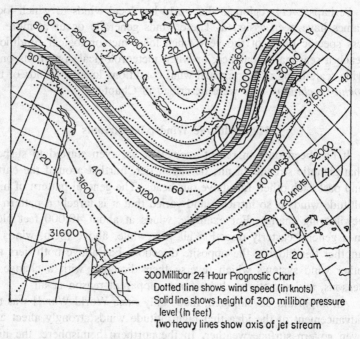

300 Millibar 24 Hour Prognostic Chart
Dotted line shows wind speed (in knots)
Solid line shows height of 300 millibar pressure
level (in feet)
Two heavy lines show axis of jet stream

Fig. 57. Jet streams. (Adapted from the U. S. Department of Commerce, Weather Bureau)

Jet streams were encountered by American bombing planes on their way to Japan in World War II but the existence of such high velocity winds had been suspected by some meteorologists since

1922, after a certain weather balloon made an astonishingly fast journey from England to Germany.

It is now known that there are several high altitude jet streams in both the northern and southern hemispheres and that the jet streams all more or less thrash about in the belt of the high altitude westerlies, sometimes displacing themselves by 1000 miles or so, from season to season. As yet, very little is known about why or how they form, although their proximity to the base of the stratosphere, the fact that they change their positions with the seasons, and the fact that they are horizontal currents, may be due to the tropopause being "fractured" in several places. These fractures, overlaps between the troposphere and the stratosphere, may somehow aid in the formation of the jet streams, perhaps by a combination of temperature differences and by the air also being made to flow at increased velocities, longitudinally, through the "fractures," etc.

Whatever the cause of the formation and maintenance of jet streams, their positions are often associated with major surface weather disturbances approximately beneath them. But as there must be interchange of air between at least some near-surface winds and the high altitude winds, the formation of jet streams, it might be postulated, is somehow associated with the activity of lower winds. As a matter of fact, it has been only recently that low-altitude jet streams within 2000 feet of the earth's surface were recognized as such, and are now being studied. This leads to the interesting thought that, someday, some now so-regarded "random" deviations in near-surface phenomena might be the collective key to a fairly accurate long-range forecast of the positions of the major jet streams. Once this can be done, assuming that it may be possible, a large percentage of the northern hemisphere's most crippling and destructive storms could be forecast. Whether the jet streams finally steer the air masses or whether the upper westerlies steer the jet streams, or whether it is a combination of the two, the statistical correlation of jet stream position with surface storm activity seems incontrovertible.

World Distribution of Precipitation

The world distribution of precipitation is shown in Figure 58. In general, and as may be seen from Figure 58, the following observations regarding world precipitation may be made:

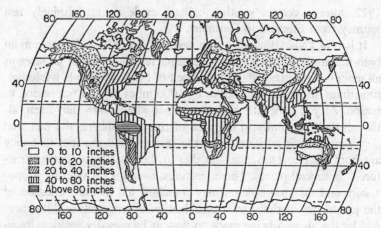

Fig. 58. Distribution of precipitation over the earth. (Adapted from Thomas A. Blair & Robert C. Fite, *Weather Elements,* 4th edition. © 1957, by permission of Prentice-Hall, Inc., Englewood Cliffs, New Jersey)

1. Due to masses of warm, moist, rising air, equatorial regions have the most precipitation.

2. The amount of world-wide precipitation becomes less as the poles are approached.

3. A major exception to (2) above is that major desert and semi-arid areas occur in the belt of the "horse latitudes," due to descending warming air.

4. World precipitation is associated with major wind belts, such as the westerlies.

5. The precipitation pattern is strongly controlled by mountain systems.

6. Monsoon circulation usually brings about arid to semi-arid central interior conditions and moist coastal areas. (See North America, Asia, Australia, and the Spanish peninsula, Figure 58.)

7. The parallel of 60° N roughly separates the northern hemisphere into two parts, the southernmost receiving, by far, most of the hemisphere's precipitation. (To the reader: Why?)

In addition to the above, and as will be explained in later chapters, ocean currents also play a major role in determining precipitation, particularly near coasts.

REVIEW

1. Explain the chief advantage of a mercurial barometer over a water barometer.

2. What is an isobar?

3. What is a "west" wind?

4. Discuss the general circulation of air near the earth's surface, and the formation of pressure belts.

5. Describe and explain the direction of wind in a cyclone and in an anticyclone.

6. Why does wind spiral into a cyclone and spiral out of an anticyclone? Your explanation should include the terms "gradient winds" and "surface friction."

7. Discuss monsoonal circulation and name three continents where monsoons occur.

8. What is a gradient wind? A "geostrophic" wind?

9. Contrast the jet stream shown in Figure 57 with the big bulges of the polar front of Figure 54. Would you explain the similarity of the curves as being by mere chance, or do you think it possible that the jet stream overlies a "front" of some kind?

10. Discuss the formation and characteristics of katabatic winds and of *chinook* winds.

EXERCISES

(Answers are given in the answer section at the back of the book.)

1. Sea water weighs about 65 pounds per cubic foot. What is the pressure in pounds per square inch due to the weight of sea water on a submarine 200 feet beneath the surface?

2. Sketch a typical "low" by drawing isobars. Place typical readings in millibars on the isobars. Show (a) the pressure gradient; (b) a gradient wind; (c) winds spiraling in toward the center crossing the isobars at angles of about 30°.

3. Assuming that a cyclonic disturbance is in the westerlies and is traveling about 25 miles per hour, how many days would it take for the storm to travel from the Pacific coast of the United States to the Atlantic coast in a general NE direction?

4. Assume that a certain jet stream is 300 miles wide, 2 miles deep, and

150

PHYSICAL GEOGRAPHY

8000 miles long. How many cubic miles of air are in the jet stream at any one instant?

5. Place tracing paper over Figure 58 and make a rough tracing of the continents.

Many mountain systems are indicated on a precipitation map by long, fairly narrow adjacent strips of differing precipitation. As nearly as can be determined by the precipitation patterns, plot on the tracing paper:

(a) The mountain system on the west coast of North America.
(b) The mountain system on the west coast of South America.
(c) The mountain systems in North Africa.
(d) The mountain system in Australia.
(e) The mountain systems of southeastern Asia.

(NOTE: Monsoon circulation here brings about heavier than average precipitation near the coasts, and over larger areas, hence mountains are extensive regions of high precipitation.)

Compare your results with a map showing the mountain systems of the world.

CHAPTER 11

Air Masses, Fronts, and Storms

Air Mass Classification

An *air mass* is a large body of air in which temperature and moisture conditions are approximately the same in a given horizontal plane through the air mass.

Air masses can be described according to several separate classifications but a general classification system will be used in this presentation. The major air mass types involved in weather in North America are tropical (T), polar (P), and superior (S). The origin of tropical and polar air masses is apparent. The superior air masses apparently originate high in the troposphere and then descend as extremely dry air.

Tropical and polar air masses acquire their temperature and moisture characteristics over either continents or oceans, and the letters c (continental) and m (maritime) are used to designate the parent surface. For example, a tropical air mass formed over the ocean is designated mT while a polar air mass formed over a continent is designated cP. As the air mass moves, a third letter (w or k) indicates if the air mass is warmer (w) or colder (k) than the surface beneath it. This third letter is of far more than academic interest in meaning. The designation mTk, for instance, means that a mass of maritime tropical air is cooler than the surface over which it is passing. It will therefore be warmed at its base and may become unstable, the process possibly resulting in heavy thundershower activity such as often occurs when moist maritime tropical air from the Caribbean passes over the southeastern continental United States.

North American Air Masses and Source Regions

The principal air masses which dominate weather in North America, and their sources, are conveniently discussed in terms of summer and winter weather on the continent of North America. The student is advised to refer now and then to Figure 59 while reading the following.

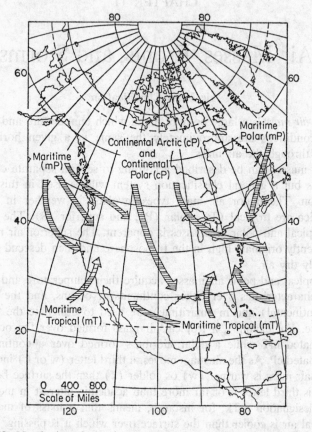

Fig. 59. North American air masses, source regions, and directions of movement. Generalized. Base map copyright Denoyer-Geppert Company.

1. Air masses dominating summer weather in North America.

a. *Continental polar air masses* (*cP*). The source regions of continental polar air masses in summer are in north-central Canada and Alaska. These air masses are cool and contain a relatively small amount of moisture. This air usually becomes cPk air over the continental United States, and in passing over the Great Lakes (its usual path) takes on moisture which is commonly precipitated over the Great Lakes and over mountains to the east.

b. *Maritime polar air masses* (*mP*). Maritime polar air masses in summer originate in two source regions: the region of the Aleutian low in the North Pacific, and in the high pressure area in the North Atlantic, between the Newfoundland-Labrador region and Greenland.

Off the Pacific coast, the air masses from the Aleutian-low source region move in a general southeast direction as mPk air and have their bases further cooled by the ocean water. This causes the persistent thick summer fogs and stratus clouds of the Pacific coast.

Any summer mP air which comes onto the Atlantic coast usually originates in the North Atlantic, between the Canadian maritime provinces and Greenland. This air, spiraling out from a high pressure center, is cool and generally stable, bringing cool weather to much of the eastern seaboard as well as to the entire New England area. It becomes mPk air over the land.

c. *Maritime tropical air masses* (*mT*). Maritime tropical air masses rarely cause any storm activity in summer on the Pacific coast. What little does come onto land is usually mTw and thus is stable.

To the east, the source regions for maritime tropical air are in in the Gulf of Mexico and in the Caribbean. These air masses have elevated temperatures and much moisture. Thunderstorms and humid weather often accompany the journeys of these air masses over land where they become mTk, increasing the instability. These air masses also frequently climb aloft over colder air, bringing rain over large areas. It is this mT air which accounts for most of the summer rain east of the Mississippi, and for much of the hot, humid weather experienced in the eastern part of the United States during the summer season.

d. *Superior air masses* (*S*). Superior (S) air usually overlies mT air, thus acting as kind of a ceiling. It is possible that, in limiting vertical storm extent, the superior air may at times considerably increase the areal extent of storm activity due to mT air. The characteristics of a typical superior air mass—high temperature and little moisture—apparently result by subsidence from aloft. Superior air is therefore usually found higher than one mile above the earth's surface. In summer, however, this air sometimes descends to cover the entire Great Plains region and all of the southwestern states, bringing hot, dry weather and drought conditions. Superior air probably results mainly from the subsidence of air in the high pressure belts at about latitudes 30° N and S, a phenomenon explained in Chapter 10.

2. Air masses dominating winter weather in North America.

a. *Continental polar air masses* (*cP*).   Continental polar air masses have winter source regions in Canada, Siberia, and the Arctic Ocean. Very cold air originating over the Arctic ice and the Greenland icecap is called continental Arctic, or cA, air. Continental polar air coming into the continental United States in winter usually originates over Canada but Siberian "cold waves" are not unknown, causing some of the most bitter cold experienced in the United States.

Continental polar air from Canada commonly passes over the Great Lakes, from west to east, acquiring moisture and a warmer base as it travels over the lakes. The air mass is thus made unstable, the warm, moist air rising until precipitation occurs. It is for this reason that the eastern sectors of the Great Lakes region receive much more snow than the western sectors. Duluth and Chicago, for example, may receive little snow from a given storm while Buffalo, New York, may receive up to a foot of snow from the same storm.

b. *Maritime polar air masses* (*mP*).   The source regions for maritime polar air masses in the winter are the same as for the summer: the general area of the Aleutian low, and the high between the maritime provinces of Canada and Greenland. Actually, most of the mP air in the Pacific starts out as cP air formed over Siberia. The maritime polar air on the Pacific coast varies in its characteristics in accordance with the time it takes to cross the Pacific. Some, taking a relatively short time, is still stable as it comes onto the Pacific coast. Other air masses, being warmer and more humid because of a longer time over the ocean, may bring about heavy orographic precipitation as they lift over coastal mountains. Farther south on the Pacific coast, with fewer high mountains directly on the coast, these air masses cool to mPk over the land, bringing fog and some rain.

On the Atlantic coast, some maritime polar air masses originating in the ocean region southwest of Greenland come onto the east coast causing "northeasters," strong, cold winds with moderate rain which may last for several days.

c. *Maritime tropical air masses (mT)*.   Maritime tropical air invading the United States in winter has these possible source regions: the Gulf of Mexico; the Caribbean; the general area of the Sargasso Sea; and the cell of high pressure southwest of Baja California.

Maritime tropical air seldom comes onto the Pacific coast of the continental United States. When it does it is in response to very low pressure off the California coast, and heavy precipitation occurs, due to either frontal or orographic precipitation, or both.

The maritime tropical air masses originating in the Gulf of Mexico and the Caribbean areas bring about more rain in the continental United States than is caused by any other type of air mass. These maritime tropical air masses commonly lift aloft over mammoth wedges of colder air to the north changing from mTw to mTk. This instability brings about warm rains of long duration over the central eastern continental United States.

Cyclones and Anticyclones

General Features of Highs and Lows.   The general wind systems in areas of low and high pressure were discussed in Chapter 10. It was also explained that "lows" are called *cyclones* while "highs" are called *anticyclones*. It is the traveling lows which bring much of the cloudy and rainy weather and many of the storms to middle and high latitudes. The traveling highs, commonly interspersed between the lows, generally bring fair weather. In general, both highs and lows move from a southwest-northeast direction in the belt of the westerlies.

As was brought out in Chapter 10, the winds in a cyclone spiral in toward the center of low pressure, counterclockwise in the northern hemisphere and clockwise in the southern hemisphere. Another fact is now considered: that the central area of a cyclone, with all winds spiraling into it, must be a region of convergence. The air must therefore rise, just as converging air rises in the vicinity of the intertropical or equatorial convergence zone. As it rises, the air in the cyclone cools. The relative humidity increases until clouds and precipitation commonly result.

In highs, or anticyclones, on the other hand, the air spirals outward from the center, clockwise in the northern hemisphere and counterclockwise in the southern hemisphere. The mere fact that air continues spiraling outward means that the anticyclone has a continuing source of air supply coming into its center. This air cannot, obviously, come into the anticyclone near the earth's surface where the flow is strongly outward. The air must therefore be furnished from above. Being subsiding air, it is adiabatically warmed as it descends and is "whirled" out over a large area as stable air, thus in general creating fair weather.

There are three major kinds of cyclones: the extratropical cyclone, the tropical cyclone, and the tornado.

The *extratropical* (*out of the tropics*) cyclone is found in middle and high latitudes. It may cover thousands of square miles and may be evidenced by anything from slight cloud cover to severe storms.

The *tropical cyclone* originates in the general equatorial area, over oceans. It is of smaller areal extent than the extratropical cyclone but is commonly of far greater intensity.

The *tornado* is a cyclonic disturbance commonly associated with thunderstorm genesis and activity. It is therefore of restricted size and occurrence but is of extreme intensity.

Weather Fronts and Cyclones. Figure 60 illustrates four stages in the development of an extratropical cyclone, according to the wave

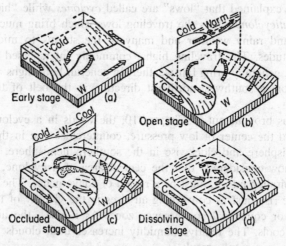

Fig. 60. Development of an extratropical cyclone in middle latitudes. (Courtesy of John Wiley & Sons, Inc. Adapted from A. Strahler's *Physical Geography*, 2d edition, 1960)

theory of cyclones advanced by Vilhelm Bjerknes in 1915. In the early stage (Block A) warm air going to the northeast contacts southwest-moving cold air at the *polar front* and a bulge, or wave, develops. Once this center of low pressure represented by the wave is formed, the air will of course spiral in a counterclockwise direction as explained in Chapter 10.

The exact mechanics of the formation of this wave are not fully understood but, as the air masses are of different temperatures, the line between them, or polar front, must essentially be a low pressure trough, which agrees with what has already been said about the polar front in Chapter 10. The bulk of the cold air mass would therefore be attracted southward and, being denser, would run under the warm air. The warm air would then tend to do two things: rise over the cold air and keep on going toward the northeast. This would shove some of the cold air back toward the northeast to create the initial bulge, *if* the warm air were now somehow turned northward as indicated in Block A, and the cold air were turned southward.

A simple experiment will demonstrate how this *could* happen, although it is not intended to be anywhere near a complete solution of what is evidently a highly complex phenomenon. The principle, however, probably plays an important role in the development of many cyclones:

Suspend each of two objects such as a pair of rubber erasers or small blocks of wood from a string held by either hand. A pair of men's shoes, each shoe suspended by its laces, also makes handy demonstration equipment. The object suspended below your right hand represents the warm air mass headed east. The object in your left hand represents the cold air headed south. Now, bring the objects together so that they barely touch. The line of contact between them represents the polar front which, say, is pointing straight at you so that you are looking in a general "eastward" direction.

Now, move your right hand away from you and your left hand toward you. It will be seen that, due to what may be called a "shear reaction," the objects start going around in a counterclockwise direction as viewed from overhead. In terms of air masses, the warm air invades the territory of the cold air, pushing it back, and the cold air invades the territory of the warm air, pushing the warm air back and lifting it. This action can not only institute the bulge, but can also intensify it as shown in Block B, creating a more or less definite center of low pressure.

Block B also shows a cross section of the cyclone in the advanced stage. A *cold front* is shown where cold air is pushing in under the warm air. On the other side of the cyclone, a *warm front* exists where warm air is climbing over the cold air. An intensifying area of low pressure is at the "V" where the fronts meet. It will be noticed that in both fronts cold air, being denser, underlies the warm air. The criterion for distinguishing the two types of fronts, then, is which air is the aggressor. In a cold front the cold air is the aggressor; in a warm front the warm air is the aggressor. The slope of a warm front is usually between $\frac{1}{100}$ and $\frac{1}{250}$, while that of a cold front is usually between $\frac{1}{50}$ and $\frac{1}{125}$. (A slope of $\frac{1}{125}$ is a slope which rises—or falls—1 unit vertically for every 125 units horizontally).

It is important to note here that Blocks B, C, and D represent the cyclone, not only in its stages of development, but also in different geographic locations as the cyclone during its development is being swept along in the belt of the westerlies. The average rate of travel for lows is around 30 miles per hour and their diameters may be from 400 to 1200 miles.

Frontal Weather. As warm fronts have gentle slopes, warm air moves up these slopes fairly steadily and slowly and the precipitation associated with warm fronts is usually of the two- or three-day type, of medium or slight intensity. If the warm air is unstable, however, *frontal thunderstorms* may develop.

Cold fronts have fairly steep slopes, especially when moving at such a rapid rate that the cold air aloft, moving more rapidly than the lower layers held back by surface friction, tends to lunge ahead. Warm air is then lifted very swiftly over the cold air and quickly reaches the dew point. Cold fronts are noted for the violent weather conditions, especially great thunderstorms, which often accompany them. Many times, most of this bad weather occurs 100 miles or so ahead of the cold front, as a *squall line*. This is caused by strong winds racing ahead of the cold front and forcing the warm air up even more quickly than would be accomplished by the cold front itself.

It is probably obvious from what has already been said, and from Figure 60, that as a cyclone moves from west to east, the warm front will pass a given point first, followed by the cold front (assuming that both fronts do pass over the point, as is commonly the case). This of course is the reason why, many times, a warm rain of a few days duration (from the warm front) seems to be terminated by sudden thundershowers and cooler temperatures (due to the cold front).

Cold fronts tend to move faster than do warm fronts, commonly about twice as fast. The speed of a typical cold front is about 20 miles per hour while that of a typical warm front is about 10 miles per hour. In a cyclone, a cold front commonly overtakes a warm front after a few days, punches into the cold air of the warm front and lifts both this cold air and the warm air aloft as shown by Block C. The warm air is thus lifted entirely above the earth's surface and becomes an isolated air mass, cut off from the main body of warm air, and *occluded*. Its fuel supply now cut off, the storm weakens and dies and the low pressure center disappears. A polar front is again formed as shown in Block D.

The Heat Transfer Role of Cyclonic Precipitation. It will be remembered from previous chapters that water vapor possesses considerable heat energy, or *latent heat,* and that this heat is released to the atmosphere upon condensation. As most of the moisture present in cyclonic disturbances comes from tropical air masses, most of the heat released during condensation is latent heat coming from the vicinity of the tropics. Tropical air can carry an amazing 5 percent moisture by volume. As extratropical cyclones of varying degrees of intensity are formed in the mid latitudes and high latitudes during most of the year, extratropical cyclones play a major role in the general heat transfer system of the earth, literally releasing tropical heat into the mid latitudes and higher latitudes.

Anticyclones. Anticyclones or *highs* can develop in several ways but the highs to be discussed here are the moving highs which seem to follow cyclones across the country. A weather map of the world commonly shows this low-high-low-high sequence.

What happens is apparently something like this. As a cyclone develops, the polar front is broken along a considerable length on the west side of the cyclone where polar air is advancing southward. Polar air on the cyclone's west side, near the surface, tends to move toward the center of the cyclone. Polar air aloft on the cyclone's far west side will tend to sink because of its density. As it sinks, it warms itself adiabatically and becomes a region of high pressure from which winds spiral out. The anticyclone carried along in the belt of the westerlies as it formed now roughly trails the low, from west to east, bringing good weather and high pressure, usually to extensive areas.

It is not uncommon for one anticyclone to cover an area equal from one fourth to two thirds that of the continental United States.

Weather Maps

The weather map of Figure 61 illustrates a cyclone near New-

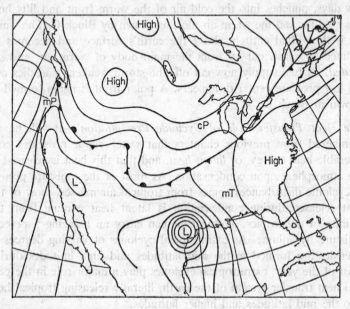

Fig. 61. This unusual weather map shows a tropical cyclone (hurricane) moving onto the Texas shore, and an extratropical cyclone centered near Newfoundland. (Adapted from the U. S. Department of Commerce, Weather Bureau)

foundland, and its trailing high pressure area. The map shown is a surface weather map. In conjunction with a storm track map—a map which shows the usual paths of storms—surface weather maps are used to accurately forecast weather.

This method of forecasting is very satisfactory if the storms actually do follow the tracks shown on the maps. They usually more or less do, but at times their paths are changed by conditions in the upper air layers. For example, a cell of low pressure at a high altitude can make a storm veer strongly from the usual track.

If no upper cell of low pressure is present the storm will usually move in a direction paralleling the isobars in the *upper* air levels. The winds aloft are essentially *geostrophic* winds (see Chapter 10) as the isobars in the upper air levels just above the storm are usually fairly straight and parallel. The upper air, in effect, moves along these "tracks" pulling the storm beneath it along in the same direction. The final path of the storm, of course, can be and commonly is altered by topography and by other appreciable changes in the characteristics of the surfaces or air masses in or near the storm's projected path.

Tropical Cyclones

Violent tropical cyclones are variously called *hurricanes, typhoons,* or *cyclones,* depending upon the world location of the storms. Like extratropical cyclones, they spin counterclockwise in the northern hemisphere; clockwise in the southern hemisphere. Tropical cyclones can vary from very weak disturbances to great storms. Contrary to popular impression, most tropical cyclones are of the weak, harmless kind. However, the great destruction which can be caused by the violent variety of tropical cyclone focuses—and rightly so—attention upon this type to the virtual exclusion of public knowledge of the weaker but far more prevalent kind.

Source Regions. Tropical cyclones form in the intertropical convergence zone (ITCZ) over the ocean when the zone is appreciably north or south of the equator. Considering the approximate six-week lag in the migration of the wind and pressure belts as they follow the sun, the zone would be expected to be well north of the equator from August through October. Records over a fifty-year period of hurricanes born in the West Indies bear this out, over 80 percent of the hurricanes during this fifty-year period having occurred from August through October.

Hurricanes apparently never form on or very near the equator and this may be due to the fact that the Coriolis effect, which starts the air spinning, is absent at the equator. Tropical cyclones develop principally in six general regions. These regions and the regional names of violent tropical cyclones are: (1) from the West Indies to the Caribbean Sea and Gulf of Mexico (*hurricanes*); (2) in the general area between the Marshall Islands and the Philippines (*typhoons*); (3) the area to the west of Mexico and Central America (*hurricanes*); (4) the Bay of Bengal and the Arabian Sea (*tropical cyclones*); (5) the general area of Samoa and the Fiji Islands (*typhoons*) to the northwest coast of Australia (*willy-willies*); and (6) in the south Indian Ocean, near Madagascar (*cyclones*).

Hurricanes and Their Structure. Hurricanes are the subject of intense current study in the United States and the study will undoubtedly go on for many years to come. Attempts are now actually being made in the field to control some of the energy in hurricanes and indications are that man will some day be able to control appreciably at least some of these violent storms. The everyday implications of such control for people who live in hurricane areas are obvious; perhaps not so obvious are the military implications of tropical cyclone control.

As seen on a weather map, a hurricane appears to be an extremely simple type of storm (see Figure 61). The interior isobars are almost perfect circles, spaced closer together as the storm's center is approached. A hurricane has no warm front and no cold front and it further differs from the extratropical cyclone in having an *"eye"* of low pressure and relative calm which is about 15 or 20 miles in diameter as contrasted with the cyclone's usual diameter of from 350 to 400 miles. The eye of a hurricane is deceptive in that this little zone of fair weather is right in the middle of the hurricane, which means that even greater storm fury will usually be encountered as the hurricane eye slowly moves along only to be succeeded by another 200-mile-thick towering wall of violent winds. The wind velocity in destructive hurricanes ranges from 75 miles per hour to over 200 miles per hour, anything over 75 miles per hour being known as "hurricane velocity." In the United States the wind systems in tropical cyclones must reach 75 miles per hour before the tropical cyclone is recognized as a "hurricane."

Hurricane Formation and Development. Despite simple appearances as seen on a weather map, and despite all that is known about hurricane structure, hurricanes are only incompletely understood in terms of their birth and development.

Some generalities can be cited. As already mentioned, hurricanes form over oceans, in the intertropical convergence zone when that zone is appreciably north or south of the equator. Being formed over oceans, the hurricanes have an inexhaustible supply of moisture, or "fuel."

In some cases hurricanes may be formed by a wave action in the trade winds, somewhat similar to the wave action believed to underlie the birth of extratropical cyclones. This wave action, in the case of hurricanes, is apparently caused by the *easterly wave,* along the intertropical convergence zone. At other times, the actual beginning of a hurricane is preceded by giant cumulus clouds which, for some reason, form a circle aloft. If air descends from aloft to fill the resulting "cylinder" with air warmer than that in the surrounding air masses, this apparently forms a hurricane "eye," and a hurricane results. At still other times, hurricanes develop from apparently weak low pressure systems which for some reason develop a considerable area of low pressure.

Once a hurricane does form, it typically pulls in approximately 20 million tons of air every minute in its lower levels and whirls it upward and out at the top of the storm at an elevation of about 8 miles above the ocean's surface. The U. S. Weather Bureau has calculated that a typical hurricane produces heat energy equivalent to 600 or so atom bombs exploding every minute.

This heat results, of course, from the condensation of water vapor and the attendant release of latent heat. As more and more heat is released within its system the hurricane can take in more and more water vapor. New air masses continually spiral in toward the storm's center of increasing heat and low pressure, adding to the fury of the hurricane's wind system. In this manner the hurricane's size and intensity grow.

Hurricane Tracks. Like the extratropical cyclones of the continental United States, strong tropical cyclones have preferred "tracks" as shown in Figure 62. Hurricane tracks are largely determined by strong atmospheric conditions some distance from the storm itself.

Hurricanes travel from about 10 to 20 miles per hour in the tropics. When a hurricane reaches a coast, however, its speed of travel usually greatly increases, sometimes up to 60 miles per hour, or one mile per minute. On the coast, the hurricane may cause the ocean water to rise up to 15 or 20 feet above the level of the normal tide, in phenomena called *storm surges.* Hurricanes on the east coast of the United States often travel into the belt of the westerlies as far as New England before passing out to sea. The typical hurricane lasts about ten days. In that time it releases enough energy—equal to about

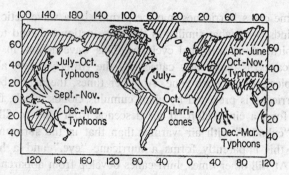

Fig. 62. Typical hurricane and typhoon tracks. (Adapted from the U. S. Navy Department)

10 million atom bombs—to satisfy the anticipated electrical power needs of the United States for the next five hundred years.

It is interesting to note that, as tropical cyclones are formed in the zones of the trade winds, the storms receive an original westward impetus. As Figure 62 shows, though, most hurricane and typhoon tracks eventually tend to curve toward the pole of the parent hemisphere, and many of them finally curve into a definite eastward direction at about latitudes 30° N and S. These tracks therefore dramatically indicate the existence and approximate boundaries of major wind belts, and also emphasize the absence of the Coriolis effect at the equator itself.

Tornadoes

The most violent storm on earth is the cyclonic storm called the *tornado*. Tornadoes are commonly associated with the thunderstorms and heavy rains of cold fronts, and many times they are formed in the *squall lines,* in advance of the cold fronts. Being a form of cyclone, tornadoes spiral counterclockwise in the northern hemisphere and clockwise in the southern hemisphere. Tornadoes occur in many regions of the world but the continental United States has more, and more violent, tornadoes per year than any other region, as far as is known. About 125 tornadoes occur in the continental United States per year. Although occurring principally in the more or less "plains" areas, most states in the continental United States report at least one tornado per year. The heaviest yearly concentration of tornadoes is in the Mississippi Valley area.

Tornadoes result from the interaction of highly unstable air masses. They are commonly associated with the undersides of cumulonimbus clouds from which a tornado seems to dangle as a twisting funnel whose "spout" may commonly be anywhere from 250 to 2000 feet in diameter. Tornadoes are also sometimes formed in the spiral bands of hurricanes.

Tornadoes often seem to "wander" along the surface rather slowly at a rate usually between 15 and 30 miles per hour but the winds within a tornado often exceed 300 miles per hour. Like the hurricane, the tornado also has an "eye," but the eye of a tornado is really a very small vortex of very low pressure and violent updraft in which the upward wind velocities often reach 200 miles per hour. The low pressure in the vortex sometimes causes houses actually to explode, much of the wreckage then being whirled aloft in the vortex at almost unbelievable speeds.

Tornadoes commonly occur on spring or early summer afternoons. It is during that time of year that air masses having widely differing properties are present over much of the continental United States. These air masses are the continental polar, the maritime polar, and the maritime tropical air masses. The convergence of any two of these types over land may well result in air mass instability. The highest temperatures occur in the afternoon, which is therefore the time of maximum instability due to convection and conduction. Combining the two factors, then, explains why tornadoes occur more often on spring or early summer afternoons than at any other time.

Waterspouts, related to tornadoes, form over the ocean and sometimes over large lakes by convectional precipitation and the release of latent heat. This type of waterspout is of little consequence; however, true tornadoes also form over the oceans, to form waterspouts. The funnel in either type of waterspout, contrary to popular belief, contains relatively little sea water being sucked up from the ocean surface, but is mostly condensed water vapor.

Weather Observation, Weather Forecasting, and Weather Control

This chapter and Chapters 8, 9, and 10 have presented fundamentals of meteorology, or weather study. Such a presentation would be incomplete without at least mentioning some of the work now being done and contemplated in weather observation, weather forecasting, and in the study of weather control.

The use of radar in tracking storms is generally known, and many people have heard or read about *radiosondes,* small transmitters carried aloft by balloons. These instruments send electrically coded data concerning atmospheric temperature, moisture, and pressure back to earth. And, of course, the weather satellites circling the earth are by now far from being news, in themselves.

Weather satellites will become increasingly more significant as time progresses. As the outcome of a program first tested early in 1963, weather satellites are now sending cloud cover pictures directly to weather stations all over the world, rather than to just a few master stations. By this new method, a particular receiving station obtains instantaneously a good photograph of local cloud patterns twice a day, a procedure which has virtually revolutionized short-range weather forecasts in many areas.

Rockets are valuable space-age tools in meteorological study, instruments in them radioing all kinds of pertinent data to stations on earth. A recently developed method of studying high winds entails the use of a rocket which ejects quantities of copper foil at high altitudes. The copper "chaff" is then tracked by radar. This method not only determines upper wind velocities but can also outline the positions of the jet streams from day to day, an extremely important advance in weather forecasting.

One of the major goals in meteorology and climatology is the ability to express definite mathematical relationships between meteorological data and related meteorological effects, such as storms. This work is being rapidly developed with the help of high speed computers and mathematical models (equations, etc.) of the atmosphere. Today five-day weather forecasts are of a high order of reliability and a thirty-day forecast of equal reliability is only a matter of time. As more and more information about the atmosphere is sent back to earth by various types of orbiting and space vehicles, the science of weather forecasting will advance and probably ultimately reach the point where all long range weather forecasting will largely be a matter of observation, screening data by computers and then processing, also by computers, the screened data into forecasts whose high accuracies would now seem fantastic to us.

It is becoming more and more evident that any long range weather forecasts must take upper atmosphere conditions into strong consideration. Recent studies indicate high correlations between bursts of solar energy and distinct changes in the earth's atmosphere and weather. For example, the long droughts in the southwest continental United States, associated with superior (S) air masses which descend from the upper troposphere, usually abruptly cease during sunspot activity. There are many other apparent correlations between weather and solar activity. Perhaps one of the most significant concepts involving sun-weather relationships is the determination that the sun's atmosphere engulfs the earth, and that winds of charged particles, "solar" or "plasma" winds from the sun, are constantly blowing against the outer atmosphere.

As for weather—and climate—control, virtually the whole path stretches ahead. At present writing, very little has yet been attempted in the field along the lines of weather control, much of this having been in the form of seeding storms, including hurricanes, with silver iodide or other compounds. However, some of the results obtained have been as encouraging as others have been disappointing and, all in all, many expert meteorologists think that at least partial control of storms and climate is a practical possibility which even now is entering the probability stage as an ever increasing amount of meteorological information is made available. It is perhaps apparent that some aspects of weather control have significant military implications.

REVIEW

1. Name the air masses which dominate weather in North America and state their source regions.

2. Explain why the eastern part of the general Great Lakes region commonly receives more snow than the western part of the Great Lakes region.

3. What air masses bring more rain to the continental United States than any other? Where do these air masses originate?

4. Distinguish between "cyclone" and "anticyclone."

5. Name the three major types of cyclones. Discuss the formation of each type.

6. What is experienced first as an extratropical cyclone passes a point, the cold front or the warm front? Why?

7. Discuss the heat transfer role, on a more or less world-wide basis, of cyclonic precipitation.

8. Discuss the formation of an anticyclone, according to the theory presented in this chapter.

9. Explain how extratropical cyclones are "steered."

10. What is "hurricane velocity"?

11. State the six general areas where hurricanes originate.

12. Why do not hurricanes originate precisely on the equator?

13. Explain why tornadoes commonly occur during afternoons in spring or early summer.

EXERCISES

(Answers are given in the answer section at the back of the book.)

1. A typical extratropical cyclone track over the continental United States is sometimes very similar to the plotted path of the principal jet stream. Do you think that there is any relationship between the two? Explain your answer.

2. Some of the major hurricane tracks shown in Figure 62 are roughly parallel to coastlines of continents. Can you offer a logical explanation for this, or do you think that the relationship occurs purely by chance?

3. On an outline map of the world plot the source regions of the air masses which dominate North American weather.

4. On an outline map of the world, plot the major source regions of hurricanes. Draw typical tracks from each source.

5. The warm front in a certain cyclone starts moving at 10 miles per hour; the cold front at 20 miles per hour. If the greatest distance between the fronts is 200 miles, how long will it take for complete occlusion to occur?

6. Assume that a cold front is traveling at 20 miles per hour and that its slope is $\frac{1}{100}$. How long will it take for a mass of warm air traveling up this slope, from the ground, to reach an elevation of 3000 feet?

7. Study the weather map of Figure 61 and list the characteristics of the isobars near Newfoundland as they (a) cross the cold front, (b) cross the warm front, (c) cross the area between the warm front and the cold front, on the south sector of the cyclone, (d) approach the center of the cyclone.

8. The pressure on a flat surface due to wind velocity is given by the formula Pressure (in pounds per square foot) $= 0.004\ V^2$ where V is in miles per hour. Assuming wind velocities in a typical extratropical cyclone as 10 miles per hour, in a hurricane as 100 miles per hour, and in a tornado as 300 miles per hour, calculate the respective pressures in pounds per square foot.

9. Sketch a typical hurricane by means of isobars and place typical barometric pressure values on the isobars. Show a scale on your sketch.

10. A weather satellite which transmits pictures of local weather conditions to receiving stations is launched in a north-south orbit, the time for a complete orbit being 1½ hours. It passes over station *A*, on the equator at 8:00 A.M. on a certain day. At what time will it pass directly over the same station again?

11. Winds of 500 miles per hour have been assumed as existing in some hurricanes. How many feet per second is this?

CHAPTER 12

The Influence of the Oceans upon Climates

The science of *oceanography* covers an extremely wide range of studies as can be inferred from the fact that ocean water covers about 72 percent of the earth's surface. In a sense, of course, there is but one ocean and this fact brings about some interesting relationships. This chapter, however, deals only with those phenomena of *physical oceanography* which have direct and important effects upon climates.

Sea Water

Fundamental facts about sea water are presented here as background for subsequent discussions.

Sea water contains about 3.5 percent of dissolved minerals by weight. Sodium chloride, "table salt," comprises about 78 percent of the dissolved minerals by weight. If all the salts in the ocean were precipitated and then spread out upon the earth's surface, they would form a crust almost 160 feet thick.

In addition to holding minerals in solution, the oceans also absorb an amazing volume of atmospheric gases, notably nitrogen, carbon dioxide, and oxygen. For example, the oceans hold approximately 20 times as much carbon dioxide in solution as is contained in the atmosphere. The amount of carbon in the ocean due to absorbed carbon dioxide, is approximately 25 times the amount of carbon in the estimated total coal reserves of the world. The significance of this lies not in the statistics as such, but in the fact that if the oceans did not absorb carbon dioxide to this extent, life forms on earth would be very different than they are.

The density (see Chapter 2) of sea water is about 1.027 grams per cubic centimeter, a cubic foot of sea water weighing about 64 pounds. The density of sea water depends mainly upon *salinity,* or salt content, and temperature. The density increases with an increase in salinity, and also increases with a decrease in temperature.

Ocean Currents

Causes and Importance of Ocean Currents. Ocean currents are caused by wind and by differences in ocean water temperature and salinity. Figure 63 shows the major surface ocean currents of the

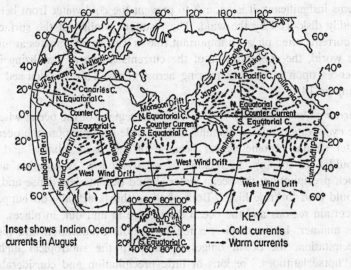

Fig. 63. Ocean currents, February. (Adapted from the U. S. Navy Department)

world. These currents, to be discussed in more detail later, are kept in motion mainly by prevailing winds, as can be seen from Figure 63 by mentally superposing the trade winds and westerlies belts upon the map. Ocean currents are of major importance in exchanging heat between regions, on a world-wide basis.

Deflection of Ocean Currents. It will be noticed that surface ocean currents are deflected by coastlines and that ocean current deflections agree in general with what has been said about the Coriolis effect. In the northern hemisphere where the coastline is not obviously the controlling factor, the current deflects to the right of its direction of travel; in the southern hemisphere the deflection is to the left.

Cold Currents and Upwelling. Current systems are also formed when cold water in high latitudes sinks because of greater density and makes its way equatorward. This particular cold water may also replace warmer water in a surface current by a process called *upwelling.* Upwelling results when warmer surface water in currents is literally drifted away by prevailing winds, and the colder water rises to take the place of the warmer water. Although the mathematical difference in densities between the warmer and the colder water seems insignificant, it is enough to prevent the cold water from being readily dislodged by the wind. The resultant cooling of the surfaces of currents often plays an important role in west coast climates around the world, the cool surfaces of the currents acting as stabilizing influences upon air masses moving across them. This is discussed in Chapter 14.

Currents Due to Salinity Differences. In regions of the ocean where the evaporation rate is high and there is little precipitation, the ocean water should become denser because of increased salinity, and it should tend to sink. In regions of relatively low evaporation and much precipitation, the ocean water should become less dense and it should tend to "ride high." Both of these things actually do happen in certain regions and the ocean does bulge in and out, in places, in this manner. In the tropics, a region of little evaporation and high precipitation, the ocean bulges upward. In the subtropical highs, or "horse latitudes," regions of little precipitation and considerable evaporation, the ocean bulges downward. Therefore ocean water tends to flow from the region of the equator toward the subtropical lows. This movement, however, is also subject to the Coriolis effect, and the resultant motion should eventually be to the east, in both hemispheres. This could contribute to the movement of such "compensating" currents as the equatorial countercurrent shown in Figure 63. Another notable example of currents formed by differences in salinity occurs in the Mediterranean Sea. The water of the Mediterranean becomes so dense due to high evaporation and little rainfall that it actually sinks and flows out through the Strait of Gibraltar to the Atlantic, beneath lighter water from the Atlantic which flows into the Mediterranean. It is believed that the Mediterranean Sea receives a complete change of water in this manner in less than every hundred years.

Subsurface Countercurrents.   Two of the most amazing discoveries made during the International Geophysical Year were those of a south-flowing countercurrent approximately beneath the Gulf Stream and of an east-flowing countercurrent beneath the west-flowing South Equatorial Current. This latter countercurrent, a tremendous river over 200 miles wide, carries about 1000 times more water in it than does the Mississippi River. It flows at about 2½ miles per hour, which happens to be the same velocity as that of the density current which flows from the Mediterranean into the Atlantic. One of the most interesting facts concerning the discovery of these countercurrents is that the existence of the current underneath the Gulf Stream was predicted by a mathematical model of ocean circulation.

The General System of Ocean Circulation.   From what relatively little has been presented above concerning ocean currents, it is obvious that the circulation in oceans is a highly complex subject directly dependent upon factors such as winds, temperature, salinity, and the rotation of the earth. Other factors, not previously mentioned, involve certain technical considerations such as torque and inertia. To all of these and more must be added the existence of currents themselves because, as recently became apparent, surface currents are intimately associated with subsurface currents. Recent studies indicate that some surface currents have a series of associated subsurface countercurrents somewhere beneath them, going in various, roughly parallel, directions for at least some distance. This new concept of a surface current having one or more subsurface countercurrents in the general vicinity leads to the interesting speculation as to the influence of ocean floor topography and other subsurface conditions upon the course of a subsurface current and thus upon the course of the associated surface current and ultimately upon climate.

All in all, the complexity of ocean circulation is due to the simple fact that the ocean is trying to maintain temperature and salinity balances against many opposing factors of time, space, and substance. The ocean approaches a balance in temperature mainly by means of currents. Thus the surface and subsurface ocean currents, many of the latter undoubtedly yet undiscovered, play a major role in distributing heat over much of the world.

The Climate-Current-Climate Cycle. Major surface ocean currents are intimately related to wind systems, as stated before. Most currents are also associated with salinity and temperature differences. Near-surface salinity is a reflection of the precipitation-evaporation ratio. Hence surface currents can be said to be induced largely by wind, precipitation, humidity, and temperature, all elements of meteorology and climatology. To a large extent, the same can be said of subsurface currents, in the light of recent findings which indicate an almost gear-mesh relationship between some surface currents and their sub-surface countercurrents.

As pointed out, currents play a major role in heat distribution and they are important controls and modifiers of some climates. Ocean currents are therefore part of a remarkable system of heat exchange: climate induces and maintains currents; currents affect climate; climate maintains currents, and so on.

Surface Currents. Figure 63 illustrates the basic fact that between the equator and the latitudes of about 40° the major surface currents tend to carry warm water past the east coasts of continents and to carry cool water past the west coasts. (The terms cool and warm, as here applied to currents, are relative.) At latitudes higher than 40°, as Figure 63 also shows, it is more common for warm currents to sweep past the western edges of continents while cool currents roughly parallel a continent's eastern shores. Contrasting (warm and cool) currents are, then, likely to be found *converging* along east coasts; along west coasts contrasting currents commonly *diverge*. This is also illustrated in Figure 63. It is noted here, again, that the relative coolness of some of these currents on west coasts is due in large part to *upwelling*.

If warm currents parallel a coast they tend to heat the bases of incoming air masses, making them more unstable and therefore increasing precipitation. Warm currents, due to decreased atmospheric pressure in their vicinity, actually also attract masses of denser air to some extent. The greatest temperature contrasts, and therefore the greatest density contrasts, occur in winter, setting up a steepened pressure gradient. One seemingly anomalous result of this is that southern states on or near the east coast of the United States receive some of their coldest and stormiest winter weather, with the most snow, when the Gulf Stream is warmer than usual.

The general circulation of surface ocean currents are very similar, a good example being the surface current circulation in the North Atlantic Ocean:

The trade winds tend to move water before them, in a southwest direction. The Coriolis effect turns the drift to the right and the resultant North Equatorial Current moves generally westward. Part of the current enters the Gulf of Mexico through the straits between Yucatán and Cuba. Some of this water eventually passes through the Florida Straits and rejoins that part of the North Equatorial Drift which has been deflected to the north by the West Indies, and has become the Gulf Stream.

The Gulf Stream, warm from its long journey through the tropics, parallels the Atlantic coast until it is well into the zone of the westerlies. At about 35° N latitude, the westerly winds and the Coriolis effect start strongly to deflect the Gulf Stream to the northeast. At about 45° N, the current splits. The southernmost division follows southward along the Spanish peninsula and the northwest coast of Africa as the relatively cool *Canaries* current until it rejoins the North Equatorial Current.

The northernmost part of the divided current swings strongly to the northeast, to pass the western coasts of the British Isles and of Scandinavia as a relatively warm current called the *North Atlantic Drift*. The North Atlantic Drift finally enters the Arctic Ocean. As an apparent adjustment to this receipt of relatively warm surface water, the Arctic Ocean releases cold water, some of which, going southward, passes the northeast coast of North America as the *Labrador Current*.

Surface Currents and Isotherms.   Surface ocean currents, if appreciably cooler or warmer than the ocean water near them, will obviously affect land temperatures to some extent, especially if in a region where the prevailing winds are from sea to land. The influence of ocean currents upon isotherms is well illustrated in Figure 48 of Chapter 8. Attention is called to the effects of the cold currents on the west coasts of South America and Africa, and especially to the effects of the Gulf Stream on the January 40° isotherm as it goes toward the British Isles and the Scandinavian peninsula.

Climatic Influences of Nonflowing Ocean Water

This section deals with the climatic influences of what might be called nonflowing ocean water, in contrast to ocean water which moves in currents. From what has been said about subsurface currents it will probably occur to the reader that no ocean water can possibly stay in the same place over a period of time and this is true. However, the time required for water to make a complete circuit in the North Atlantic surface current system, for example, is in the order of from one to two years, while it takes from 300 to 2000 years for surface water to be completely renewed by water below. Hence the following discussion will relate to the great volume of what, for our immediate purposes, may be called nonflowing ocean water. Some readers may wonder about the use of the term "nonflowing" in conjunction with bodies of water whose most familiar features are waves. As will be shown in Chapter 24, though, a given particle of water changes its position very little due to normal wave action, although under the influence of extraordinary wave action a very slow drift may be set up locally.

The Oceans as Temperature Controls. It was brought out in previous chapters that oceans heat up much more slowly than land and that they also lose their heat much more slowly. The result is that the oceans are really reservoirs of heat whose temperatures stay within a comparatively narrow range between summer and winter. As such, the oceans of the world exert considerable direct and stabilizing influence upon world temperatures, especially in coastal regions where the prevailing winds are from ocean to land. An illustration of this is commonly seen in winter, in the United States, when a cyclonic storm may bring rain to the Pacific coast at an average temperature of 65° F. Inland, losing their marine characteristics, the air masses quickly grow colder over the colder land and by the time the disturbance reaches the New England states it may be causing heavy snowfall at subfreezing temperatures. There, the prevailing winds are flowing from land to sea, thus tending to cancel the local marine influence.

The indirect influence of oceans upon world temperatures is of considerable importance. Most of the moisture in the atmosphere comes primarily from the oceans by evaporation, as explained in Chapter 9. As also explained in that chapter, condensation of this moisture releases heat, a fact which was also referred to in Chapter 11. In Chapter 11, the important role of cyclonic storms in the global transferral of heat was described. As most of the moisture carrying this heat originally came from the oceans, the indirect role which the oceans play in global temperature is of major importance.

The Oceans and Atmospheric Moisture. In addition to furnishing moisture to the atmosphere the oceans apparently play an important part in precipitating moisture. In Chapter 9 it was stated that nuclei must be present for most condensation and precipitation to occur. Recent studies point toward a direct relationship between the number of bubbles occurring over an area of ocean and the number of raindrops ultimately falling from air masses moving over the area.

What happens is evidently something like this: bubbles of atmospheric gases break at the surface of the ocean and, in breaking, flip minute solid particles into the air. These particles may be salt, salt plus silica, or plain silica which has been held in suspension in the sea water. If the particles are plain salt, they may attach themselves to minute particles of silica (from volcanic eruptions, wind erosion activity, etc.) at higher elevations. It is known that particles of silica act as nuclei to change supercooled cloud droplets to ice, a process which can result in rain. By throwing potential nuclei into the atmosphere, then, the oceans apparently help to precipitate much of the same moisture they furnish to the atmosphere.

The Oceans, Atmospheric Pressure, and Winds. As outlined in Chapter 10, oceans, being major temperature controls, are also major atmospheric pressure controls. High-pressure cells in the northern hemisphere form mainly over oceans, two outstanding examples being the *Pacific high* and the *Azores high*. The general relationship of winds to areas of high and low pressure has already been discussed. This relationship will be referred to again in the chapters on climatology.

Sea Ice and Icebergs

Sea Ice. *Sea ice* results from the freezing of sea water at about 27° F, depending upon the salinity, and seldom attains a thickness of over fifteen feet except where it forms close to shore. Sea ice more or less covers the North Polar Sea all year long, but the North Atlantic Drift, being a relatively warm current, prevents ice from forming off the Norwegian coast. Sea ice which covers a large area is called *pack ice*. In the Antarctic regions the movement of pack ice is not restricted by land and the ice pack tends to move north and break up. Sea ice in the northern hemisphere is therefore of considerable yearlong consequence from the standpoint of temperature and pressure, and therefore of climate control, and of lesser importance in the southern hemisphere. Care should be taken at this point to carefully distinguish between the sea ice and the *continental* ice of the Antarctic regions which, of course, is a climate control of global proportions.

Icebergs.   *Icebergs* result when large pieces of glaciers fall, or *calve,* into the sea. Icebergs are composed of fresh, frozen water which originally fell onto a glacier or ice field in the form of rain or snow.

Icebergs are of unique value in some studies. A common current procedure in oceanographic studies is for a party of scientists to spend several months on flat, broad icebergs called *ice islands.* Measurements of radioactivity in various layers of the ice are taken for research involving former climatic conditions; the routes of the ice islands are precisely mapped, thus giving valuable information about the circulation of the surface current systems. Salinity, temperature, and wind observations are also made. Geomagnetic observations and other geophysical measurements are also part of the routine. All in all, these sea islands are extremely valuable oceanographic and climatological research "ships."

One of these ice islands, floating around some years ago in the North Polar regions, was highly interesting in itself in that its shape, size, and surface made it an almost perfect potential aircraft carrier, and certainly one which would have been the world's largest. As it floated around in the current system the ice island variously left and entered different political territories. For several years the procedure was one of Soviet scientists and military personnel evacuating the island before it floated into NATO territory and of Western scientists and military personnel leaving it before it entered Soviet waters. Finally, what was one of the most potentially strategic and most studied islands that the world has ever seen, broke up.

REVIEW

1. Discuss the occurrence of ocean currents due to salinity and temperature differences.

2. Explain how surface ocean currents are formed and maintained. Explain their deflections near coasts.

3. Explain *upwelling*. Name and locate three currents where upwelling occurs. Discuss the resultant effects.

4. Name and locate one subsurface ocean current. In what direction does it flow? How fast? With what major surface current is it associated?

5. To what is the complexity of ocean circulation due?

6. Discuss the climate-current-climate cycle.

7. Discuss the effect of surface currents upon isotherms, taking the Gulf Stream in the North Atlantic as an example.

8. How does the ocean act as a temperature control?

9. What is the relationship of the ocean to atmospheric moisture and to some precipitation?

10. Is sea ice of any importance in the northern hemisphere in global climates? Explain your answer.

EXERCISES

(Answers are given in the answer section at the back of the book.)

1. Sea water contains about 3.5 percent by weight of dissolved minerals. About 78 percent of these minerals is sodium chloride, "table salt." One cubic foot of sea water weighs 64 pounds. How many pounds of "table salt" are there in 100 pounds of sea water?

2. On an outline map of the world sketch the major surface ocean currents. Place the proper names on these currents, in the proper places.

3. The specific gravity of fresh ice is about .93 while the specific gravity of sea water is about 1.03. Assuming that a certain ice island is 200 feet thick and is an almost perfect "block" of ice, how many feet will be above the ocean surface?

Hint: An object of specific gravity a floating in a liquid of specific gravity b does so in such a manner that the fraction $\frac{a}{b}$ represents that part of the volume of the floating object which is below the surface. The ice island in this problem is an almost perfect block, hence the ratio $\frac{a}{b}$ also gives, for this particular problem, that part of the island's thickness below the water.

4. Sketch a hypothetical continent in the northern hemisphere, fixing its northern and southern boundaries by assumed latitudes. It is summer. Assume your own reasonable temperature for the continent, from north to south, and assume similar reasonable temperatures for the ocean. Also assume that a warm current parallels the west coast. Halfway up the west coast the temperature (T) of the current is midway between the temperature of the ocean at that latitude and the temperature of the land at that latitude. Sketch the "T" isotherm across the continent.

5. Records show that the Gulf Stream has warmed up considerably in recent years. Would this tend to make winters in the British Isles warmer or colder and snowier *during a major outbreak on the polar front* near the British Isles? Explain your answer and then check it by inspecting actual records during the last twenty years.

6. About 75,000 cubic miles of fresh water are evaporated from the oceans yearly. (a) How many short tons of moisture is this per square mile of the earth's surface? (b) If all of the above water fell as rain equally all over the world, how many inches of rain would this be at any point on the earth's surface? (1 short ton = 2000 pounds; the area of the earth's surface is about 197 million square miles; 1 cubic foot of fresh water weighs 62.4 pounds.)

7. Antarctica has about 7 million cubic miles of ice. Suppose that world temperature conditions suddenly became such that all of the fresh water evaporated yearly from the oceans (see problem 6) became ice on the continental United States. Disregarding present glaciers, changes in volume due to freezing, compaction, etc., in how many years would the United States have the same amount of ice as Antarctica?

8. As stated in this chapter, ocean water covers about 72 percent of the earth's surface. The surface of the earth is 197 million square miles. If the approximately 7 million cubic miles of ice on Antarctica melted to form 7 million cubic miles of water, how many feet would sea level rise all over the world?

CHAPTER 13

Climatic Classification and World Climatic Types

Climatic Classification

General Problem of Classification. Climates could be classed in a number of ways, but the most important elements of climate are temperature and precipitation. It is of course impossible to measure temperature and precipitation every day, in every small area of the world, but temperature and precipitation leave their "calling cards" in the form of vegetation. The type and amount of vegetation in a particular region is governed chiefly by temperature and precipitation, as compare the tall, heavily foliaged trees of the tropical rain forest with the mosses, lichens, and stunted trees of the Arctic.

Types and extents of vegetation can rather easily be determined, and vegetation is the one best practical means of determining the general precipitation and temperature patterns over large areas over a period of years. There is one main objection, however, to classifying climate solely on the basis of vegetation: vegetation is a result of climate rather than being a cause of climate. The logical solution seems to be to combine cause and result, to describe the climate of a region in terms of what causes climatic patterns in a particular region, and to use the geographical limits of the resulting vegetation types as rough boundary controls.

The two climatic elements which certainly must be included are precipitation and temperature. The next consideration is: how are we to use precipitation and temperature as a general approach for climatic classification? One obvious solution is suggested by the precipitation and temperature maps of previous chapters: both temperature and precipitation, in general, decrease from the equator, poleward. Some climatic classifications, therefore, have such broad latitudinal divisions as "equatorial and tropical climates," "mid-latitude climates," etc. Other classifications are directly in terms of precipitation and temperature, an example of a climate described in this manner being "the moist, mild winter climates." Still other classifications are variations and combinations of the above described systems.

The Köppen System.   In 1918 Dr. Wladimir Köppen of Germany revised a climate classification system which he had advanced in 1900. Since 1918 the revised Köppen system has been modified in several ways by several climatologists, but today the basic Köppen system is the most used method of climate classification.

Köppen based his system upon vegetation zones, temperature, and precipitation. The Köppen system contains five major climatic groups, each designated by a capital letter:

A   Tropical climates
B   Dry climates
C   Warm temperate climates
D   Cold forest climates
E   Polar climates

Each main group is next broken down into climatic types by precipitation, by means of added letters. The letters S and W, meaning steppe (semi-arid) and desert (arid), respectively, are added only to the B group. Thus any climate in the B group is either BS or BW.

The next letters added usually describe precipitation characteristics, as follows:

f   Moist all year
w   Dry winter
s   Dry summer
m   Monsoon precipitation resulting in
     rain forest climate; therefore,
     applies only to A group

The next letters usually describe temperature characteristics:

a   hot summer
b   warm summer
c   cool summer
d   extremely cold winter
h   hot; applies to B climates, only.
k   cool or cold; applies to B climates
     only

As an example of classification in the Köppen system, the New

England states in general are Dfb, the Southern states are Cfa, and various Southwestern states are BSh, BWh, etc. The foregoing description of the Köppen system is generalized and abbreviated although sufficiently precise and complete for an introductory course in geography. Actually, the system makes extensive use of mathematical values for temperatures to define "hot," "cold," etc. Also, some climatic notations can be somewhat involved. For more complete descriptions of the modified Köppen systems, the reader is referred to some of the books on climate listed in the bibliography.

The Thornwaite Systems. The system for climatic classification offered by C. W. Thornwaite in 1933 is like the Köppen system in several respects including the facts that it is based upon vegetation and that it also uses letters to describe types of climates. The Thornwaite system features the one major departure of the Köppen system wherein the B climates are mathematically delineated by a precipitation-to-evaporation ratio, by dividing monthly precipitation by monthly evaporation. The first Thornwaite system uses this ratio throughout.

In 1948 Thornwaite advanced another idea, that of the evaporation and transpiration which would result if sufficient vegetation were available in various regions, that is, *potential evapotranspiration.* The chief drawback to the second Thornwaite classification is that mathematical ratios used in the system are dependent upon values for potential evapotranspiration, which itself is difficult to measure directly.

Climatic Classification in Terms of Air Masses. The Köppen and similar systems of climate classification might be described as being empirical in that they are based upon observed values such as observed extent of vegetation, average measured precipitation, and average measured temperature. Although temperature and precipitation patterns do, to large extent, determine climate, climate itself is a general picture of weather over a period of time. So, the temperature and precipitation patterns of climate are summations of the temperature and precipitation patterns of weather. Weather is controlled principally by air masses. (Chapter 11)

To many authors, therefore, a system of climate classification based upon the "why" of climate, as well as upon the "what, where, when, and how much," has considerable merit. Such a system is used in this book.

World Climatic Types

Climatic types to be discussed in later chapters are listed below. The numbers before each type also appear on the world map of Figure 64. Köppen system equivalents, or near-equivalents, are given after each climate type.

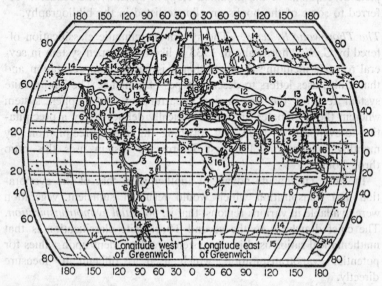

Fig. 64. World climates. (Courtesy A. J. Nystrom & Co., Chicago, Van der Grinten projection. Howard J. Critchfield, *General Climatology*. © 1960. Prentice-Hall, Inc., Englewood Cliffs, N. J.)

I.   Climates Controlled by Equatorial and Tropical Air Masses:
     1. Tropical Rain Forest (Af)
     2. Rainy Tropics, Monsoon Type (Am)
     3. Wet-and-Dry Tropics (Aw, Cwa)
     4. Tropical Desert (BWh)
     5. Tropical Semi-Arid (BSh)

II. Climates Controlled by Tropical and Polar Air Masses:
     6. Mediterranean (Csa, Csb)
     7. Humid Subtropical (Cfa)
     8. Marine Climate (Cfb, Cfc)

9. Mid-Latitude Desert (BWk)
10. Mid-Latitude Semi-Arid (BSk)
11. Humid Continental, Hot Summer (Dfa, Dwa)
12. Humid Continental, Warm Summer (Dfb, Dwb)

III. Climates Controlled by Polar and Arctic Air Masses:
13. Subarctic (Dfc, Dfd, Dwc, Dwd)
14. Tundra (ET)
15. Polar (EF)

IV. Climates Controlled Principally by Altitude:
16. Highland Climates (H)

It is suggested at this point that the reader, by means of colored pencils, color the areas in Figure 64 according to number so that the world-wide distribution of climatic types can be seen at a glance. The exercise will also have the added effect of "learning by doing" and is one of the most effective ways of becoming acquainted with climatic type distribution.

It will also be helpful and interesting to roughly indicate on the map the wind and pressure "belts" of the earth, showing wind directions, and then to refer to the map as one reads the descriptions of the various climatic types in following chapters. The boundaries stated below are very rough in that they encompass the entire regions covered due to seasonal shifts. Some overlapping therefore occurs. Characteristics of each "belt" are also briefly reviewed:

Belt	Boundaries (Latitude)	Characteristics
Equatorial (Intertropical Convergence Zone, ITCZ)	6° N to 6° S	Converging, moist, rising air. Heavy rains.
Tropics	23½° N to 23½° S	Maximum insolation during year.
Subtropical Highs	25° to 35°, N and S	Descending air. High pressure. Stable air. Horse latitudes.
Trade Winds	35° to 0°, N and S	Winds blow in a general SW direction in northern hemisphere, NW in southern hemisphere.

Belt	Boundaries (Latitude)	Characteristics
Westerlies	25° to 65°, N and S	Winds blow in a general NE direction in northern hemisphere, SE in southern hemisphere.
Polar Fronts	Location varies widely. May be located anywhere from 30° to 70° N and S. Generally pictured as a wavy line centered about 50° N and S.	Converging air masses. Rising air. Low Pressure. Region of cyclonic storms.
Polar Easterlies	From polar regions to 50° N and S. Equatorward limit varies widely, like polar front.	Winds blow in general SW direction in northern hemisphere, NW in southern hemisphere.

It should be held in mind that the above described belts and zones, in general, migrate after the sun, lagging about five or six weeks behind. For example, on June 21 the sun is over the Tropic of Capricorn and starting southward. On June 21 the major pressure and wind belts of the earth are still moving north and will not reach their maximum northern position until late July or August.

It must also be remembered that the pressure and wind belts described above are very generalized and that in many cases they are nonexistent as true zones. This is especially true of the pressure belts which, as already explained, tend to break down into separate cells. The reader will find, however, that the basic picture of the world being girdled by parallel wind and pressure belts is extremely helpful in understanding climate and is in fact not too far removed from actual truth much of the time.

REVIEW

1. Explain the general relationship of temperature and precipitation to extent and kind of vegetation.

2. Give one reason why climate classifications are not based upon vegetation alone.

3. Describe the Köppen system of climate classification. Is the Köppen system primarily based upon controls of climate or upon elements of climate?

4. How would the climate of your area be expressed in the Köppen system?

5. One of Thornwaite's climate classification systems is based upon "potential evapotranspiration." Explain what this means.

6. Name the sixteen chief climatic types described in this chapter, and give their Köppen classification. Arrange your list in terms of air mass controls.

7. It would be expected that climates controlled by equatorial and tropical air masses (Types 1–5, inclusive) would be restricted, at least roughly, to the tropics, between 23½° N and 23½° S latitudes. How does this statement agree with the actual locations of Types 1 through 5 as shown in Figure 64?

EXERCISES

(Answers are given in the answer section at the back of the book.)

1. Make a tracing of the outline of North America from Figure 64 without indicating the climatic zones. Show parallels of latitude. Now, without referring to Figure 64 assume that a certain isotherm comes onto Alaska from the ocean at 60° N. Due to the fact that the west coasts of continents at a fairly high latitude are warmer than the east coasts at the same latitude, assume that this particular isotherm will shift 10° to the south as it crosses Canada and that it will leave the continent around the mouth of the St. Lawrence River.

Sketch the isotherm across the tracing of the continent. Compare your result with the southern boundary of Climate Type 13 in Figure 64. Also compare the northern boundary of Climate Type 13 with its southern boundary. State any general conclusion you may arrive at concerning the general direction of these boundaries, and the reason for the general directions.

Now examine the southern boundary of Type 13 on the Eurasian continent. Does this boundary agree with your conclusion? Explain the northward bulge of the northern boundary of Type 13, on the Eurasian continent.

2. Coloring Figure 64 as suggested brings up an interesting cartographic fact known as "the map problem." In order to delineate countries or areas by the use of colors, and in order that not too many colors be used, the same color is often used more than once on maps showing boundaries.

It can be proven mathematically that, given any number of adjacent

areas of any shape or position, no more than five colors are needed to
completely define each area, assuming that each area is fully colored. In
practice, it has never been found that more than "x" colors are needed.
Sketching the most complicated hypothetical intersection of areas you can,
and remembering that a full color or a design of particular color, such as
crosshatching, may be used more than once as long as it does not overlap
onto itself in another area, what is the value of "x"?

Check this value against your most complex junctures of your variously
colored climatic types in Figure 64.

CHAPTER 14

Climates Controlled by Equatorial and Tropical Air Masses

1. The Tropical Rain Forest Climate (Af)

The tropical rain forest type of climate typically occurs at low elevation within 10° of the equator and it also occurs on some higher-latitude tropical coasts which are exposed to the trade winds. The major world areas having tropical rain forest climate are the Congo Basin, the Amazon Basin, Malaya, Sumatra, Borneo, Java, New Guinea, the Solomon Islands, areas along the east coasts of South America and Central America, the east coast of Madagascar, and the eastern sector of the Philippines.

As the tropics receive maximum insolation during the year and as almost unvarying conditions for producing rain are always present, the tropical rain forest climate has no great variations in either temperature or precipitation from month to month. A typical area having this climate has from 5 to 6 inches of rain every month for a yearly total of over 60 inches and has an average monthly temperature of about 80° F.

The popular picture of the rainy tropics as a "steaming jungle" is far from usual actuality. Daytime temperatures rarely exceed 88° F on the average and, at night, temperatures are usually on the relatively cool side, around 70° F. Rainfall in interior locations is mainly convectional, resulting from thunderstorm activity. Rainfall on the coasts may be entirely convectional near the equator but at higher latitudes usually results from the trade winds blowing across east coasts and just beginning their ascent over inland mountains.

The air masses which control the tropical rain forest climate are part of the subtropic high-equatorial low interchange. The trade winds blow from the "horse latitudes" toward the equator, leaving some precipitation on some east coasts as outlined above, and converge near the equator at the intertropical convergence zone (ITCZ). There they are forced aloft and heavy, erratic convectional rainfall results.

Rain forest, or *selva,* is the main type of vegetation of this climate. Tall, broadleaf trees grow to average heights of about 80 feet, although it is not uncommon to see trees more than 100 feet in height, especially where trees whose bases are in small valleys or depressions have grown taller in competition for the sunlight.

It was once a more or less popular belief that the rain forest province is one of dense jungle. Now, the opposite idea is sometimes advanced, this being that real jungle is almost nonexistent and occurs only thinly along the margins of open spaces and along riverbanks. This picturization would be strongly challenged by many who have traveled through the rain forest. Actually, jungle does exist and in considerable quantity in those regions of rain forest climate where conditions are suitable for the growth of smaller trees, bushes, thickets, smaller vines, etc.

2. The Rainy Tropics Climate, Monsoon Type (Am)

As its name indicates, this type of climate has a dry season but is similar in many respects to the tropical rain forest climate. Major world regions having the rainy tropics climate, monsoon type, are the southwestern coast of India, the coasts of Burma and Thailand, the northeastern coast of South America, and the northern coasts of Puerto Rico, Haiti, and the Philippines.

The average monthly temperatures of this climate are somewhat lower than those of the rain forest climate, being about 70° F. The average annual precipitation is usually over 60 inches, some areas having more than 200 inches per year. Thus, although there is a dry season of from two to three months, the precipitation is sufficient throughout all regions having this climate to support a rain forest type of vegetation. The dry season may occur in winter or in summer, depending upon geographical location, although the general pattern is that of dry winters and moist summers.

In the dry winter, large land mass variety of this type of climate, the controlling air masses are of the equatorial and maritime tropical (mT) varieties, pulled onto land by a genuine monsoonal circulation, as over India and southeast Asia. In other regions the dry season and its characteristics are determined mainly by seasonal changes in the force of the trade winds—the "surge of the trades"—and is not due to true monsoonal circulation.

Precipitation, like that of the tropical rain forest climate, is primarily from thundershowers originating from the updraft of air in the intertropical convergence zone. Due to the fact that most regions having this type of climate are not directly on the equator but are north of the equator, hurricanes and typhoons, and their accompanying heavy rainfall, are seasonal occurrences.

Another factor in the precipitation pattern is of importance. It may have already occurred to the reader that, despite a dry season and despite the fact that this climate is centered some degrees north of the equator instead of on the equator, the rainy tropics, monsoon type of climate has just about as much rainfall as does the tropical rain forest climate where precipitation is never absent during any month. The chief reason for this is that the rainfall, when it does occur in the monsoon type, is heavier than it would otherwise be, because of added orographic effects due to mountains.

This effect is very noticeable over the Western Ghats mountains on the southeast coast of India where another notable, associated

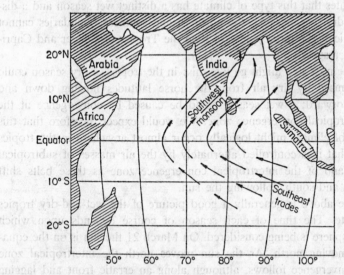

Fig. 65. Trade winds and the summer monsoon in the Indian Ocean, showing deflection by Coriolis effect. (Adapted from George F. Taylor, *Elementary Meteorology.* © 1954. Prentice-Hall, Inc., Englewood Cliffs, N. J.)

phenomenon occurs. In that region the trade winds blowing from the southeast blow well across the equator only to be deflected to the northeast because of the Coriolis effect. (See Figure 65.) These moist winds thus bring heavy precipitation to the mountain-rimmed coast and become part of the monsoon system of India. Thanks to the Coriolis effect India captures moisture originally headed for Africa. This accounts in part for the arid to semi-arid eastern equatorial coast of Africa.

The vegetation associated with the rainy tropics, monsoon type of climate is essentially rain forest growth or selva. Due to the added effect of orographic precipitation, however, the vegetation on mountain ranges often grades rather sharply from tall trees on the windward side into dense thicket and thornbush on the leeward side.

3. The Wet-and-Dry Tropics (Aw, Cwa)

It is interesting and informative at this point to try to deduce, using the information of previous chapters, just where the wet-and-dry tropics type of climate might be found, and why. First, the name indicates that this type of climate has a distinct wet season and a distinct dry season. Next, the northern and southern boundaries cannot technically be more poleward than the Tropics of Cancer and Capricorn, respectively.

The next step might go like this: in the tropics, a dry season could be caused by dry air from the horse latitudes flowing down and equatorward; a wet season could be caused by convergence at the intertropical convergence zone. We would expect therefore that this type of climate might logically occur almost anywhere in the tropics and that it is controlled alternately by the air masses of subtropical high and of the intertropical convergence zone as these belts shift north and south, following the sun.

The above is generally a good picture of the wet-and-dry tropics climate. The time of each season of course depends upon which hemisphere is being considered. On March 21 the sun is on the equator, moving north. As the sun moves north the intertropical zone of convergence follows, although along an erratic front and lagging about 1½ months behind. The northern subtropical high also moves north, also along an erratic front made even more erratic by land-sea temperature contrasts, mountain systems, trade wind surges, etc.

The result is a wet season for some tropical regions in the northern hemisphere.

At the same time the southern subtropical low and its warm, stable air is moving equatorward on the heels of a departing wet season in the southern hemisphere. Thus, typically, the wet season of the wet-and-dry tropics climate occurs in the southern hemisphere from October through May, approximately, while in the northern hemisphere the wet season occurs from May through October, approximately.

Major areas having the wet-and-dry tropics climate include parts of Central and South America, Africa, Australia, India, and southeast Asia which lie between the latitudes of 5° and 25°. The western part of Madagascar also has this climate.

The average monthly temperatures, as would be expected, show a higher yearly range than that for either the tropical rain forest or the rainy tropics, monsoon type of climate, from a minimum of about 60° F to a maximum of, at times, 90° F. The precipitation, up to about 60 inches per year, is mainly from thundershowers and from tropical lows formed near the intertropical convergence zone.

The effect of a fairly long, very dry season is strongly reflected in the type and amount of vegetation, the vegetation of the wet-and-dry tropics being of the *savanna* type. Savannas—grasslands—are primarily made up of tall, very coarse grass which grows in tufts. Here and there, low trees give the savanna a parklike look. Before the savanna grades into regions with more moist climates the *savanna forest* appears, which in turn may grade into a tropical rain forest, typical examples of such transitions occurring on the Amazon Basin of South America. Riverbanks in the savanna forests, and their floodplains, often feature thick masses of tall trees which arch over stream courses and are called *galería* forests, the word *galería* meaning "corridor" in Spanish.

4. The Tropical Desert Climate (BWh)

5. The Tropical Semi-Arid Climate (BSh)

Tropical desert and semi-arid climates are associated with the subtropic highs and are therefore centered a few degrees poleward of the Tropics of Cancer and Capricorn. The controlling air masses of these climates are thus compressed and adiabatically warmed as they descend in the "horse latitudes." Warming decreases the relative humidity of the air. Then, as the air passes over land, major evaporation of any surface moisture results. As much of the upper air descends on a slope and is deflected back toward the equator as a result of the Coriolis effect, the aridity due to the descending air extends appreciably into the zone of the trade winds in either hemisphere. This equatorward extension of arid conditions is increased along the west coasts of continents where, as brought out in Chapter 12, cool ocean current water, due to *upwelling,* stabilizes the bases of maritime air masses moving onto land. The combination of descending dry air plus offshore dry air results in some of the world's greatest deserts: the Sonoran of California, Arizona, and Mexico; the Atacama-Peru desert of Chile and Peru; the Sahara and Namib deserts of Africa. These four regions, with central Australia and a 500-mile wide strip from Arabia eastward to Afghanistan, constitute the world's principal areas of tropical desert climate.

A desert or arid climate is generally considered to be one whose annual precipitation is less than 10 inches, and a semi-arid climate one whose annual precipitation is between 10 and 20 inches. Precipitation in tropical deserts is usually from thunderstorm activity. Due to lack of vegetation, "flash floods" are the rule rather than the exception during and after a desert storm. Some deserts have very little precipitation, however. For example, one region in the Atacama Desert of Chile had a total of less than one inch of rain for a period of forty-five years.

Tropical semi-arid, or tropical *steppe* regions, usually surround or abut the tropical desert regions as fairly thin strips which are intermediate, meteorologically as well as geographically, between the desert and moist climates. Precipitation in the semi-arid regions may occur from both thunderstorm and true cyclonic activity, the latter type usually occurring seasonally.

Temperatures of the tropical semi-arid climate are not materially different from those of the tropical desert climate. Desert climates commonly have daytime temperatures of 120° F or over, while night temperatures may drop to 80° F or lower. The highest official temperature on record is 136° F, recorded in the northwestern Sahara Desert in 1922. Temperatures over 130° F have been recorded in several regions in the southwestern United States.

Many people visualize a desert as a waste of drifting sand dunes. Sand dune areas of deserts, however, usually comprise only a small fraction of the entire desert area. The Sahara Desert, for example, is only about one ninth covered by sand. The typical desert also has a wide variety of vegetation growing on it, contrary to popular belief. If every desert plant had leaves the size of average oak leaves, many so-called "barren" deserts would seem to be covered with vegetation.

As it is, however, desert plants cannot maintain thin broad leaves through which moisture would easily transpire into the atmosphere. Rather, the typical desert plant which has any noticeable leaves at all has them in a thick-skinned, pulpy form which distributes moisture slowly throughout the plant and not quickly to the atmosphere.

The vegetation of the tropical semi-arid climate includes much of the tropical desert type of vegetation but usually gradually grades through cactus, etc., into grass, many times into the savanna and therefore into the wet-and-dry tropics climate. An outstanding example of the geographical transition from tropical desert to tropical semi-arid to wet-and-dry tropics climates occurs in Africa, starting at about 30° N latitude and going south.

REVIEW

1. State the principal world areas having the tropical rain forest type of climate.

2. What air masses control the tropical rain forest type of climate? What wind and pressure belts are they associated with?

3. Describe the rain forest vegetation.

4. What is the chief difference between the tropical rain forest climate and the rainy tropics, monsoon type of climate?

5. Define *selva, steppe, savanna*.

6. What major world areas have the wet-and-dry tropics type of climate?

7. Name four great desert regions associated with both the tropical desert climate and with cool ocean currents.

8. What is the general geographical relationship of regions having tropical semi-arid climates to regions having tropical desert climates?

9. Discuss the tropical rain forest climate, the wet-and-dry tropics climate, and the tropical desert climate in terms of precipitation and temperature.

EXERCISES

(Answers are given in the answer section at the back of the book.)

1. The highest natural surface air temperature ever officially recorded was 136° F. How would this temperature be expressed on the Centigrade scale?

2. Descending air in the regions of the subtropical lows (horse latitudes) warms itself adiabatically and thus helps to bring about arid conditions in those latitudes. Assume that a mass of air in so descending is compressed into $9/10$ of the volume it had aloft and that its temperature changes from 75° F to 90° F. Assume also that its relative humidity aloft was 50 percent. What is the new relative humidity of the air mass? Will this change in relative humidity speed up or retard evaporation on the ground surface?

3. On an outline map of the world sketch the principal areas of the tropical rain forest climate, the rainy tropics, monsoon type of climate, the wet-and-dry tropics climate, and the tropical desert and tropical semi-arid climates. Color each type according to the legend you place on your map.

CHAPTER 15

Climates Controlled by Tropical and Polar Air Masses

This chapter is a continuation of the descriptions of climate types which began in Chapter 14. As before, the number in front of the name of each climate type is keyed to the map of Figure 64. The symbols following the name of the climate type indicate equivalent or near-equivalent types in the Köppen system.

6. The Mediterranean Climate (Csa, Csb)

The Mediterranean climate is found between the latitudes of 30° and 40°, usually on the western coasts of continents. The major regions where it occurs are southern California, central Chile, the Mediterranean Sea area, the tip of South Africa, and some areas in Australia. The unique meteorological characteristic of this climate is that it has almost absolute drought in summer and, usually, an average of about 20 inches of rainfall in winter. The marine or coastal version of this climate is defined in the Köppen system as Csb, the interior version as Csa. Precipitation characteristics for adjacent marine and interior regions having the Mediterranean climate are much the same. Temperature contrasts between the marine and interior types are often striking, especially in summer. It is not unusual, for example, for the San Fernando Valley of southern California to be experiencing a temperature of almost 100° F under a blazing sun while, a few miles distant, on the coast, the city of Santa Monica may be shrouded in ocean fog, at a temperature of 65° F. Cool ocean currents contribute to the very cool summers of many coastal locations having the Mediterranean type of climate. The ocean currents also stabilize maritime air masses which might otherwise tend to cause precipitation. The summer temperatures of inland locations having the Mediterranean climate are much like those of the tropical semi-arid climate, as the Mediterranean climate is transitional between the tropical semi-arid and the humid climates.

The main reason for the summer drought and the winter rains of this climate is simply stated: in summer, the regions having this climate lie in or near the descending, stable air of the subtropical highs or horse latitudes; in winter, due to migration of the belts, the regions lie in the path of the westerlies and their moving fronts. Snowfall is of course rare in lowland Mediterranean locations as are thunderstorms. In summer, the air is dry and descending. In winter, the air masses of the westerlies have their bases stabilized by cool ocean water. Thus thunderstorm activity in the tropical Mediterranean climate is usually confined to mountain areas. The yearly precipitation is almost entirely frontal in character and results from convergence of air masses having different temperature and humidity characteristics.

The vegetation associated with the Mediterranean climate reflects the fact that the precipitation comes during the cooler months when evaporation is least. Although the moisture is thus utilized to almost maximum extent it is still far from being a copious amount. The usual result is that vegetation can be either dense or fairly big but not both, in the same region. This leads to two main types of Mediterranean climate vegetation. One type is exemplified by the *chaparral* of southern California and the *maquis* of Europe. Both are dense tangles of stunted trees, shrubs, and bushes. The other main type of Mediterranean vegetation is *Mediterranean woodland,* or *Mediterranean scrub forest.* This kind of general vegetation consists of widely spaced trees which are usually some type of oak or olive, and grass which turns brown in the summer drought season.

7. The Humid Subtropical Climate (Cfa)

The humid subtropical type of climate is found on the east coasts of continents, at about the same general latitudes as the Mediterranean climate, but extending farther equatorward. It might seem, therefore, that the two climates would be much the same.

In reality they are very different. The middle latitude west coasts of continents where the Mediterranean climates typically occur are strongly affected by the stabilizing marine influence and rather readily allow the migration of pressure and wind belts. Monsoonal type circulation does not normally tend to occur on the west coasts of continents, also because of the dominance of the stabilizing marine control, and the shift of the belts from subtropical high to westerlies and back again in a year is unopposed.

On the other hand, continental east coasts in middle latitudes are not dominated by marine-stabilized air. Land-sea temperature differences on east coasts in summer often set up a monsoonal type circulation which is strong enough to upset the latitudinal shifting of the wind and pressure belts. The result is that many east coasts in the latitudes of the subtropical high, rather than having a dry Mediterranean summer like their west coast counterparts, have very humid, uncomfortable, rainy summers as moist maritime tropical (mT) air moves onto the continent. These air masses are made even more unstable as they pass over the warm currents which commonly flow off east coasts.

The major world areas having the humid subtropical climate are the southeastern United States, southeast China, parts of Japan, parts of Brazil, Paraguay, and Uruguay, the east coast of Australia, and the extreme southeastern coast of Africa. In all of these regions the summers are controlled by masses of maritime tropical air moving inland in response to a monsoonal type circulation due to land-sea temperature differences. In winter, in most of these regions, the land-sea temperature differences are less and a strong reversal of wind, from land to sea, does not occur except in Asia where a true monsoon circulation exists the year round. This results in less precipitation in southeast China and northern India during the winter months. The other regions having the humid subtropical climate, however, now have no strong wind flow to interrupt the normal shifting of the wind and pressure belts to the south. The belts shift and these regions now come under the winter control of air masses at or near the polar front. Winter precipitation is therefore mainly of the frontal type from cyclones carried along in the belt of the westerlies, the fronts resulting from the convergence of continental polar (cP) and maritime tropical (mT) air masses.

The average monthly temperature in summer is around 80° F but temperatures of over 90° F are far from uncommon. Many days are extremely humid and night generally brings little relief at such times as any appreciable temperature drop is more than offset, from the standpoint of comfort, by a corresponding increase in relative humidity.

In winter months, these latitudes are the battleground of tropical and polar air masses. A succession of warm fronts and mild rains might be followed by violent cold front activity and associated thunderstorms and then by many days of pleasant, balmy weather which in turn might be abruptly terminated by a tongue of polar air which brings snow and plunges the temperatures to far below freezing.

Considering the differing air masses which control the humid subtropical climates throughout the year, the amount of monthly precipitation is remarkably similar, varying from about 3 to 5 inches. An exception to this is, of course, southeast China where the monsoonal circulation causes a noticeable dry season in winter. The total annual precipitation even there, though, is comparable to other humid subtropical locations, being about 45 inches.

A notable departure from the usually comparable precipitation figures for regions having the humid subtropical climate occurs in Cherrapunji, India, in the Khasi Hills. There, with the added effects of orographic precipitation, the average yearly precipitation is over 400 inches. The highest yearly precipitation ever recorded for an area was in Cherrapunji in the latter part of the nineteenth century when 1041 inches of rain fell in one year.

The typical vegetation of the humid subtropical climates are the broadleaf and mixed broadleaf-coniferous forests. The trees may be oak, hickory, ash, pine, spruce, etc. The forest floor, especially where the broadleaf trees dominate, is commonly well covered in areas by bushes, ferns, and creeping vines which in swampy regions often grow in a variety and profusion characteristic of swamp areas in the tropical rain forest.

8. The Marine Climate (Cfb, Cfc)

As already developed, the Mediterranean type of climate extends from 30° to about 40° latitude and it is there that the prevailing westerlies and their associated air masses begin to exert considerable influence on the climate of continental west coasts. The marine climate, or the "west coast marine climate," typically starts at about 40° latitude on the west coasts of continents and extends to about 60° latitude. The considerably greater-than-average poleward extension of this type of climate is due to the stable, mild characteristics of the marine air in these latitudes and to the existence of stabilizing cold currents along the continental west coasts.

The Cfb type of marine climate is "temperate, with warm summers"; the Cfc type is "temperate, with cool summers." The principal world areas having the marine climate are the west coast of North America, from southern California to Alaska; the British Isles; the west coasts of France and Germany; the Netherlands and Belgium; Denmark; the southwest coasts of Sweden and Norway; New Zealand; southeastern Australia; and the southern tip of Chile.

As the general passage of the air masses is from west to east and as some continents have high mountains on their west coasts, the amount of precipitation is greatly influenced by the presence or absence of coastal mountains. Where England, France, the Netherlands, and Denmark, for example, may receive 40 inches of precipitation per year, the west coasts of Alaska, Chile, and Norway within these latitudes receive up to 90 inches per year.

The marine climate is chiefly characterized by mild winters and cool summers, 50° F being a good annual average except at high elevations. Temperatures seldom drop to freezing for any length of time nor do they often go over 80° F. Some west coast areas having the marine climate have a noticeable decrease in monthly rainfall during the summer months. The reason for this is that it is during the summer that the belt of the subtropical high reaches its highest latitudes. This brings the equatorward portion of the marine climate under partial dominance by the descending, dry air of the subtropical high and reduces the amount of precipitation.

The vegetation of the marine climate is of course largely dependent upon the amount of precipitation which, in the marine climate, as explained, is strongly dependent upon the presence or non-presence of coastal mountains. Various kinds of grasses and shrubs thrive in both situations. That part of the low-lying west coast of Europe having the marine climate has good stands of oak and beech and similar trees, but the fabled oak and pine trees of England have all but disappeared due to cutting. On North American west coasts having the marine climate, the great coniferous forests and luxuriant broadleafs associated with heavy rainfall grade into each other on the mountain slopes and represent the major marine climate vegetation of that continent.

9. The Mid-Latitude Desert Climate (BWk)

10. The Mid-Latitude Semi-Arid Climate (BSk)

It will be remembered that the tropical desert and tropical semi-arid climates result chiefly from their rough latitudinal correspondence with the subtropical highs and the resulting descending, warm, stable air. The mid-latitude desert and mid-latitude semi-arid climates result mainly from the fact that most of the regions having these climates are interior regions. They are either far removed from sources of maritime air, or are shut off from moist air by mountains, or both. Further, those regions in the northern hemisphere are often inundated in winter by masses of cold, dry polar air. The principal regions of the world having these climates are, in North America, the basin-and-range structure to the east of the Sierra Nevada, and the Great Plains; in Eurasia, the Central Asia Desert which extends across the south of Russia and north China; in South America, much of Argentina.

The average annual temperature of the mid-latitude desert climate and the mid-latitude semi-arid climate of about 63° F is some 12° below the average temperature of their tropical counterparts and this delineates the two climates, tropical and mid-latitude, where they happen to abut each other as in the western United States. The cooler temperatures, as the reader has probably already concluded, are due to the more poleward locations of these climates.

Due to the fact that these mid-latitude deserts are at higher latitudes, annual extremes in temperature for a particular region may be considerable, varying from −55° F in winter to 110° F in summer. Extremes between day and night may also exhibit a large range, particularly in summer when the desert heats up rapidly during the day and at night loses its heat rapidly into the still, clear air by radiation.

The mid-latitude semi-arid climates typically abut the mid-latitude desert climates and, where the true desert climates are associated with relatively small areas, the semi-arid climates involve tremendous areas, such as the steppes of Russia. Where the desert areas usually receive about 4 inches of rainfall annually, the semi-arid, steppe regions usually receive from 10 to 20 inches per year. The typical steppe climate in mid-latitudes occurs on hills between the desert and the sources of moisture, hence intercept by orographic precipitation whatever modest amount of rain may be left in the air masses after their long journey inland.

The vegetation of the mid-latitude desert is similar to that of other deserts, with some variations in type and quantity due to colder winters. The vegetation of the mid-latitude semi-arid climate is, typically, shrubs, clumps of short grass, and trees like the cottonwood. The preferred routes of old covered wagon trails of the United States, west of the Rockies, skirted the deserts and led through the grass-covered steppes. Now this region is a vast commercial cattle and sheep range, as are the mid-latitude steppes of Argentina. Vast herds of beef cattle and sheep also roam the semi-arid regions of central Asia, Russia at present writing being second to Australia in sheep production.

11. The Humid Continental, Hot Summer Climate (Dfa, Dwa)

12. The Humid Continental, Warm Summer Climate (Dfb, Dwb)

The humid continental climates lie between the latitudes of 35° and 55° in the northern hemisphere. These climates are virtually absent in the southern hemisphere because of the absence of continental land masses in these latitudes. The latitudes of 35° to 55° are invaded by several types of polar and tropical air masses during the year, hence this is a region of seasonal temperature and precipitation contrasts.

The Humid Continental, Hot Summer Climate (Dfa, Dwa). The humid continental, hot summer climate is sometimes called the Corn Belt climate as it is in this climate that a considerable portion of the world's maize is grown. The hot summer version of the humid continental climate extends from about latitude 35° to 45° N. The three major world occurrences of the climate are, in the United States, from about longitude 100° W, passing south of the Great Lakes and wedging out to the east coast; in Europe the Danube Valley, the Balkan States, and the Po Valley; in Asia, north China, most of Manchuria, Korea, and the northern part of the island of Honshu, Japan. The climate in much of this latter area is described by Köppen as Dwa, or cold snowy forest climates having dry winters, with hot summers.

In winter the humid continental, hot summer type of climate is largely controlled by continental polar air masses (cP) but these latitudes are those of the polar front, a term which is both highly descriptive and factual. This is the region of battling air masses, and tropical maritime air masses (mT) invade the territory from time to time in winter and precipitate cyclonic activity. In summer the regions are controlled mainly by continental tropical (cT) and maritime tropical (mT) air masses. Like the wind belts and other pressure belts, the polar front, in places actually an extremely mobile and undulating wide zone of low pressure, moves northward in summer in the northern hemisphere. Continental and maritime tropical air masses then largely take over and control the "battleground" as the polar front and its colder air masses retreat.

The term "temperature extremes" is applicable to the humid continental, hot summer climate. Temperatures below freezing are common in winter while temperatures above 90° F are not uncommon in summer. In summer, the fact that tropical air masses dominate the climate is reflected by the generally small temperature change from north to south for a large region. In winter, the existence of a true "front" of opposing air masses is apparent from the sharp drop in temperatures as one goes north, leaving the warmer air masses behind.

Precipitation is in the form of rain and snow, with some hail and sleet. The rain occurs generally in the warmer months and is principally convectional in nature. At times in the winter months the presence of both cold and warm air masses in the same general region is demonstrated by large snowflakes which apparently melt in the air before the eyes of observers. As explained in Chapter 9, snowflakes are formed in temperatures close to 0° F and what is happening is that snow is forming in the polar sector of a cyclone and is precipitating in the warm sector. Thus a mass of freezing polar air is often adjacent to a mass of warm air, a fact which is well known to dwellers in this climate who are all accustomed to seeing, at times, temperatures changing from deep winter readings to spring values and back again within the course of a few days. Precipitation in this climate is generally from around 25 inches to 55 inches per year, the amount of precipitation usually being greater in the lower latitudes.

In October or early November the regions having the humid continental, hot summer climate begin to come under the control of polar air masses but the tropical air masses, although retreating, are still strong. The result is that in autumn, cold, clear weather may be interspersed for a week or two by typically summer weather. This is the "Indian Summer" of this climate.

Vegetation in the humid continental, hot summer climate is characterized by the broadleaf and mixed broadleaf-conifer forests. The conifer forests become more and more dominant in the higher latitudes. Grasses vary from the short, vivid green grasses of the more humid areas to the prairie grasses of the less humid regions.

The Humid Continental, Warm Summer Climate (Dfb, Dwb).   The humid continental, warm summer climate is located between the general latitudes of 50° and 60° N. The principal world occurrences of this climate are: in North America, in the northern United States east of longitude 100° W, and in southern Canada; in Eurasia, in Poland, Czechoslovakia, eastern Germany, southern Sweden, and a large area in Russia; in Asia, in southeastern Siberia, northern Manchuria, and the island of Hokkaido, Japan. Parts of the above regions are designated by Köppen as Dwb, cold snowy forest climates having dry winters and warm summers.

As the name of this climate indicates, summers are generally not as hot as the humid continental, hot summer type. The reason for this is that the polar air masses have increasing influence as the poles are approached. Similarly, winters are more severe, the severity increasing toward the poles. Temperatures in winter commonly fall far below freezing.

Because of the strong effect of the polar air masses, yearly precipitation in this climate is often not much more than 20 inches, the upper "limit" of a semi-arid climate. This general situation is notably altered on the east coasts of North America and Asia. In both these regions, slow-moving cyclones hover over the coasts long enough to precipitate considerable moisture from maritime air drawn into the cyclone system. Due both to the warmer temperatures of the maritime air and to the release of latent heat, the temperatures are considerably modified. Such higher temperatures and higher precipitation are characteristic of the Maritime Provinces of Canada, New England, and Hokkaido, Japan. This unique pattern is designated by some geographers as the "New England-Hokkaido" type of climate.

Forests in the humid continental, warm summer climates are primarily conifer, especially in the most northern areas. The northern limits of the humid continental, warm summer type of climate, due to a short growing season, the quality of soil, and topography, roughly represent the northernmost limits of man's attempts to till the land.

REVIEW

1. Explain why large semi-arid regions commonly occur in continental interiors.

2. If the city in which you live has one of the climates discussed in this chapter, state its Köppen designation.

3. As stated in this chapter, about 1040 inches of rain fell in the area of Cherrapunji, India, in one year. Explain this precipitation, comparing it with the average precipitation for the humid subtropical climate.

4. Explain each one of the climates 6 to 12 in terms of shifting wind and pressure belts and controlling air masses. Where wind and pressure belts are modified by other factors, state and explain these factors and their effects.

5. What is the "Corn Belt" climate?

6. What is "Indian Summer"? In what climate does it occur, and why?

7. Relative humidity increases as air gets colder and thus the dew point is brought closer. Continental polar air (cP) is cold but it is regarded as relatively stable air, not in itself a source of great precipitation. Explain the apparent discrepancy.

EXERCISES

(Answers are given in the answer section at the back of the book.)

1. In 1896 about 990 inches of rain fell during the year in one area in India. How many feet of rain was this?

2. Show, on an outline map of the world, the distribution of climates 6 to 12, using a different color or shading for each climate type.

3. The humid continental climates are more or less restricted to areas between the latitudes of 35° and 55° N. Sketch a world map to show why these climates do not occur in the southern hemisphere, on land.

4. Except for continental west coasts, the longest lines delineating climate types lie in a general east-west direction rather than in a general north-south direction. Why? (Compare Figure 64 with the rainfall and the temperature maps of previous chapters.)

5. The marine climate, or marine west coast climate, is typically somewhere between the latitudes of 40° and 60°. About how many miles is it from 40° N to 60° N, measured along the same line of longitude?

6. A few years ago, Russia seriously suggested that a dam be built across the Bering Strait and that cold water be pumped out of the Arctic

Ocean and replaced with warmer water. If such a scheme actually worked, to give Russia about 3000 miles more of ice-free coastline, discuss the effects of this plan upon the climates of the world, especially upon those of the United States. As part of your discussion, sketch, on an outline map of the world, the present wind and pressure belts of the world, the present boundaries of climate types and your conception of the future boundaries of wind and pressure belts and of climate types. Then, on an outline map of the United States, draw the boundaries of the present and anticipated climates.

7. It is seen on Figure 64 that the boundary between climate types 11 and 12 in the United States makes an abrupt turn, thus placing the general Great Lakes region in the climate 12 area.

Review the characteristics of these two climates and then, on an outline map or sketch of North America, draw the boundaries of the climates as they would exist if there were no Great Lakes.

8. Referring to Figure 64, near the east coast of the United States the boundary line between climate types 11 and 12 and the boundary line between types 11 and 7 show a pronounced loop toward the southwest. Examine a relief map of the United States, and explain these loops in terms of topography, air masses, temperature, and precipitation.

CHAPTER 16

Climates Controlled by Polar and Arctic Air Masses; Highland Climates

The climates controlled by polar and arctic air masses are the subarctic, tundra, and polar climates. Highland climates are discussed in conjunction with the above named climates because of major similarities and relationships between the four climates.

13. The Subarctic Climate (Dfc, Dfd, Dwc, Dwd)

The subarctic climate is also known as the *taiga* climate, a Russian expression for the forests of the far north. The subarctic climate is found, roughly, between the latitudes of 50° and 65° N. The two major world occurrences of the climate are: across North America, from Alaska to Labrador and Newfoundland; in Eurasia, from upper Scandinavia across the entire continent to the Kamchatka peninsula of Siberia. Most of these regions are Dfc, in the Köppen system. The Dfd (extremely cold winters) version is restricted to northern Siberia, while the Dwc and Dwd versions, cold snow forest climates with dry winters, occur only in parts of northern Asia.

The latitudes of the subarctic climate are the latitudes of the breeding grounds of the continental polar (cP) air masses. Winters are long and very cold, and summers are short and very cool. Temperatures considerably below freezing are the rule in the winter months, while the average for the warmest summer month is around 55° F. An official world's lowest temperature of −90° F was recorded at Oimekon, Siberia, in 1933, a mark which stood until 1959, when a temperature of −125.5° F was recorded in Antarctica.

It is not uncommon for daily temperatures in regions having the subarctic climate to reach around 75° F in summer, even in regions which in winter experience some of the coldest weather. Precipitation in the subarctic climate is primarily cyclonic and may reach 20 inches per year, although it is usually less. Snow is responsible for less than an inch of the total yearly precipitation.

The vegetation of the subarctic climate is primarily represented by great expanses of coniferous forest. To the north this forest grades through dwarf trees into the treeless tundra.

14. The Tundra Climate (ET)

The principal areas of tundra climate lie roughly within the latitudes of the Arctic Circle and 75° N. The tundra climate is therefore found in the Arctic Sea areas of North America and Eurasia.

The controlling air masses of the tundra climate are usually continental arctic or continental polar, but maritime polar air is a fairly frequent invader near the coasts during the year. Spring and autumn are the warmest seasons, and it is during these months that the tundra climate has its greatest precipitation. Total precipitation for the year is usually less than 10 inches. Precipitation is mainly cyclonic and because of the contrasts between the temperature of ice of the Arctic Ocean and the temperature of land, strong pressure gradients are set up which result in some storms throughout the year. The coldest temperatures, however, are on land, and not over the ocean. Despite the fact that the Arctic Ocean is frozen over during much of the year, its heat actually raises temperatures throughout much of the tundra.

Average yearly temperatures are below 32° F, a good average probably being around 20° F, and only about three months of the year have average temperatures above freezing. Like the subarctic, winters are long and cold, and summers are short and cool.

Lands having the tundra climate are relatively flat. Thus, when summer comes and frost in the upper surface layers of the ground melts, the resulting water does not drain but stays in the same area to form the well-known, insect-infested, bogs and swamps of the tundra.

The vegetation of the tundra is primarily lichens, grasses, marsh grasses, and the springy, tufted, and peat mosses of the tundra's more moist regions. Trees, if they exist at all in the northern regions of the tundra, are dwarfed or stunted. In the south, the tundra may be dotted with willows and birches which gradually merge into the coniferous forest of the subarctic.

15. The Polar Climate (EF)

Polar climate, or *ice-cap* climate, is associated with the continental ice caps of Greenland and Antarctica and the permanent ice of the North Polar Sea. As might be expected, polar climate temperatures are coldest of all. A record temperature of −125.5° F was observed in Antarctica in 1959.

For the world at large the average annual temperatures of the various polar climate regions (−25° F or so for Greenland, −10° for the North Polar Sea, and the wide range of below zero temperature in Antarctica) are important mainly from the standpoint of the earth's heat exchange and wind systems. As explained in previous chapters, the wind pattern of the earth is basically dependent upon warm tropical air moving toward the poles, because of a mammoth temperature gradient resulting in an equally extensive pressure gradient. It has also been explained how this air is deflected and how surface pressure and wind belts are thus formed. What is still largely a mystery, however, is just what the continental ice caps and the north polar ice do with all the air that flows to these regions, and specifically just how these areas of bitter cold play what are known to be key roles in all atmospheric circulation, horizontal and vertical. One reason for the mystery surrounding the effects of these climates upon other climates is that these climates were not extensively investigated until the IGY. Then it was found that the world had about 40 percent more ice on it than was formerly believed, a fact which has considerable bearing upon the importance of the polar climates in an understanding of world climates, weather, and wind systems.

Precipitation in polar climates is relatively meager, possibly about 3 inches per year, and results mainly from cyclonic activity. A peculiar type of "storm" sometimes occurs on ice caps when cold air flows down a steep slope, by gravity, and creates a katabatic wind. Frost particles are formed in the air by sublimation and are swept along as a "snowstorm" whose vertical extent is only a few feet above the ground but whose winds are often of hurricane velocity, 75 miles per hour or more.

The Antarctic, contrary to popular belief, is not all snow and ice. Brilliantly colored mosses and lichens grow in a few strange, Shangri

La-type valleys sheltered from the snow. Several types of grasses grow in some regions, and even some flowering plants. It is worth noting that extensive coal deposits in the Antarctic indicate its former equable climate and its former extensive, lush vegetation.

16. The Highland Climates (H)

The so-called highland climates may be considered to include the varieties of climate occurring over 6000 feet above sea level. In general, climates occurring below this altitude are considered to be controlled more by air masses than they are by altitude and mountain topography. To put it another way, altitude and topography in a given highland mountain area largely determine what air masses will control the climate in that area. Major world areas having this climate are: in North America, the Sierra Nevada and Cascades; in South America, the Andes Mountains; in Eurasia, the Himalayas, the Alps, and the mountains of Tibet; and in Africa, the Eastern Highlands.

As is immediately evident, there is no one "highland climate." Further, highland climates may differ considerably in their characteristics depending upon their altitude, whether they are on windward or lee slopes, whether they are in coastal or in interior locations, etc. There are, however, some general similarities which can be described.

First, mountain climates are, in general, cooler than other climates. As outlined previously the lapse rate in still air is about 3.5° F for every 1000 feet, vertically. On this basis, then, a mountain area 7000 feet above a plain would theoretically have a temperature about 25° lower than that of the adjacent plain. Actually, of course, the rate is usually considerably altered in mountain regions due to topography. It can be said, though, that highland climates on the average have cooler temperatures than adjacent and lower climates.

One very noticeable effect of highland climates is the sharp decrease in the percent of oxygen as one goes higher. The effects of oxygen deficiency, or "mountain sickness," have been felt by many first-time travelers in highland areas, sometimes causing a complete "black-out" of the senses. Due to effects of oxygen deficiency upon the human system, it is currently believed by many that regions of the earth above 9000 feet or so in elevation will never be thickly populated. Such use of our high land, however, certainly should seem to have more to offer in the way of feasibility than the currently often stated proposals to meet the problem of exploding population by colonizing the moon or some planet. Humans can adapt to the highland climate. In Peru, for example, native Indians and foreigners alike live and work at altitudes well over 15,000 feet above sea level, and there is much workable land at these and lower elevations. It may be that the lower highland areas of the world will experience the beginnings of an influx of population within our lifetimes.

The vegetation of the highland climates is zoned vertically rather than horizontally. Subarctic type forests commonly give way to tundra type vegetation at higher levels and, still higher, mountain glaciers may dominate the landscape. It is an education in climatology in itself to journey over the Andes Mountains by car. In the course of eight hours journey from the coast, one may pass through the tropical arid climate, the highland equivalents of the subarctic tundra, and polar climates (with possible heavy snow around 16,000 feet), down through the tundra and the broadleaf version of a subarctic equivalent and then rather abruptly into the tropical rain forest.

REVIEW

1. The precipitation of subarctic, tundra, and polar climates is primarily cyclonic in origin. Why?

2. Describe the vegetation of (a) the subarctic, (b) the tundra, (c) the highland climates.

3. What is the general relationship of altitude to the amount of oxygen in the air?

4. Explain how the bogs and swamps of the tundra regions are formed.

5. Why is so relatively little known about polar climates?

6. The southern boundary of the tundra climate is, roughly, on the Arctic Circle. Do you think that this has anything to do with the fact that the tundra grades into forests at about this latitude? Explain your answer.

7. What are the two major controls of highland climates, as explained in this chapter?

EXERCISES

(Answers are given in the answer section at the back of the book.)

1. A given mass of air over a glacier at an elevation of 12,000 feet is cooled to 0° F and starts to descend the mountain. At what elevation will this mass of air have the same temperature as that of the surrounding air if the air temperature at the bottom of the mountain, on the seacoast, is 60° F? Assume that the lapse rate and the adiabatic rate are not affected by topography, etc. (NOTE: Such descending air masses create katabatic winds called *fallwinds* in Norway.)

2. On what date or dates does the noon sun reach its highest elevation at latitude 70° N? How much is this elevation?

3. In the northern hemisphere, what latitude experiences the longest day? What latitude experiences the longest night? How long are these days and nights?

4. A certain temperature, commonly recorded during IGY on the Antarctic continent, has the same numerical value on the Centigrade scale thermometers as on the Fahrenheit scale thermometers. What is the temperature?

5. On a map or lined paper "move" Australia by drawing it in various positions so that it is successively centered at latitudes (a) 35° S, (b) 55° S, (c) 70° S, and show what climates Australia would have in each position.

CHAPTER 17

Rocks; Weathering and Erosion of Rocks

It might be assumed that the chief concern of physical geography with the study of rocks lies not in how rocks are formed but in how they weather and erode to produce or modify landforms and contribute to soil formation. Satisfactory understanding of the breakup and decay of rocks, however, is impossible unless one knows something of the structure and composition of rocks. This in turn can be understood only by also knowing something about how rocks are formed.

There are three main types of rocks, according to formation: *sedimentary, igneous,* and *metamorphic.* The composition, origin, and structure of the most important crustal rocks of each group will be discussed first, to be followed by discussion of the kinds of weathering.

The Rock-Forming Minerals

A rock is an aggregate of minerals. A *mineral* is a naturally-occurring inorganic substance whose physical properties and chemical composition are fixed or vary within definite known limits. Minerals commonly show *crystal* shape but some lack this property and are *amorphous*.

The informed reader may question the above restrictive definition of "mineral" as the term is, of course, also commonly used in reference to coal, oil, and gas; also, many minerals are made in industry today and these cannot be said to be "naturally occurring." The reason for the latter restriction is, of course, that this book deals only with man's natural environment. As for coal, oil, gas, etc., these never show true crystal shape and their compositions can vary widely. They will be discussed in later chapters.

As a rock is composed of minerals, the characteristics of a rock are determined by the characteristics of its minerals. The study of minerals, *mineralogy,* therefore goes hand in hand with *petrology,* the study of the origin, composition, and structure of rocks.

Almost 99 percent of the earth's crust is made up of the following named elements, in order of decreasing abundance: oxygen (O), silicon (Si), aluminum (Al), iron (Fe), calcium (Ca), sodium (Na), potassium (K), magnesium (Mg). It seems rather amazing that only 8 *elements* comprise 99 percent of the crust and it seems just as remarkable that only 9 *minerals* make up almost 75 percent of the earth's crust. These 9 minerals are described immediately following.

The Rock-Forming Silicates. Silicates are formed when silicon and oxygen combine chemically with each other. Other elements are commonly present. Most rocks and soils are primarily made up of silicates. Silicates account for 90 percent of the earth's crust, and the 9 most common minerals which make up 75 percent of the crust, as mentioned above, are all silicates. These silicates are *orthoclase, plagioclase, microcline, quartz, muscovite, biotite, amphibole, pyroxene,* and *olivine.*

Orthoclase, plagioclase, and *microcline* are *feldspars,* aluminum silicates which normally contain either potassium, sodium, or calcium. The feldspars are the most common of all rock-forming minerals but are fairly easily weathered. Orthoclase has the formula $K_2O \cdot Al_2O_3 \cdot 6SiO_2$, sometimes expressed $KAlSi_3O_8$; plagioclase normally has either sodium (Na) or calcium (Ca) replacing the potassium (K) in the orthoclase but is otherwise the same in composition. Microcline has the same chemical composition as orthoclase but crystallizes differently.

Quartz, SiO_2, the hardest of all common minerals, is the next most frequently occurring mineral in rocks. Being hard and abundant, it is also the commonest constituent of sands. Quartz may be of various colors but is usually white or even clear, giving it the appearance of glass. Its hardness distinguishes it from glass. Some colored varieties of quartz, such as *amethyst* and *rose quartz,* are considered as gemstone material.

Muscovite, $KAl_3Si_3O_{10}(OH)_2$, is the name used to describe the family of "white" micas. Muscovite noticeably occurs in many rocks.

Its crystal structure is such that it can be split into sheets. Its name derives from the fact that thin sheets of mica were once commonly used in tsarist Russia as window "glass."

Biotite, or the family of "black" micas, has the same formula as muscovite except that biotite also contains magnesium and iron.

The *amphiboles* are complex silicates, dark in color, from dark green to black. The most common amphibole is *hornblende,* a complex silicate of calcium, magnesium, iron, soda, and alumina. Some amphiboles whose crystals are long six-sided "fibers" are used as a form of asbestos.

The *pyroxenes* are complex silicates. The most important rock forming pyroxene is augite, $Ca(Mg,Fe,Al)(Al,Si)_2O_6$. Like the amphiboles, the pyroxenes are dark in color, also ranging from dark green to black.

Olivine, $(Mg,Fe)_2SiO_4$, is a glassy mineral. As its name indicates, olivine ranges from olive green to greenish yellow in color. Olivine generally occurs in granulated form, its appearance in rocks being much like that of granulated sugar which has been colored green.

Other Minerals. Although the above described silicates are by far the most abundant minerals in the earth's crust, the following named minerals are also important rock-forming minerals.

Calcite, $CaCO_3$, *calcium carbonate,* is an important constituent of many sedimentary rocks and is the main constituent in the sedimentary rock known as "limestone." *Dolomite,* calcium magnesium carbonate, resembles calcite but has slightly different chemical and physical properties.

Gypsum, $CaSO_4 \cdot 2H_2O$, calcium sulfate, occurs in several types of sedimentary rocks. It is a product of evaporation and is generally light colored and glassy-appearing. Commercially it is used in manufacturing gypsum *plaster*.

Anhydrite, $CaSO_4$, *anhydrous calcium sulfate,* is also a common mineral in sedimentary rocks. It has the same formula as gypsum, but without water. It has the same general appearance as calcite.

Serpentine, $Mg_3Si_2O_5(OH)_4$, *hydrous magnesium silicate,* results from the alteration of olivine, hornblende, and some of the pyroxenes. It is from green to black in color and commonly occurs in fairly large masses. A type of serpentine, *chrysotile,* furnishes high-grade *asbestos.*

Halite, $NaC1$, which has the same formula as common table salt, is a product of evaporation and is found in certain types and layers of sedimentary rocks.

Chlorites are hydrous magnesium iron aluminum silicates whose compositions and physical properties vary relatively widely. They resemble mica in structure but their characteristic dark green color helps to distinguish them from mica. Another distinguishing feature is that a leaf of mica will spring back when bent whereas chlorite will stay bent.

Sedimentary Rocks

Sedimentary rocks result from the consolidation of rock and other particles or from the precipitation of substances from solution. On the basis of their origin, sedimentary rocks can be separated into three main classes: *clastic, organic,* and those of *physical-chemical* origin.

Clastic Rocks. *Clastic,* or *fragmental,* rocks are derived from particles resulting from the breakup of other rocks. The particles are then transported by streams, wind, or ice, etc., and deposited. If the particles are subjected to pressure, such as that furnished by new material being laid down overhead, and are also *cemented* together by some substance, a consolidated sedimentary rock is formed. As is apparent, river beds, lake beds, and the oceans are major regions of sedimentary rock formation. Many sedimentary rocks therefore show a layered or bedded structure, due to sorting action by the water.

Sandstone is a clastic sedimentary rock which consists of grains of sand cemented together. The term "sand" really refers to size rather than to composition although the world-wide prevalence of quartz (SiO_2) sand particles has resulted in the association of "sand" only with beach sand, etc., which is mainly quartz.

The sand particles in sandstone are also usually mostly quartz for the reason that quartz is highly resistant to chemical and physical attack. These particles after deposition are ultimately bonded together by the deposition of cementing substances such as silica (SiO_2), calcium carbonate ($CaCO_3$), or some type of iron oxide. These cements are furnished by ground water which percolates through the sand. By that time the particles are usually under great compressive force from the layers overhead. This reduces the amount of pore space and a fairly rigid bond is commonly established.

Despite even extreme pressure and cementation, however, there is probably no such thing as a perfectly solid sedimentary rock. The porosity, or amount of open space in a rock, may go as high as 40 percent for some poorly compacted and cemented sandstones. The relatively high porosity of sandstones is of great economic importance as sandstones are thus natural underground "pipelines" and reservoirs of water, oil, and gas. For example, one cubic foot of a sandstone whose porosity is 25 percent could hold almost two gallons of water or oil.

Conglomerate and *siltstone* are formed in much the same manner as sandstone. Conglomerate, however, is made up of more or less smooth and rounded particles ranging in size from a diameter of about one foot to about ¼ of an inch, while siltstone particles are smaller than those of sand. The chief cementing substances in conglomerate and siltstone are the same as for sandstone, namely silica, calcium carbonate, and iron oxide. A variety of conglomerate, whose particles are rough and angular, instead of fairly smooth and rounded, is called *sedimentary breccia.*

Shale is composed of extremely fine particles, smaller than those of siltstone. Although most shale is highly compressed mud or clay, some shales are largely composed of compressed organic material such as diatoms, with just enough cementing substance to weakly bond the material into a rock. All shales show a platy structure and most of them can easily be split into thin sheets. Due to their soft composition and weak structure, shales are usually very easily worn away by weathering.

Pyroclastic rocks result from the consolidation of volcanic ash which may be deposited either on the surface or under water. If deposited on the surface, the ash may be covered by more ash or by other sediments and be cemented by the action of minerals precipitated from ground water. When deposited under water the ash is commonly sorted into beds or layers.

The chief clastic type of *limestone* is called *coquina.* Coquina is formed by the cementing together of sea shells, shell fragments, etc., by calcium carbonate.

Organic Sedimentary Rocks. The limestone, *coquina,* may also be properly considered as an organic rock, in that the particles cemented together are former parts of organisms. A form of limestone called dolomitic limestone results when magnesium combines with the calcium carbonate. If *dolomite,* discussed previously in the section on minerals, is in greater abundance than calcite, the rock is known as *dolostone.*

Coal is also considered as a rock despite the fact that it is not made up of what we have defined as "minerals." Coal results from the decomposition of organic material such as trees, grasses, etc., and subsequent burial and hardening. Coal is discussed in more detail in Chapter 20.

Sedimentary Rocks of Physical-Chemical Origin. Limestone is sometimes formed as the result of physical-chemical action such as the combined effects of a change in water temperature and a simultaneous change in carbon dioxide content, resulting in the *physical-chemical* precipitation of calcium carbonate.

Some minerals, such as *anhydrite, gypsum,* and *halite,* all previously described in this chapter, are *evaporites* in that they result from the evaporation in shallow water. They often precipitate in such quantities that the resulting mass, although primarily of only one mineral, can properly be called a deposit of rock.

Igneous Rocks

Igneous rocks comprise about 95 percent of the earth's crust. They are rocks which solidify from *magma.* Magma is molten rock and its included gases. An igneous rock is either *intrusive* or *extrusive,* depending upon whether it was formed beneath or on the surface of the earth. Although the exact origin of magma is debatable, it is known that it moves through cracks and fissures, and that it also forces itself through solid rock. Interestingly, the most widely known of all rocks, *granite,* is an intrusive igneous rock and was formed at least ½ mile beneath the earth's surface. Subsequent erosion has revealed much granite to our view.

In general, the texture of intrusive igneous rocks is coarser than that of the extrusive rocks. A magma which is solidifying beneath the earth's surface loses its heat much more slowly than a magma solidifying on the surface. Thus, in an intrusive rock, the crystals have more time to grow, and crystals of some minerals which have solidified at depth are as large as 35 feet long and 5 feet wide. At the other extreme, magma flowing out upon the surface is often chilled so rapidly that the resulting structure has no apparent crystal structure and may look like glass.

Intrusive Igneous Rocks.   *Granite* typically consists of about 60 percent feldspar, 30 percent quartz, and 10 percent of, usually, a combination of biotite and hornblende. Granite is coarse-grained. The chief feldspar in granite is usually orthoclase, which gives the granite a pink appearance. When the chief feldspar is plagioclase, the granite may be gray or white.

Diorite is coarse-grained and results from a combination of plagioclase with, usually, hornblende. Its typical overall appearance in color is whitish gray. The hornblende may be replaced by biotite or by a pyroxene.

Gabbro is coarse-grained and is a mixture of plagioclase and dark minerals such as olivine and pyroxene. The chief distinction between gabbro and diorite is that gabbro contains a higher percentage of dark minerals. Thus the color of gabbro varies from gray to black and has a higher specific gravity than that of diorite.

Peridotite is a coarse-grained rock with very little feldspar, if any, and a preponderance of olivine. Other dark minerals which may be present are hornblende and pyroxene. Peridotite is dark in color.

Extrusive Igneous Rocks.   Magma that flows out upon the earth's surface is called *lava.* If the lava cools very quickly, as already mentioned, a glass results. This is called *volcanic glass,* or *obsidian.*

Rhyolite, a fine-grained rock, is formed when magma, which if solidified at depth would result in granite, flows out upon the surface. Rhyolite has a distinctly glassy appearance or may resemble a very fine-grained granite.

Andesite is the extrusive version of diorite and has the same chemical composition. It is usually dark gray in color and may or may not contain glassy particles.

Basalt is fine-grained and is the extrusive equivalent of gabbro. It is typically dark brown to black in color.

Volcanic ash, as already outlined, may form pyroclastic rocks. It is also properly included as an extrusive rock as the "ash" particles are actually very small particles of solidified magma. They are not products of combustion (like wood or coal ash), as is commonly believed.

Metamorphic Rocks

Metamorphic rocks result from the alteration of sedimentary, igneous, or sometimes other metamorphic rocks. The metamorphism is usually a result of chemical action, pressure, or heat or, usually, some combination of these. Metamorphic rocks are generally hard and dense and are sometimes so extremely changed that it is impossible to determine whether the rock altered was sedimentary, igneous, or another metamorphic rock. Actual formation of new minerals in metamorphic rocks is not uncommon.

Metamorphic rocks are important in that they indicate the geologic processes which have been operating in a particular region. For example, a highly compressed and folded rock normally indicates horizontal compressive stresses while, in the same rock, changes in mineral structure may indicate at about what depth the metamorphism took place, and how it occurred.

Slate, as a specific example, results from the metamorphism of shale. Slate is much harder than shale and is used in some regions for blackboards, flagstones, coverings for roofs, etc. It might be expected that cleavage in metamorphic rocks such as slate which have been formed from layered sedimentary rocks would more or less parallel the original bedding planes. Often, however, the main cleavage is at distinct angles to the bedding planes. The reason behind this may be illustrated by the simple experiment of squeezing some clay, moist soap, or other material, between thumb and forefinger. The material elongates in directions at right angles to the direction of pressure and its thinnest dimension is parallel to the direction of pressure. Roughly the same thing happens to old minerals and minerals being newly formed in the metamorphic rock. Thus "slaty cleavage" in metamorphic rocks often parallels the flatter, longer faces of the minerals and commonly takes place directly across the bedding planes.

Phyllite results when shale is metamorphosed even past the slate stage. Phyllite also breaks into "plates" and typically shows a shiny cleavage surface. Further metamorphism results in *schist* which has much mica and a leaf-like cleavage. *Gneiss,* a coarse banded rock, sometimes results when sedimentary rocks are altered by molten granite.

Whereas slate is the so-called *metamorphic equivalent* of shale, the metamorphic equivalent of conglomerate, siltstone, or sandstone is *quartzite.* Quartzite is conglomerate, siltstone, or sandstone which has been so thoroughly further cemented by silica that upon fracture, quartzite breaks through the grains instead of around them as happens in the case of its sedimentary parent rock. Quartzite therefore resists weathering more successfully than any other rock.

Marble is the metamorphic equivalent of limestone. During metamorphism, which may be due to a combination of heat, pressure, and resultant shearing, the crystals in the limestone grow larger, the dark minerals tend to align themselves in bands or disappear altogether, and the whole rock becomes harder. Despite the phrase "as hard as marble," marble is extremely susceptible to some types of weathering.

Gneiss, in addition to being formed by the alteration of sedimentary rocks as already explained, more commonly results from alteration of granite by extreme heat and pressure. These *granite gneiss* structures are characterized by a bold, possibly highly contorted, banded arrangement of dark and light minerals, many times roughly giving the appearance of zebra skins. Other gneisses are apparently formed in other ways but, as a gneiss is definitely the result of extreme metamorphism at high temperatures and probably high pressures, it is normally a very hard and resistant rock.

Weathering

Weathering is the alteration of crustal rocks and rock material by natural processes. Such alteration is accomplished by either mechanical or chemical means or, usually, by a combination of the two. Without an atmosphere there would be very little alteration of surface rock, hence the atmosphere is the chief agent of weathering.

Mechanical Weathering. The mechanical breakup of rocks is also called *disintegration.* Disintegration may occur in several ways, one way being *frost wedging.* Frost wedging is confined to regions which experience freezing temperatures. When water in cracks or fissures in rocks freezes and expands, it creates tremendous pressure which forces the rock to split.

Plants and *animals* are responsible for an amazingly large amount of disintegration. Probably everyone has seen pictures of tree roots which have actually split large rocks and the same thing happens with roots of smaller plants and smaller rocks. Burrowing animals turn up great amounts of earth each year as do earthworms, estimates for the latter running as high as 12 tons of earth turned up per acre per year in good soil. The effect of such movement of soil upon the breakup of underlying rock is to allow water and atmospheric gases to penetrate to the rock far more quickly than would otherwise be possible.

Temperature changes also play a part in disintegration. Many campers, for instance, have experienced the explosive bursting of a rock which has been placed close to the campfire. The similar generation of steam in outer rock layers by forest fires undoubtedly has caused the partial disintegration of many rocks throughout geologic history.

One formerly widely held theory was that extreme changes in temperature between day and night in desert regions could bring about such disintegration. Laboratory experiments involving subjecting rocks to temperature extremes have failed to support this theory but the fact remains that evidences of otherwise hard-to-explain surface breakup of rocks are commonly seen in desert regions.

Exfoliation, although a mechanical process, is actually a result of chemical weathering. The sequence of events, well developed in granites, is this: rain water penetrates a rock to a thin depth, through cracks and pore spaces; the water reacts with the feldspar in the granite (see Chemical Weathering) and small amounts of feldspar turn to clay; the clay minerals swell in growing and, like ice in frost wedging, exert pressure in all directions; this causes thin shells or leaves to separate from the rock, hence the term "exfoliation" (L. *folia*—"leaf").

Chemical Weathering or Decomposition. The reader who has studied chemistry may have wondered in the above just how and why rain water reacts with feldspar. Actually, any rain water is a mild form of carbonic acid as it picks up some carbon dioxide in its journey through the atmosphere. Feldspars attacked by this acid ultimately break down into *kaolinite,* a common clay mineral, and *silica* (SiO_2). Thus granite, geologically, is not highly resistant to weathering, especially in the more humid climates. Furthermore, decomposition of granite is considerably accelerated where the granite lies just beneath the surface where it can be attacked by acidic water percolating through the upper surface layers.

"Decomposition" of rocks is of course really the decomposition of the individual minerals in the rocks, a fact which is strikingly illustrated by chemical weathering of rocks which contain relatively large amounts of the dark-colored minerals. These rocks, in general, are igneous rocks or metamorphosed igneous rocks. The dark minerals most often involved are biotite, amphibole, pyroxene, and olivine. These all contain iron and magnesium and are therefore *ferromagnesians*. These particular four minerals are also all silicates. The intermediate and end products of the weathering of these minerals depends upon many factors, but one thing is very apparent as these minerals decompose within a rock: the resulting iron stains. An iron-stained rock invariably indicates that the rock is or was being chemically weathered and it often also indicates that the soil which results in part from the decomposition of the rock will contain relatively high proportions of iron and magnesium, and that most of the soil minerals will be silicates.

Chemical Weathering by Solution.   Any rock is soluble to some extent in some fluid or other and so it is possible to have many degrees of decomposition by solution in the same rock type in different areas.

For example, rain falling upon the earth is already acidic. It becomes more acidic as it trickles through the humus layers of the soil and if it now encounters a rock like limestone, it can accomplish considerable solution of the rock. This particular process is discussed more fully in Chapter 18.

On the other hand, suppose that there is a large deposit of limestone in an arid region. Little rain falls and that which does fall percolates through soil which has little decaying vegetation. The rain therefore gains little in acidity. Being small in amount, and only weakly acidic, the water will have little effect upon the limestone. As a matter of fact it is entirely possible that some alkali minerals in the upper soil layers would, thanks to the slightly acidic water, be dissolved and then precipitated lower down as a protective covering on the limestone.

Rocks, Erosion, and Topography

Weathering is only a prelude to the removal of the rock material. The weathered material must be transported by some agency such as wind or water before any appreciable change in topography occurs.

The amount of weathered material available for transportation is determined by the intensity and kind of weathering, by the rock structure, and by time. The amount of weathered material actually transported in a given period of time depends upon many factors such as the agent of transportation—that is, whether it is water, wind, or ice, or gravity alone—the size and kind of material, whether it is on a slope, the steepness of the slope, potential valleys, resistant rock layers, etc.

Erosion is therefore an extremely complicated process, as far as determining how much is going to take place and what topographic relief it will bring about in a given area in a given period of time. On the other hand some generalizations concerning rock types and topography can be arrived at on the basis of rock structure and composition. These generalizations are discussed in Chapter 21 as part of the introduction to landforms.

REVIEW

1. Explain why a physical geographer is concerned with the origin, composition, and structure of rocks.

2. Define "mineral."

3. What is "muscovite"? What is the origin of the name?

4. What are the three main types of rock, according to origin?

5. What percentage of the earth's crust is composed of igneous rocks?

6. Explain why the texture of intrusive igneous rocks and of extrusive igneous rocks differ, and describe each texture.

7. What is "granite," in terms of composition?

8. State the metamorphic equivalents of (a) sandstone; (b) shale; (c) limestone.

9. Define "weathering" and "erosion."

10. Name the two kinds of weathering.

11. What is "slaty cleavage" and how does it develop? Is its occurrence confined to slate?

EXERCISES

(Answers are given in the answer section at the back of the book.)

1. One cubic foot of a certain sandstone weighs 120 pounds. The grains and the cementing substance are silica (SiO_2), whose specific gravity is about 2.7. What is the percentage of pore space in the sandstone? Hint:

Let $x =$ the volume of pore space, in cubic feet. Then $1 - x =$ volume of silica. Therefore, $2.7(1 - x) = ?$

2. In general, light-colored rocks are relatively light in weight while dark-colored rocks are relatively heavy. Why?

3. "Chalk," as used on blackboards, is popularly believed to be made of "limestone," or calcium carbonate. What is this type of "chalk" actually made of? Why, in your opinion, is calcium carbonate not used for blackboard "chalk"?

CHAPTER 18

Soils

The scientific study of soils is called *pedology*. Soil is at once one of the least glamorous and one of the two most important natural resources. The average observer of a landscape is liable to give much more attention to the bold outlines of a forested mountain or to the gentle slope of a grassy valley than to the type of soil in the vicinity. Yet, without soil, there would be no forests and little grass, and there would be no one to look at landscapes. The great bulk of the animal and plant life of the continents is dependent upon the existence of soil. Next to air and water it is man's greatest need.

Soil Development

Soils are composed of the products of rock weathering and of decomposing organic material. The idea that soil, once formed as such, is unchanging is a prevalent but ill-founded assumption. Rock particles in soil continue weathering and organic material in soil continues decomposing until the soil reaches maturity. In addition, organisms including soil bacteria perform important work in the whole complex process which is chemical, physical, and biological in nature.

If soil remains over the bedrock from which it formed, it is *residual* soil, otherwise it is *transported* soil. Residual soil is the type whose origin is so well illustrated in road cuts where solid rock grades upward into "rotten" rock. This in turn grades into *mantle rock,* or rock debris, which grades upward into the darker debris which is the soil. *Soil can be generally described as the part of the mantle rock which supports plant growth.* (The term "mantle rock" should not be confused with the word "mantle" used to describe an interior zone of the earth.)

In understanding how soil is formed it will be helpful to recon-

struct what happens when a large exposure of, say, granite weathers
in a fairly moist climate. It will be recalled from Chapter 17 that
granite is composed of about 60 percent feldspar, 30 percent quartz,
and 10 percent dark minerals.

The feldspar in granite is usually orthoclase, which contains potassium, and there may be plagioclase which contains sodium. The
feldspars decompose to form *kaolinite,* a silicate mineral of clay,
while much of the potassium and sodium are carried away in solution to be deposited throughout the potential soil. Whatever the
dark minerals in the granite are, they are mostly silicates. Some of
them almost certainly contain iron and magnesium while others contain calcium. The weathering of the dark minerals will therefore result in silicates of some kind and in calcium, magnesium, silica, iron,
and other elements being dissolved and apportioned among the soil-
to-be.

During all this time, organic material is being incorporated into
the rock debris which is getting finer and finer in size. Leaves and
grasses, blown into the area, are decomposed by bacteria. Finally
there comes a day when one part of the dirt, just barely rich enough
to support the growth of one plant, receives a wind-blown plant
seed. The seed germinates and the plant grows, its roots taking the
mineral elements from the soil about them. The soil bacteria furnish nitrogen to the plant and are aided in the process by other microorganisms. As the plant matures it too drops seeds, some of which
come to life. By now, other plants have developed from wind-blown
seeds. Finally the original plant dies and it itself becomes part of the
soil. It decomposes as untold hosts of microorganisms extract nitrogen from its remains and pass the nitrogen on to the new plants and
to the soil. Billions of organisms come to life every day, and billions
die, their remains being immediately processed. Elements such as
iron, calcium, and potassium which were in the leaves of the original
plant are now released and distributed by percolating rain water to
the soil again, only to be then taken up by the roots of the new plants,
some of which are now dropping their own seeds into the soil and
some of which have already died and are being decomposed by increasing numbers of bacteria. The parent rock continues weathering,
furnishing more gross material and more mineral nutrients. The
procedure is tortuously slow. Finally, in from 300 to 3000 years,
about 4 inches of soil has been formed. In many regions of the United

States that same 4 inches is being eroded and forever lost to our use in, shockingly, a period of ten years.

The Soil Profile

A *soil profile* is a cross section through the layers of soil. A soil profile is normally considered to have three horizons, A, B, and C, the A horizon being uppermost, the B next, and the C horizon being the weathered parent rock material. A typical depth in the United States of the combined A, B, or true soil, or *solum,* is about 4 feet. Few soil profiles are more than ten feet in depth except in some tropical, moist regions, a point to be explained later. When a soil profile reaches the stage where its layers are unchanged by the agents of soil formation, the soil is *mature.* It should not be thought, however, that a mature soil is one in which all action, reaction, and interchange have stopped. Instead, a mature soil is in equilibrium for the simple reason that all of its multitudinous component activities are in equilibrium. Acids react with alkalis to maintain the soil's pH, or acid-alkali ratio; growing plants in the soil use the same amount of nutrient being returned to the soil; and colonies of billions upon billions of microorganisms maintain a life-death ratio in accordance with the now closely fixed amount of dead organic material constantly being processed in the soil. A mature soil is an outstanding example of natural balance and it is unique in the respect that it encompasses both organic and inorganic materials and processes.

How Soil Profiles Develop

The chief agents of soil formation are *water, air, plants,* and *animal life.* Any change in quantity or composition in even one of these will normally result in a change in soil, between two regions. Soil differences are commonly reflected in the varying appearances of the soil profiles.

Water as a Soil-Forming Agent. Water which enters soil may pass downward between the soil particles, or coat a soil grain, or be held between the soil particles as *capillary water.* Capillary water supplies most of the moisture in plants.

Whether water in the soil will or will not be held as capillary water in appreciable quantity depends mainly upon the size of the spaces, or pores, between soil particles. Capillary action of a fluid depends upon the size of the "tube" which the fluid occupies. If the passageway is too large in cross-sectional area, the weight of the water exceeds the force of surface tension tending to hold the water in the passageway and the water will move downward due to gravity. A capillary passageway is one of such small cross-sectional area that the molecules of water can pull themselves up the tube. The process is much like that of a mountain climber who climbs a "chimney"—an almost vertical narrow opening in rock—by pushing with his feet and his back against opposite sides of the chimney, and thus inching his way upward. The pressure he is exerting is comparable to the surface tension of water molecules. Where the chimney starts to widen, however, the force he can now exert against the chimney sides becomes less and his weight will cause him to fall if he still tries to climb in this manner. The same thing happens to water in an opening: if the weight of the water is greater than the pulling force due to surface tension—and this, as in the case of the mountain climber, is due to too wide an opening —the water will move downward as *gravitational water*.

In addition to being the chief source of moisture for plants, capillary water in the soil often brings about major changes in soil during periods of drought. The ground surface dries out and capillary water moves higher, thus still furnishing moisture to the plants. The water usually contains dissolved salts of some kind and these salts will therefore be deposited in the upper soil zones if the drought continues. The upper soil layers may thereupon become so alkaline that little will grow there. In many southwestern states, carbonates deposited in this manner have formed a hard subsurface layer or *caliche* which makes agriculture almost impossible in some southwest regions. Furthermore, the caliche prevents normal soil profile development.

Where capillary water is always of major importance to plant growth, and therefore to the soil itself, hygroscopic water, which merely coats the soil grains, is apparently of little importance in soil development. Of the three, capillary, hygroscopic, and gravitational, it is the gravitational water which does the most work in establishing the appearance of a soil profile.

Gravitational water, moving down through the A horizon, picks up very small particles of material and moves these down to the B horizon, and deposits them there. This process of *eluviation*—the carrying away of fine particles—plus the subsequent deposition, results in increased pore space in the A horizon and decreased pore space in the

B horizon. This in turn causes decreased capillarity in the A horizon and increased capillarity in the B horizon.

As the gravitational water moves downward it also dissolves some mineral substances from the upper A horizon and commonly deposits some of these in the B horizon. In humid regions the A horizon is, then, a horizon of "leaching" while the B horizon is commonly a horizon of deposition, or *illuviation*. As the A horizon has lost both capillarity and minerals to the B horizon, it is the B horizon in which most plants have the ends of their roots. The process of leaching is considerably affected by the amount of humus in the upper layers. Water percolating through the humus becomes more acidic, a fact which is often of great importance in the dissolving of certain minerals in the A horizon.

In humid regions, then, it is gravitational water which is mainly responsible for the texture and composition of the soil. It is also chiefly responsible for soil color. Sometimes the water composition is such that it leaves iron compounds in the A horizon, in which case the A horizon may be any color from yellow to reddish brown. On the other hand, most of the visible iron may be leached out of the A and deposited in the B horizon, coloring the B horizon and leaving the A horizon with a typical leached, pale appearance. Another typical reaction is that of acidic water, containing metallic elements in solution, reacting with the humus to form various dark-colored compounds which may be precipitated at various depths to give the soil a number of almost black layers.

Air as a Soil-Forming Agent.   Probably anyone who has lived in a humid region has noticed the numbers of earthworms on the surface of the ground after a heavy rain. It seems to be a common belief that earthworms are "washed out" of the soil, and easily at that, during a heavy rain, a belief which would be disputed by anyone who has ever tried to pull a resisting earthworm out of the soil. The fact is that earthworms do not dislodge easily and that they come to the surface of the ground after a heavy rain to get oxygen, the rain having filled in most of the soil's pore spaces and cut off their oxygen supply.

This points up the fact that most ground plants and animals need a direct supply of air. Without air, most of the microorganisms and other animal life, and the plant life, could not live. There would be little plant life to supply dead plant material to the soil, and few organisms to connect the plant material to humus. Without air, there

would be only dirt, not soil. Furthermore, the soil air always contains
a certain amount of water vapor and carbon dioxide, most of the carbon dioxide coming from organisms and plant life in the soil. The soil
air is therefore a not inconsiderable agent of soil alteration by chemical means, especially in humid region soils which have considerable
air space.

Plants and Animals as Soil-Forming Agents. The general role of
plants and animals in soil development has already necessarily been
presented in conjunction with previous explanations in this chapter,
but it should also be noted here that some soil bacteria, such as those
which colonize on the roots of leguminous plants like clover, alfalfa,
beans, peas, etc., can extract nitrogen directly from the air and pass
it on to the plant roots. This process is called *nitrogen fixation.*

The purely mechanical work done by small animals is also of importance. For example, earthworms eat humus and help to distribute
it among the soil by transporting it in their bodies and then discharging
it in some other place. Many other small animals in the soil do essentially the same thing.

The Controls of Soil Formation

It was explained in the previous section that the chief agents of soil
formation are *water, air, plants,* and *animal life.* The amounts of water, air, plants, and animal life available to a particular soil are determined by several controls which may vary widely between regions.
These controls are (1) parent material, (2) climate, (3) vegetation,
(4) local topography, and (5) time.

Parent Materials as a Control of Soil Formation. The parent material of a soil is the rock which furnishes the body of the soil. It might
be thought that the type of parent material largely determines the type
of resulting soil but, on a world-wide basis, this is not true. Parent material of course is closely associated with such things as a soil's mineral content and color, especially in an immature soil, but the fact is
that the world's soils can be classified by astonishingly few categories,
and the type of parent material plays little part in determining what
kinds of soil finally result under different conditions of climate and
vegetation growth. In other words, the same type of granite will help
produce very different soils in Canada and Panama. On the other
hand, given enough time, two dissimilar rocks such as a sandstone and

a granite will help produce the same general type of soil in the same locality.

Climate as a Control of Soil Formation. Climate is the most important control of soil formation in that it controls the amount of water available to the soil, and the temperature of the soil water and of the soil air. In general, chemical decomposition accelerates with an increase in temperature.

In moist, tropical regions both leaching and eluviation are at a maximum. In arid or perennially very cold climates, leaching and eluviation are at a minimum. It could be correctly assumed therefore that the depth of the soil profile, in general, grades from a maximum depth in tropical regions to a minimum depth in polar regions. This fact has considerable bearing upon the development of agriculture around the world.

Vegetation as a Control of Soil Formation. Vegetation is the chief source of humus and humus results from the processing of the vegetable material by bacteria and other microorganisms. The amount of humus in a soil therefore primarily depends upon the amount of vegetable material available and also upon the number of microorganisms. Assuming a sufficient supply of dead vegetable material and water, then the next thing required is microorganisms.

In northern climates, although there is a mat of leaves, pine needles, etc., on the forest floor, the cool climate precludes a large number of bacteria. Thus humus is formed very slowly and is very often concentrated at the bottom of, say, a mat of brown pine needles, in the form of about one inch of dark material which comes up attached to the pine needles when the needles are kicked. This humus is extremely acidic, however, and makes the water sinking into the soil very acidic. Iron salts are therefore commonly leached out of the A horizon.

In moist tropical climates, and in areas other than swamps, the great hordes of microorganisms literally eat up most of the plant material which would otherwise form tremendous deposits of humus in the A horizon. The water in the A horizon, in the tropics, commonly becomes of such a composition that it does selective leaching, removing many soluble minerals from the A horizon, but leaving a few other minerals behind.

Topography as a Control of Soil Formation. It is obvious that soil being formed on a steep slope is exposed to more erosion than soil being formed on a gentler slope. Also, soil being formed on a steep slope will not have the opportunity to take in as much water as soil on a gentler slope, due to increased runoff. In addition, soils on south-facing slopes north of the Tropic of Cancer will have much of their water evaporated by the sun, in spring and summer.

Where the water table is close to the surface or intersects it, as in the case of a slough or swamp, soil cannot form in the usual manner. With all possible pore spaces occupied by water there is: no directly downward leaching, very slow mechanical removal of material from the upper horizon, and no air spaces. Therefore, although there is usu-ally abundant dead plant material in a swamp, it tends to form a slightly decomposed mat which is processed to a certain point by bac-teria while being mechanically pushed down as more and more ma-terial accumulates. Under some conditions, a *bog soil* develops which may become very productive if drained.

Time as a Control of Soil Formation.   From what has already been said it is probably apparent that the present immature soil of any re-gion does not look like its mature version, say, one thousand years from now, nor does it resemble an almost mature soil now in the same region. This is assuming that the soils have been derived from differ-ent parent rocks, and that the differences in the soil profiles are very apparent.

The astonishing thing, though, is that these soils will some day look almost exactly like each other. It may take one hundred, one thou-sand, or ten thousand years, but if both soils are exposed to essen-tially the same controls of climate, vegetation, and topography for a long enough time, they will be the same in appearance and also almost identical in internal structure, composition, and texture.

Processes of Soil Formation

There are three major processes of soil formation: *podzolization, laterization,* and *calcification.* These processes singly or in combina-tion, are responsible for all major soil types.

Podzolization.   Podzolization is the main soil-forming process in cool humid climates where the humus, as previously explained, tends to stay near the surface but makes the soil water more acidic. The result is that elements such as iron and aluminum are leached out of the A horizon and deposited below along with the clays. Much of the silica remains in the A horizon, however. The removal of iron gives the A horizon a rather pale, washed-out look.

The material leached and mechanically carried from the A horizon and deposited in the B horizon reduces the pore space of the B horizon. The resulting soil, known as a *podzol,* is acid and is generally unproductive. Podzol soils are common in mountainous areas, especially in regions of conifer forests. Podzol soils are rarely more than two feet in depth as the process is commonly interrupted or slowed down each winter. Podzolic type soils are found from the subarctic to the middle latitudes, and in some cases even to the tropics.

Laterization. Laterization takes place principally in moist tropical regions where, as it was previously stated, most of the potential humus is devoured by bacteria. This results in soil water which leaches out most of the nutrient minerals and brings them far below the surface. The water has very little effect upon the hydroxides of iron and aluminum although it commonly dissolves silica. The result is that *laterite,* a hard red or yellowish crust of iron and aluminum minerals, develops to depth in some tropical countries. The process of laterization continues without interruption all year long, therefore the lateritic soil profile is deeper than any other. Lateritic soil of a thickness of twenty feet is not uncommon in some countries.

Calcification. Soils of near-dry climates reflect the little amount of rainfall. The vegetation control of this process is, of course, of a grass or shrub type rather than trees, due to the lack of rain. Grass is high in calcium and, when it dies, it returns calcium to the soil. What rain does fall readily leaches calcium and magnesium from the A horizon, depositing these elements in the B horizon. The A layer is characterized, near the surface, by a mat of organic material and humus.

Pedocals and Pedalfers

The 97° W meridian roughly divides the continental United States into an eastern humid area and a western drier area. (See Figure 66.) The actual dividing line passes along the eastern boundaries of North Dakota, South Dakota, and Nebraska, and splits off the eastern third of Kansas, Oklahoma, and Texas. East of this line are the *pedalfers,* soils whose B horizons have had much clay and iron added (*al,* aluminum; *fer,* iron). This of course is due to the increased precipitation and the resulting leaching, eluviation, and illuviation.

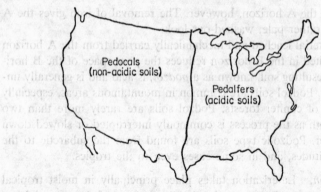

Fig. 66. A line dividing the humid from the subhumid sections indicates where soil processes tend to develop acid soils. (Adapted from the U. S. Department of Agriculture)

The soils west of the line are, in general, the *pedocals*, soils whose upper layers contain much calcium (*cal,* calcium). As explained before, these soils are characteristic of drier regions. There are major exceptions, of course, such as in the general area of the Pacific Northwest where abundant rainfall has brought about the formation of pedalfers.

The Great Soil Groups

Soils can be classified, according to the soil-forming processes, as *zonal, intrazonal,* or *azonal.* The term "zonal" arises from the fact that resulting soils in the same climatic and vegetation "zones" tend to be of the same type, assuming the added general conditions of gentle slope of land, etc. Therefore a *zonal soil*—a soil characteristic of a large region—has a profile with well-differentiated horizons.

An *intrazonal soil* is one whose profile has been altered from that of the representative zonal soil of the area. The alteration is brought out by local differences in climate, vegetation, topography, etc. These soils are found in all climatic and vegetation zones, hence the name *intrazonal.*

Other soils seem to have been little affected by the controls of climate and vegetation. These soils are usually young soils. As they do not reflect the existence of climatic and vegetative zones, these soils are called *azonal soils.* As examples, *lithosols* (stony soils) and *rego-*

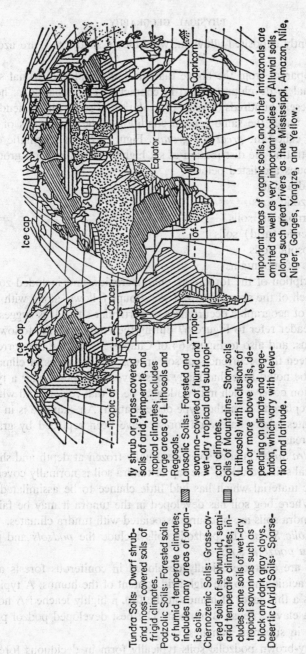

Important areas of organic soils, and other intrazonals are omitted as well as very important bodies of Alluvial soils along such great rivers as the Mississippi, Amazon, Nile, Niger, Ganges, Yangtze, and Yellow.

☐ Tundra Soils: Dwarf shrub- and moss-covered soils of frigid climates.

▨ Podzolic Soils: Forested soils of humid, temperate climates; includes many areas of organic soils.

▧ Chernozemic Soils: Grass-covered soils of subhumid, semi-arid temperate climates; includes some soils of wet-dry tropical savannas such as black and dark gray clays.

▦ Deseric (Arid) Soils: Sparse-ly shrub or grass-covered soils of arid, temperate, and tropical climates; includes large areas of Lithosols and Regosols.

▨ Latosolic Soils: Forested and savanna-covered of humid and wet-dry tropical and subtropical climates.

▥ Soils of Mountains: Stony soils (Lithosols) with inclusions of one or more above soils, depending on climate and vegetation, which vary with elevation and latitude.

Fig. 67. World distribution of the principal zonal soil groups. (Adapted from the U. S. Department of Agriculture)

sols (recently deposited alluvium, wind-blown sand, etc.) are azonal soils.

It is apparent from the above that the intrazonal and azonal soils are regional in development and in character. The zonal soils, however, represent hundreds of years of evolution of soil over tremendous areas and under the same general conditions. The zonal soils of the world are called the *great soil groups*. Figure 67 is a schematic diagram illustrating the distribution of six highly generalized soil groups. These groups are listed below:

1. Tundra soils
2. Podzolic soils
3. Chernozemic soils
4. Desertic (arid) soils
5. Latosolic soils
6. Soils of mountains

A description of the formation, characteristics, and included zonal soils of each of the six generalized soil groups follows, along with descriptions of geographic occurrences of particular soils. It is suggested that the reader refer to Figure 67 during the reading of the following descriptions, and also to Figure 64 of Chapter 13, noting the correlations between the occurrences of soil groups and the types of climate. It should be noted here that many soils have developed under a type of vegetation cover which may no longer be in that region, and which has been replaced by another type of vegetation. An example is in the United States where hardwood forests have been replaced by grass, in some areas.

1. Tundra Soils. Tundra soils are usually frozen at depth and show little normal soil evolution. The top of tundra soil is normally covered by organic material which has had little chance to be assimilated in the soil. Where bog soil has developed in the tundra it may be fairly fertile. Tundra soils are of course associated with tundra climates.

2. Podzolic Soils. The podzolic soils include the *podzols* and the *gray-brown podzolic soils*.

Podzols are characteristically developed in coniferous forests and are highly acidic due to the high acid content of the humus. A typical podzol has a thin layer of humus at the top, a highly leached A horizon, and a clayey, dense B horizon. The best developed podzol profiles occur in subarctic climates.

The gray-brown podzolic soils typically form in deciduous forests and less often in mixed deciduous-conifer forests. The gray-brown podzolic soils are not as acid as the podzols and the A horizon is therefore not as thoroughly leached as the A horizon of a true podzol. The addition of organic material to what is usually a brown hydroxide of iron gives the soil its gray-brown color. The B horizon is denser than the A because of illuviation, or deposition from above. The gray-brown podzolic soils are very productive, agriculturally, and are associated in general with the humid continental climates.

3. Chernozemic Soils. The chernozemic soils include the *chernozems,* the *prairie soils,* and the *chestnut and brown soils.*

Chernozems are the most fertile soils formed under grass cover. They contain much organic matter and the resulting dark color often extends several feet below the surface. They typically occur on the more humid margins of the steppe climates and are therefore intermediate between steppe soils and prairie soils. Due to the presence of much calcium from grass, chernozems are characterized by *calcification,* and there is always a concentration of calcium carbonate or lime, at some depth. Chernozems occur from north to south in the central United States; from east to west in the central USSR; in Africa; and in Argentina.

Prairie soils are formed under grass, rather than under forests. They are thus associated with intermediate quantities of rainfall. As grass readily forms humus, prairie soils are very fertile. The color of the soil varies from brown-black near the surface to what may be an extremely light-colored parent rock. The depth of the profile is usually from 2½ to 6 feet. Due to relatively little leaching the A horizon has high mineral and organic content, a fact of considerable importance to early homesteaders in the United States and Canada, who, after "busting the sod" with simple tools, had merely to sow seed for their first crops. Prairie soils occur in the corn-belt regions of Illinois, Iowa, and Missouri, in Russia, South America, Africa, and northeastern Australia.

The chestnut and brown soils are associated with steppe, or semiarid, climates. The chestnut and brown soils are intermediate between the chernozems and the desert soils.

The color of chestnut and brown soils is due to the fact that they have evolved under a grass cover which is thinner than that overlying the chernozem soils. The reduced amount of humus and precipitation results in a chestnut or brown color.

The chestnut and brown soils also have an accumulation of lime in their profile but, due to decreased precipitation, it is commonly within a foot or two of the surface. The chestnut and brown soils are associated with the livestock industry around the world. These soils are extensively developed in the western Great Plains of the United States, in Russia, in part of the Argentine region of South America, and almost completely rim the Australian Desert.

4. Desertic Soils. Due to the slight vegetation cover in deserts, desert soils contain little organic matter. Thus they are typically light in color. Because of little precipitation, alkalis are commonly found near or on the surface. The main type of salt present determines whether desert soil can or cannot be successfully irrigated for crop production. This fact is sometimes overlooked. A large dam was recently built at great expense by a foreign country for such irrigation of desert land. After the dam was built it was discovered that, water or no water, due to the high content of sodium salts in the soil, the land would never grow crops.

5. Latosolic Soils. The dominant process in the formation of latosolic soils is laterization. Latosolic soils occur under conditions of heavy precipitation and above-normal temperature, thus their occurrence is roughly in the rainy tropics, the wet-and-dry tropics, and the monsoon tropics. Latosolic, or "lateritic," soils contain much iron and aluminum in the A horizon and have relatively deep soil profiles. The associated vegetation is that of the tropical forests.

Red and yellow podzolic soils result from a combination of the podzolization and the laterization processes. Due to their color, they are usually classed with latosolic soils. They are found in the rainy tropics and in the humid subtropics. The A horizon typically contains clays, silica, and organic matter and is leached. The B horizon is where the red or yellow colors typically occur. The A horizon of these red and yellow soils closely resembles the B horizon of a podzolic soil, while the B horizon of the red and yellow soils resembles the very young A horizon of lateritic soils. Red podzolic soils often evolve in mixed broadleaf-conifer forests while yellow podzolic soils often occur in conifer forests such as those in the southeastern United States.

6. Soils of Mountains. These soils, which include the soils of mountain valleys, generally are "alike only in their unlikeness" and on this basis alone are classed as zonal soils. The complex mountain and valley soils vary widely, from region to region and from altitude to altitude. The use of these soils therefore varies widely from none at all in unpopulated areas to extreme use in widely separated regions of the world.

Cultural and Economic Effects
of the Distribution of Zonal Soils

The primary use of soil is for agriculture and it is agriculture which has largely determined the population patterns and the welfare of many nations. The pattern of global distribution of zonal soils has therefore played, and will continue to play, a major role in world affairs. There is a definite correlation, on a world-wide basis, between type of soil, cultural inheritance, and use of soil. It is interesting to consider the effects of types and usages of soil upon the development of the United States, and to then compare these soil types and usages with those in some other countries.

Soil Distribution and the Growth of the United States.   The early settlers on the east coast of the United States, from New England far into the south, were faced with the same necessity: clearing trees from the land in order to grow food. The forests were mainly broadleaf and mixed broadleaf-coniferous in type. The forests before these had been similar. There was one difference between the northern and southern colonies, however, and that difference was climate. Today we describe this difference by saying that the southern states have a subtropical climate while the northern states have a continental climate.

Due to these differing climates, different soils had developed. Settlers north of 37° latitude found gray-brown podzolic soils in the forest clearings. The soils were like those in Europe, the pioneers saw. Settlers in the south found strange, reddish-colored soils, resulting from varying degrees of laterization. These red soils, they discovered, could grow crops like cotton, tobacco, and peanuts, in addition to others. By this time, some of the settlers in the northern and middle colonies had pushed west, taking with them their hard-won knowledge of how best to clear the land and work the gray-brown soil. Gradually the southern plantations and small farms also spread west, staying in the same reddish soil the southern settlers now understood. Where both migrations met the treeless prairie and the unfamiliar prairie soil, they stopped. This roughly marked the frontier for many years. Today, the bulk of the crop and livestock farming in the United States still lies in that same area of gray-brown podzolic soils in the northeastern one sixth of the United States. That area is also the most densely populated area of the United States. Also, the plantations and small farms of the United States are still all largely in the lateritic red soil of the southeastern one sixth of the country.

Those settlers who had worked the gray-brown soil farthest to the north had immediately discovered a major drawback—glacial rocks in the soil which made it almost impossible to till the soil in many places. The glaciers, however, had also done a thorough job of plowing the soil, and grass grew green and profusely on the hills. The land was unsuited for large-scale tillage but it was perfect for dairying. Thus the "dairybelt" of the United States extends, in gray-brown but rocky soil, from the New England states westward and past the Great Lakes region to the prairie.

By 1840 the tide had once more started to flow west. The treeless prairies and Great Plains were something to be passed over as quickly as possible, in order to get to Texas, California, and Oregon. Trees were associated with good soil; there weren't any trees; *ergo,* the prairie and dry plains soils were worthless. Within a decade such thinkers were astonished to see that worthless soil or not, the dairy industry, the crop and livestock industries, and the plantations and small farms had each successfully encroached upon this prairie soil. Today, this great area of prairie soil is known as the "corn belt," which includes Iowa, Illinois, eastern Nebraska, southern Minnesota, northern Missouri, and much of Kansas.

Some hardy pioneers ventured onto the Great Plains where the black prairie soil gives way to the chernozems and, further west, to the chestnut and brown soils. Those early years on the Great Plains were, providentially, wet years, and good harvests of grains such as wheat were made. Now the frontier, which had paused briefly at the western edge of the prairie soils, moved west again, spurred on by the Homestead Act of 1862, onto the Great Plains and its chestnut and brown soils. Some dry years followed. Longhorn cattle drives from Texas to northern markets demonstrated to some pioneers occupying the chestnut and brown soils of the western, more arid portions of the Great Plains that cattle stood a much better chance of surviving the long periods of drought than did grain. They brought in Herefords and Shorthorns and thus began the great livestock industry of the western states, an industry which is associated world-wide with the chestnut and brown soils. In many regions the industry widely overlaps onto areas of what is properly called desert soil.

World Agriculture and Zonal Soils. Agricultural practices are closely associated with cultures and thus it would be expected that peoples having allied cultural backgrounds would, although widely separated by distance, make about the same use of familiar soil types. Thus the original agriculture in the United States was determined by Europeans from many countries, including Russians from the Ukraine who brought hardy wheat with them, Dutch settlers with their livestock, Germans with their improved methods of grain production, French immigrants with their love of wheat and vegetables, and, in California, the settlers of Spanish descent who grew the olives, grapes, and leafy vegetables of Spain. Emigrants of the above and other nationalities also left Europe for lands other than those in North America. The English went to Australia and, with the Dutch, to South Africa. English, Dutch, Germans, and Ukranians also poured into Canada where the French were already well ensconced. In almost every one of the above instances, the settlers either made the same use that had been made in Europe of a given soil group, or patterned its use after that which their ethnic groups had proved profitable in the New World. The result is that the agricultures of many geographically widely separated areas have what would appear to the uninitiated as startling similarities.

One of the most striking similarities is that occurring between the usage of chernozem, and chestnut and brown soils of the United States and the usage of the same soils in other countries. In the United States these soils are associated with the grain and livestock industries of the Great Plains and of the corn belt. In the USSR these same two soil groups, in a long east-west band, host Russia's mammoth grain and livestock industries. In South Africa, Canada, Australia, and the Argentine, the chernozems and the chestnut and brown soils are also very closely associated with livestock ranching and with grain farming. In South America, livestock ranching overlaps broadly onto prairie and lateritic soils.

The gray-brown forest soils in the northern one sixth of the United States have counterparts in western Europe and on the tip of South Africa. In the United States and Europe the gray-brown soils support the crops and livestock industries and the dairy industries. On the southern tip of South Africa a flourishing dairy industry is associated with the gray-brown soil group.

An interesting correlation between the usage of particular soil groups by various cultures concerns the coastal and inland area north and south of the mouth of the Rio de la Plata, in Argentina and Uruguay, and stretching into Brazil. These three countries received great numbers of Germans, Spaniards, Italians, Portuguese, and some English during their years of initial growth. The result is that the prairie, chernozem, and chestnut and brown soils in this area respectively host largely what they did in their respective areas in Europe: crop and livestock farms, grain, and livestock industries, in that order. In the United States, and as already explained, pioneer farmers from the same European countries established an identical pattern of soil usage in the three soils.

REVIEW

1. Describe the evolution of a typical soil.

2. What is a "soil profile"?

3. State the chief agents of soil formation and explain how each operates.

4. Explain "capillary action." What is its importance?

5. Define "leaching," "eluviation," and "illuviation."

6. What is "nitrogen fixation"? How is this accomplished in soil?

7. What are the five controls of soil formation? Explain the difference between controls and agents of soil formation.

8. Describe typical A and B horizons developed by (1) podzolization, (2) laterization, (3) calcification.

9. What is a pedocal; a pedalfer? Where, roughly, does each occur in quantity in the United States?

10. List the zonal soils and describe the characteristics of each.

11. Explain the term "zonal soil."

12. Discuss the usage of certain soil groups by peoples of the same original cultures who have migrated to other countries.

EXERCISES

(Answers are given in the answer section at the back of the book.)

1. Sketch a typical profile, for a lateritic soil, showing a typical dimension of depth, and the mineral constitution of the horizons.

2. In general, in the northern hemisphere, lateritic soils grade in color from dark red in the tropics to light yellow toward the north. The colors are principally due to oxides of iron, the yellow color being due to less oxidation of the iron. Explain the red-to-yellow change described above, in terms of vegetation, climate, extent of leaching, etc.

3. Which, fine-grained or coarse-grained soil, has the *smaller* pore spaces? Check your answer by placing three pennies, touching together, on the table and comparing the space between them with that between three quarters similarly arranged. Would you expect more capillary action in fine or in coarse soil?

4. Sketch the major boundaries of the zonal soils on an outline map of the world. Indicate some famous military fronts and settlement frontiers which have more or less approximated certain lines of division between the various soil types, and name the types of soil involved. In each case explain the development of the battle front or the civilian frontiers in terms of soil or soil forming agents and controls.

5. Write a description of possible soil evolution in the general area where you live, basing the description upon soil formation controls and agents as they now exist in your area. Describe the resulting profile. What kind of soil have you "formed"?

Compare this soil with the zonal soil of your area. Explain any discrepancies, in terms of intrazonal effects, change in climate, vegetation, etc. If possible, take a field trip to exposures where "your" soil is forming, and where the zonal soil is well shown.

CHAPTER 19

Underground Water

The evaporation of water from the ocean into the atmosphere was described in Chapter 9 as was the subsequent precipitation of the water. This present chapter deals with that part of the precipitated water which sinks into the ground. Precipitation is the main source of underground water. Other possible sources are steam from magma, and original salt water or fresh water trapped in their own sediments. These types of water are, respectively, *magmatic,* or *juvenile* water, and *connate* water.

The Hydrologic Cycle

Practically all of the water evaporated from the ocean finally gets back to the ocean in what is called the *hydrologic cycle*. The hydrologic cycle may be summarized as follows: water is evaporated from the ocean and is subsequently precipitated. If the precipitation takes place over the ocean the water is directly returned to the ocean; if the precipitation takes place over land, some water goes back into the atmosphere, some directly flows on the earth's surface, and some sinks into the ground. In the case of snow and ice, the above processes are delayed for lengths of time varying from a few minutes as in the case of spring snows, or thousands of years in the case of glaciers.

The water which goes back into the atmosphere will subsequently be precipitated; the water flowing on the earth's surface is usually well on its way to the ocean; the water beneath the earth's surface will work through the ground. Some of it will be transpired by plants or directly evaporated but much of it eventually enters some stream system. Then it, too, will be on its way back to the ocean to, some day, repeat the entire cycle. An amazingly complete description of the hydrologic cycle is given by Ecclesiastes 1:7, in the Old Testament: "All the rivers run into the sea, yet the sea is not full: unto the place from whence the rivers come, thither they return again."

The Downward Movement of Underground Water

Porosity and Permeability. The movement of underground water through rock is largely controlled by the *porosity* and the *permeability* of the rock. Porosity is the volume of pore space in the rock while rock permeability is the capacity of the rock for allowing the passage of water through it.

At first glance it might seem that porosity and permeability go together, that the greater the porosity the greater the permeability. In many instances this is true but there are important exceptions. It is possible for a rock to have fairly high porosity and low permeability, and for a rock with little porosity to have high local permeability.

Consider a shale, for example. A shale may have a porosity of 15 percent (which means that 15 percent of its volume is open space) but it may have almost no permeability. This would be the case if molecular attraction between the molecules of water and the rock prevented the downward flow of water. This happens in small openings. In the discussion on soils, capillary action and surface tension were explained in terms of a mountain climber ascending an opening in rock by pressing with feet and back against the rock walls, and moving slowly upward. Now, if the mountain climber gets himself wedged against all sides of a very narrow part of the "chimney" he might find it impossible to proceed either upward or downward, due to the increased force he is now exerting on the rock walls, and no one else could pass him. The force he is now exerting is roughly comparable to the molecular attraction between films of hygroscopic water which coats rock grains and which prevents other water from traveling through very fine openings.

This is often the situation in rocks like shale which have fairly high porosity. On the other hand a sandstone with lower porosity than a shale may allow water to pass through it relatively easily. In general, assuming rounded grains, coarse-grained rocks are more permeable than fine-grained rocks.

At the other extreme, a rock which is not truly porous throughout to measurable degree may be very permeable. For example, an igneous rock such as basalt may have various cracks in it. The rock cannot be technically described as porous, yet water passes freely through it and the rock therefore has a high degree of permeability. Any rock or soil permeable enough to allow ground water to move through it is called an *aquifer*.

The Zone of Aeration; the Zone of Saturation. Water entering the ground does so because it moves essentially downward through openings in the soil or rock. These openings are therefore normally filled with air, and the zone containing these openings is called the *zone of aeration*. The zone of aeration contains a *belt of soil water* near the top, an *intermediate belt,* and a *capillary fringe* above the water table. (See Figure 68.) The belt of soil water contains the water, de-

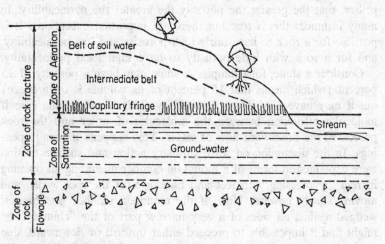

Fig. 68. Ground-water zones and belts. (Adapted from U. S. Department of Agriculture *Water*)

scribed in the previous chapter, which is held by capillary action and which is used by plants. The water in the intermediate zone is also held by capillary action but is usually beyond the roots of most plants. The capillary fringe is a belt where water from the saturated rocks below is pulled up by capillary action. The depth of the capillary fringe may vary from a few inches to a few feet, depending upon pore space.

At some depth, the rock openings are filled with water. Air ceases here and the *zone of saturation* begins. The lower limit of the zone of saturation, due to decreasing open space with depth, is usually less than 1/3 of a mile below ground surface.

The Water Table. The surface between the zone of aeration and the zone of saturation is the *water table*. The water table is an undulating surface which, in humid regions of homogeneous rock, tends to approximate the slope of the ground.

Movement of Water in the Zone of Saturation

Whereas the movement of water in the zone of aeration is primarily either downward due to gravity or upward due to capillary action, the movement of water in the zone of saturation tends to be both downward and lateral. Consider, for example, what happens during a rainstorm after a dry period in a region of homogeneous rock such as shown in Figure 68.

Water will pass through the zone of aeration quickly but, when it reaches the zone of saturation, it slows down considerably for the simple reason that all pore spaces are filled with water which is slowly moving throughout the zone of saturation. This movement through the zone of saturation is called *percolation*.

To understand the characteristics of the water table and of percolation let us assume that the water is not moving at all in the zone of saturation but that any additional force will disrupt its equilibrium. Now, consider one drop of water which has passed through the zone of aeration. This one drop is pressing downward and upon the water table and the zone of saturation. If the drop enters the present zone of saturation then somewhere some other drop in the zone of saturation must be displaced. If that drop is displaced, another must be displaced, and so on. Thus, if water quickly entered the zone of saturation, percolation in that zone would be fast. Or, conversely, if percolation were fast then water from above could quickly enter the zone of saturation.

It would also be true that if percolation were slow the water from above could not readily enter the existent zone of saturation. Rather it would hump up toward the top of the hill, saturating the rocks and thus raising the water table. This is the exact situation in that friction makes percolation a very slow process. The water table therefore rises, and the pressure on any point in the zone of saturation becomes greater due to the increased weight of water above it. The pressure at any one point is almost the same in all directions, therefore a drop of water will tend to move laterally as well as down due to gravity. The area in which the water table intersects the topography to form something like a spring or a swamp or, as shown in Figure 68, to discharge into a stream system, is the area toward which the water in the zone of saturation will naturally try to flow. Technically the water flows from a region of higher pressure to one of lower pressure which, of course, is the same reason that a liquid in a container flows through a hole or crack in the container.

Now suppose that the rain stops, followed by several weeks of fair weather. Water from the saturated zone keeps discharging into the stream system, thus lowering the water table beneath the hill. The water table beneath the hill drops beneath its former intersection with the ground and now lies beneath the stream bed. Percolation continues but now toward some other area, possibly in some place miles distant where the water table again intersects the ground. In this manner, a water table in a moist region more or less approximates the surface slopes, being higher under hills and lower in valleys.

Whether or not the water table actually intersects the ground in a particular area, water in the zone of saturation still flows essentially down the "hump" beneath a hill or mountain, toward points of lower elevation. Water in a region of homogeneous rocks is therefore commonly sought by digging or drilling wells in the lower valley sides or in the valley floors rather than near the tops of hills or mountains.

It should not be thought, however, that the bulk of the flow of water in the zone of saturation is in more or less of a straight line. If this were so, very little geological work would be done by ground water. Attention is called to the arrows indicating the various theoretical directions of flow in Figure 69. These curves result from the fact,

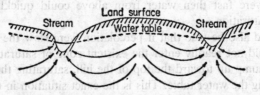

Fig. 69. Theoretical flow of water in zone of saturation. (Adapted from the U. S. Department of Agriculture)

already mentioned, that the particles of flowing water are pulled downward by gravity, and laterally and upward by the lower pressure in the area of seepage. For those readers who wish actually to see such an effect, the following simple "kitchen sink experiment" is suggested:

Fill a small cardboard or plastic container—such as those used for dairy products, etc.—with water. Wait a few minutes so that circular motion of the water will be at a minimum. Push a nail through the side of the container several times, about midway between the top and bottom of the container, arranging the holes on the same horizontal line and close together. The holes through which the water is now running represent an area where the water table intersects the ground. Drop a very small quantity of ink or food coloring onto the center of the water surface. Loops almost exactly like those shown in Figure 69 will develop, indicating various directions and speeds of flow as the particles of water move toward the holes.

The Movement of Underground Water in Regions of Unlike Rocks

So far in this chapter we have largely been discussing the behavior of underground water in regions of homogeneous material. The distribution and action of underground water is quite different in regions of dissimilar rocks and soils.

Perched Water Tables; Springs. Suppose that water in the zone of aeration, moving downward from the surface, encounters an imper-

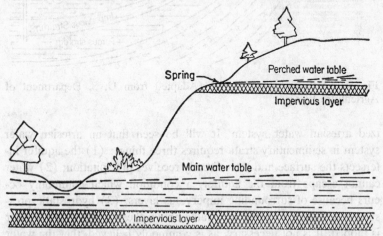

Fig. 70. Perched water table. (Adapted from U. S. Department of Agriculture *Water*)

meable layer of shale as shown in Figure 70. A local water table, known as a *perched water table,* will therefore be created in the zone of aeration above the main water table. If the perched water table intersects the surface of the ground a spring or seepage of some kind will result as is the case when the main water table intersects the surface.

Artesian Wells and Springs.   A popular belief is that artesian water is any water from far beneath the earth's surface, but this is a mistaken notion. Artesian water is water which rises toward the surface due to water pressure in the aquifer. Figure 71 illustrates an ideal-

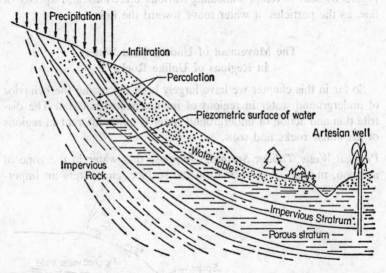

Fig. 71. Artesian ground-water. (Adapted from U. S. Department of Agriculture *Water*)

ized artesian water system. It will be seen that an artesian water system in sedimentary strata requires three things: (1) the aquifer intersects the surface and thus directly receives precipitation; (2) water cannot escape from the aquifer, a condition which commonly occurs because of surrounding impervious layers; (3) hydrostatic pressure is sufficient to force the water above the aquifer if the aquifer is tapped. It is not necessary, as is commonly believed, that the water be forced to the surface of the ground in order to be properly classified as artesian water. Many true artesian systems require pumping to get the water to the surface.

The tapping of the aquifer may be done by man for an *artesian well* or it may be done by nature in the form of a fissure or fault through which the water will move under pressure toward the surface. In this latter case and if the water actually comes out upon the surface, the result is an *artesian spring*.

Although artesian systems are commonly associated with sedimentary rocks they can occur in any type of rock, due to cracks and fissures, etc., which bring about permeability. It is still necessary, however, that the water be under pressure, in order to be truly artesian.

Thermal Springs; Geysers. If the temperature of the water in a spring is at or near 212° F the spring is called a *hot spring*. Springs whose water is at lower temperatures, but which is still above normal body heat, are called *warm springs*. In the western part of the United States, the heat is normally furnished by underground water contacting or approaching igneous intrusions or extrusions which are cooling. In the eastern United States, the underground water in some regions evidently descends far enough below the surface of the earth to be heated in accordance with the *geothermal gradient,* the increase of temperature with depth.

Geysers are hot springs which erupt from time to time. Whereas hot springs have an uncomplicated plumbing system, geysers apparently have several long feeder tubes, most of which must somehow prevent a ready circulation of water through them. This could be caused by the supply "roots" of the geysers being narrow and curved, thus inhibiting convection currents within them. At any rate what evidently happens in many cases is that the roots of the geyser are close to igneous rock which is cooling. The water in the lower parts of the roots is heated but cannot transfer much of this heat to the water's upper layers due to the lack of convection currents. Furthermore, the water is under much more pressure at the bottom than at the top and it becomes superheated. Due to the pressure, steam is not formed at first. The water in the main part of the geyser goes up and down several times, as steam is finally formed in the various feeder tubes and released. This up-and-down surge is apparently very similar to the motion which can be observed in a coffee percolator.

Finally, just as in the case of a coffee percolator, some water spills over the edge of the geyser tube. This reduces the pressure at the bottom of the geyser, steam is immediately formed, and the eruption takes place.

Although most geysers and hot springs seem to be largely fed by rain water, some apparently receive at least some magmatic water. This is very probably the situation in Yellowstone Park, the geyser region of New Zealand, and in Iceland, all known to be regions of fairly recent volcanic activity.

The Work Done by Underground Water

Where the Ocean Gets Its Salt.   The solvent action of underground water can be appreciated when it is realized that most of the salt in the ocean is in the ocean because of underground water. It used to be thought that the ocean's salt was inherent to the ocean water or to the rocks of the ocean floor. It is now known that underground water, percolating through the rocks, dissolves the salts and later discharges into stream systems which then carry the dissolved minerals to the ocean. One such salt is sodium chloride, common table salt.

Limestone Caverns and Karst Topography.   In limestone regions, underground water, especially if more acidic than usual, rather readily dissolves the host rock. One result is that *caverns* in limestone commonly develop. Such caverns, most of them probably formed beneath the water table, are often connected by tunnels through which underground streams now course. Some large caverns with their myriads of stalactites and stalagmites are among the most popular tourist attractions.

In regions of limestone, salt, or gypsum, *sinkholes* may develop on the surface. These holes which may vary from a few feet to a few miles in diameter are caused by surface water directly dissolving the rock, by collapse of the surface layers into a cavern, or by both actions. Sometimes only part of the ground layers collapse, leaving a *natural bridge* spanning what may eventually be a fairly large *solution valley*.

Regions characterized by sinkholes, caves, natural bridges, solution valleys, etc., are known as regions of *karst topography*. The name derives from an extensive limestone region having such topography in the Karst region of Yugoslavia and Italy. The major region of karst topography in the United States is in the southeast, in the states of Tennessee, Kentucky, Indiana, and Florida.

Underground Water and Deposition. The visually most striking depositional features brought about by underground water are such things as stalactites and stalagmites in caverns. However, the most important depositional work done by underground water is that of cementing mineral grains together, to form sedimentary rock. This cementing action is done largely in the zone of saturation by all kinds of underground water. Obviously, connate water is of importance here. Calcium carbonate, silica, and iron in various forms are the three major "cements" which underground water carries in solution and then deposits around the unconsolidated grains. The reason why these materials deposit in this way from solution is one of the unknowns in geology.

Economic and Cultural Aspects
of Underground Water

Water Supply, Wells, and Water Tables. Man's greatest need is water, and the geography of man is largely the geography of water. In the United States, one third of the cities whose populations are over 35,000 get most of their water from underground sources. About 20 percent of all water used in the United States comes from underground sources.

Wells of one kind or another are the links between underground water and man. Wells other than artesian wells are usually drilled to beneath the water table, into the zone of saturation. As more and more wells are drilled into the water table, and more and more water is removed from the zone of saturation, the water table falls. As a result, in many areas of the United States, water tables are from 50 to 200 feet lower than they were a decade ago, and are dropping rapidly.

Water tables of the perched variety are important sources of underground water for several cities in the southeastern part of the United States. Perched water tables can continue to be a continuing source of municipal water only in humid regions where the rainfall entering the perched system exceeds the amount of water being withdrawn.

Settlement of much of the Great Plains, discussed in the chapter on soils, is largely due to a mammoth artesian system extending from the Rockies and the Black Hills to Kansas. A layer of sandstone is tilted and exposed to the west by having been forced upward as the present Rockies and the Black Hills grew. The outcrop of the sandstone receives much of the surface water coursing down the east slopes of these mountains, and the aquifer then gently dips to the east beneath the surface. The drilling of the first well into the aquifer in the 1880s spelled the end of the "Great American Desert" and the beginning of a vast agricultural complex.

Other Uses of Underground Water. Many of the famous resort areas of the world are centered about hot and warm springs and mineral springs. The minerals result from solution of various salts by the underground water which eventually comes out upon the surface as a spring. Many hot or warm springs are heavily charged with mineral salts.

In some localities of the world, including some in the western United States, the heat from geysers is used to warm buildings and even to furnish power. Experimentation along these lines is presently continuing. In New Zealand, geysers have been made by man by boring through rock to favorable locations. One use of such geysers is in the obtaining of "heavy water" (D_2O), which is used in atomic reactors.

REVIEW

1. What is the chief source of underground water? What are two other possible sources?

2. Discuss the hydrologic cycle.

3. Distinguish between porosity and permeability.

4. Explain how a rock may be porous but not permeable.

5. Define "zone of aeration," "zone of saturation," and "capillary fringe." State where each occurs, and its characteristics.

6. Explain why a water table in a moist region more or less approximates the slope of the ground surface.

7. What is a spring? What is a perched water table?

8. What is an artesian system? Name the three factors necessary for a true artesian system.

9. Explain how a geyser may erupt.

10. What is the most important geological work done by underground water, other than furnishing salts to the sea?

11. What is "karst topography"? Name a region of karst topography in the United States.

EXERCISES

(Answers are given in the answer section at the back of the book.)

1. Glass jar "A" is filled with spheres whose diameters are 1.0″. Glass jar "B" has the same dimensions as "A" but is filled with spheres whose diameters are 2.0″. Which jar now has the more air space, or are they equal in air space? Assuming rounded grains, does grain size have any effect upon porosity?

2. A certain sandstone is composed of grains of a substance whose specific gravity is 2.7. The sandstone has a porosity of 20 percent. How much does it weigh per cubic foot?

3. Sketch a cross section of a hillside and valley and show the water table as it might exist in a moist region.

4. Most caverns seem to have been formed beneath the water table. What does the presence of stalactites and stalagmites in these caverns show?

5. Do you think that the removal of water from the saturated zone generally strengthens or weakens the rock in that zone? State reasons for your opinion. Check the validity of your reasoning by investigating the cause of ground subsidence in Mexico City, Las Vegas, and Long Beach, California, during the last decade.

CHAPTER 20

The Earth's Interior as a Control of Man's Environment

Other than the obviously important subsurface occurrences of water, minerals, soil, coal, and oil, etc., what lies beneath the surface of the earth may at first glance seem to be of little importance in our everyday lives. The fact is, however, that the earth's overall internal structure and composition play a basic part in man's environment and in human affairs. This chapter deals with some major relationships between our natural environment and the physical structure and composition of the earth as a whole. The first part, "The Zones of the Earth," will serve as background material for the remainder of this chapter.

The Zones of the Earth

Evidence from Earthquake Data. Most of what we know about the internal structure of the earth has been determined from the study of *seismic* or earthquake waves. Different types of seismic waves move with varying velocities through varying types of rock and rock structure, at different depths. These velocities are known, hence a fairly good picture of some details of the earth's interior has been obtained.

On the basis mainly of earthquake data, then, the earth is layered into several closely concentric zones or shells which grade into each other and which surround an inner *core*. The zones to be discussed, with the core, are the *crust* and the *mantle*. (See Figure 72.)

The Crust. The earth's crust, so called, is the outer shell of the earth. In continental regions, the crust is composed mainly of sedimentary, metamorphic and granite-like rocks, and its thickness varies

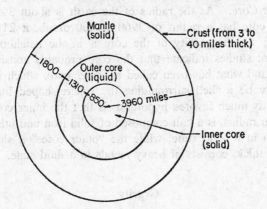

Fig. 72. The "zones" of the earth.

from 10 to 20 miles. In general, but with some notable exceptions, the thickness of the crust in a region varies with the elevation above sea level of that region. For example, the thickness of the crust in regions near sea level in elevation is often from 10 to 20 miles, in plains regions from 20 to 30 miles, while under high mountains the crust is often from 30 to 40 miles thick. The crust beneath the oceans—this part of the crust is composed of basalt, a fairly heavy igneous rock—apparently averages about 3 miles in thickness.

The Mantle and the Moho. The succession of heavier rocks which underlies the crust and extends to some 1800 miles beneath the earth's surface is called the *mantle.* The boundary between the crust and the mantle is more or less sharply defined as shown by earthquake wave behavior and is called the *Moho,* short for a seismologist named Mohorovičić who proved the existence of this discontinuity, in the early part of the twentieth century. The average specific gravity of the mantle directly beneath the crust is about 3.3, which is approximately 10 percent higher than that of the basaltic rocks in the crust beneath the oceans. (In turn, the specific gravity of basalt, about 3.0, is approximately 10 percent higher than the specific gravity of 2.8 or so for crustal rocks in continental regions.)

The density of the mantle increases with depth until, where the mantle meets the core 1800 miles beneath the earth's surface, the mantle's specific gravity is about 6.0. The density changes radically here, the specific gravity of adjacent rocks in the core being almost 10.0.

The Earth's Core.   As the radius of the earth is about 3960 miles, the earth's core has a radius of 3960 − 1800 or about 2160 miles. The overall specific gravity of the core is in the neighborhood of 12.0. Recent studies indicate that the core probably consists of an *inner core* and what has been called an *outer core,* which of course would really be a shell surrounding the sphere-shaped inner core. One presently much favored hypothesis is that the inner core, about 850 miles in radius, is a ball composed of solid iron and other heavy metals, also in a solid state, while the "outer core," a shell about 1300 miles thick, consists of heavy metals in a fluid state.

Gravity

What Gravity Is.   *Gravity* and *gravitation* are really the same thing; however, the word "gravity" is usually used to describe the attraction between the earth and relatively small particles or objects. The word "gravitation" is commonly used to describe the attraction between particles or objects throughout the universe. Although it can be said that gravity (or gravitation) involves a force of some kind, the exact cause and nature of this force are not known. We know, as brought out in Chapter 2, that the force of gravitation varies directly with the masses involved, and indirectly as the square of the distances between them. Other than that, about all we know about gravity is how to measure and predict its effects, although Einstein in 1929 did suggest that gravitation might somehow be linked to electromagnetism.

Gravity and Our Environment.   Everyone has seen "slow-motion" moving pictures in which a walking or running person seems to be suspended in air for several seconds at a time. If moving pictures were taken of moving objects at about six times the normal speed and then projected at a normal speed, the "up-and-down" rates of movement would be very much as if the objects were on the moon with its lesser gravity. Suppose that the earth's gravity were reduced to that of the moon. Description of a few of the resulting effects will point up the usually little-appreciated role of gravity in our natural environment.

Probably the first effect noticed would be that of decreased weight and "slow motion" as evidenced by the fact that our leg muscles, made relatively strong as a result of coping with the earth's actual gravity, would hurtle us six or seven feet into the air during a "nor-

mal" vigorous step. Our next sensations would be those associated
with the fact that we would be "off-balance" when not on the ground,
possibly even coming down head first and, very probably, in a nause-
ated condition after the first few such steps. The point of the above
descriptions is, of course, that the earth's gravity is at the very basis
of man's physical construction, his movements, and thus his progress.

With such decreased gravity the earth's atmosphere would no longer
be held to the earth by its present great force and our atmosphere
would gradually disappear into space, possibly in less than 1000
years. Long before then the earth would have become devoid of
practically all life as we know it now. The lack of oxygen and of
water would have killed most living things. Energy from the sun,
passing almost freely through the rapidly disappearing atmosphere,
would flood the earth with scorching radiation by day. At night the
temperatures would fall to $-300°$ F.

Coinciding with the disappearing of the atmosphere there would
be a halt in erosional processes. Finally, no rain at all would fall.
Mountains would be eroded only by strong, short-lived wind, and
valleys and canyons would be almost completely arrested in their
development. Even the slumping of material into the valleys and
canyons, and down mountainsides, would be sharply curtailed because of the reduced gravity. The face of the earth would, except for
impact of meteorites, etc., be largely unchanged for all time to come.

Weather as we know it would cease to exist almost immediately.
As the atmosphere disappeared, violent wind systems would tend to
girdle the globe from north to south and from east to west in response to extreme differences in temperature. But the winds would
soon end. The ceasing of the winds would mean that no vestige of
an atmosphere remained and that sound, having no medium of trans-
mission, would not exist above the surface. The world would have
but one climate, desert, but a desert whose extremes of heat and
cold and utter unchanging desolation and quiet are almost unimagi-
nable to us.

The above description is, of course, an extreme based upon something which is not likely ever to occur, as far as we know. The inference can correctly be drawn by proportion, however, that a very
small change in the gravitational force exerted by the earth would
bring about what we would consider as major changes in weather,
climate, topography, and in man himself. As gravitational attraction
is dependent upon both mass and distance, the earth's internal struc-

ture, as represented by the densities and positions of the various zones of the earth, is thus seen to be a very basic control of our environment.

The Effects of Some Movements within the Earth upon the Surface Environment

The interior of the earth is not the rigid, unyielding structure pictured by many people. Change, adjustment, and motion are constantly going on inside the earth. These internal processes are not, in general, well understood and in many cases they are explained by hypotheses and theories. It is notable, however, that the most widely accepted hypotheses and theories concerning internal earth movements all point toward fundamental relationships between these movements and our surface environment.

Movements in the Earth's Core; the Earth's Magnetic Field. If the hypothesis, already outlined, that the earth's outer core is composed of molten metal is accepted, then it seems only logical that convection currents would be set up in such a vast reservoir. These currents would form mainly as the result of temperature and density differences. Such movement of iron-rich metal could result in the formation and continued maintenance of the major portion of the earth's magnetic field. This is a corollary hypothesis: that the greater part of the earth's magnetic field originated and is being perpetuated in this manner. There is considerable evidence to support both hypotheses.

To illustrate, a speeding up or slowing down in the earth's rotation would of course cause the core also to rotate at a different speed. Next, if the earth's magnetic field does result largely from convection currents within a molten outer core, these currents would be disturbed by a change in rotational velocity and the earth's magnetic field would be altered. In reality, the earth's rotational velocity is far from constant. Its many periods of rotational acceleration and deceleration are carefully studied and recent findings show that the earth's magnetic field is appreciably altered when the earth speeds up or slows down its rotation.

The apparent fact that movement within the earth's core is thus responsible for the major portion of the earth's magnetic field is of much more than academic interest. For one thing, the earth's magnetic field traps certain radiation particles from the sun and from other sources and forms the Van Allen radiation belts within the magnetic field, much like foreign particles arrange themselves in banded structures in a large filter. If the earth's magnetic field suddenly ceased to exist and these radiation particles got through to earth, the entire human race would be annihilated within a very few days. It also appears certain, considering recent research, that the earth's magnetic field somehow plays a part in determining weather and climate on the earth's surface. An interesting fact here, mentioned again in Chapter 24, is that the present locations of the earth's magnetic north and south poles are near Greenland and on Antarctica, respectively, which are also the locations of the earth's two greatest concentrations of ice. At any rate, assuming that the basic hypotheses are correct, movement of material far inside the earth, in the earth's core, is probably a governing factor of surface environment to say nothing of its being a determining factor in man's very survival.

Movements along Zone Surfaces. The idea that slippage can occur at some zone surfaces as the earth rotates is a fairly old hypothesis which has been utilized in attempting to explain such phenomena as world-wide climatic changes, mountain building, and the possible "drifting" of continents. Ideally such slippage would be expected to occur, if at all, at sharply defined zone boundaries and at times when the earth is appreciably accelerating or decelerating in rotation. As stated above, the latter is known to occur. The occurrence of slippage between major zones is not actually known, although there is strong reason to believe that it is continually occurring between the core and the mantle.

The development of the idea of general zone slippage is complicated by facts such as the one that the boundaries between the three or four "sub-zones" of the mantle are not sharply defined but are gradational zones in themselves. Slippage between zones, if the hypotheses of zone slippage and molten outer core are both valid, would be expected to occur between the earth's outer core and the mantle. Here there is a sharp increase in mass and an apparent change from the solid to the fluid state. Significantly enough certain magnetic anomalies can be explained only by assuming that the earth's core and mantle are rotating at different speeds and that the core is lagging behind because of slippage.

If such zone slippage in upper layers can take place, this could explain such apparent anomalies as coal, formed only under tropical or temperate conditions and now found in Antarctica, and evidences of former intensive sea-level glaciation in what are now tropical regions. Due to slippage in the outer shells of the earth, a particular continental area could literally slide, over many years, from arctic to tropical latitudes, or *vice versa*. It may be that the climates of the world are even now being changed by some past or continuing slippage on zone surfaces, and that our present climates were appreciably determined by such movements. Lest all this may seem too fanciful to some, it will not be out of place to point again to evidence of slippage between the core and the mantle and also to state that actual large-scale slipping movements in the earth's crust are currently being studied and measured. This is discussed in the immediately following section of this chapter.

Movements in the Earth's Crust; Isostasy. The earth attains near-equilibrium in its crust by a process called *isostatic adjustment*. As Figure 73 shows, the thickness of the earth's crust in an area often

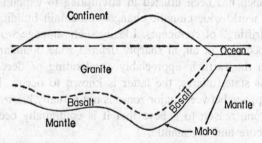

Fig. 73. Diagrammatic representation of thickness of earth's crust as a function of elevation above sea level.

varies with the elevation of that area above sea level. That is, in many instances, the higher the elevation of an area, the thicker is the earth's crust below that area. This is supposedly due to crustal rocks floating plastically in mantle rocks, much as icebergs of different sizes float in water. Ideal equilibrium between these "floating" segments of the earth's crust is called *isostasy* (Greek, "equal standing").

As an example of the effects of this mechanism, it is known that mountains are being eroded continually but that, somehow, they stay at about the same height for periods of time far in excess of what would be expected, considering erosion. Plainly, something keeps pushing them up almost as fast as they lose elevation by erosion. That "something" is largely isostatic adjustment.

Material eroded from a mountain is, say, deposited on a segment of the earth's crust at sea level. This segment is therefore made heavier while the mountain segment becomes lighter. Pressure at some depth below the sea level segment is thus increased and pressure at the same depth is decreased below the mountain segment. The rock at or near that depth therefore flows plastically from the region of higher pressure below the sea level block to the region of lower pressure underneath the mountain segment. As the rock flows, the sea level segment sinks and the plastically flowing rock pushes in under the roots of the mountain segment, forcing the mountain segment back up. The whole adjustment is due to the physical principle that, for equilibrium or actual isostasy, the pressure underneath the mountain roots must equal the pressure, at the same depth, below the sea level block. It is seen, therefore, that isostatic adjustment is a prime factor in determining the topographic features of our environment and the many important meteorological and climatological phenomena controlled or influenced by topography. Isostatic adjustment is no doubt helped by increased temperature at depth, resulting in more plastic action of the rocks involved. In the outer layers of the earth, the temperature increases downward at a rate of about 1° F per 60 feet, although, obviously, this rate or *geothermal gradient* must drop off sharply after a few miles.

The seemingly offhand inference that solid rock can flow plastically may evoke desirable curiosity if not understandable skepticism on the part of many readers. It is known to happen, however, in nature as well as in the laboratory. One instance is in California, along the San Andreas Fault which splits California from the Mexican border to the Golden Gate. The word "split" may be used literally. Precise measurements show that the portion of California to the west of the fault is moving northwest along the fault at the relative rate of about two inches per year. Similar rates of movement in the crust have been observed in several regions in the world.

One incidental observation is of interest here and this concerns the hypothesis that South America and Africa were once joined as one continent. The most dramatic visual support for this idea is, of course, the rough "fit" between the east coast of South America and the west coast of Africa. If the continents were once joined it is known when the break must have occurred: about 200 million years ago. Knowing this, and the present distance between any two matching points, the rate of relative drift can be calculated. Interestingly enough, this is also about two inches per year.

REVIEW

1. What is our one most important source of information concerning the structure and composition of the earth's interior?

2. Define the *crust* and the *mantle* and give their dimensions.

3. How thick is the crust underneath the oceans? What is it composed of there?

4. Define "moho."

5. Describe the inner and outer cores of the earth in terms of structure, composition, and dimensions.

6. Describe some of the effects if the earth's force of gravity were reduced to that of the moon.

7. Is the earth's speed of rotation constant?

8. Describe one beneficial effect of the earth's magnetic field.

9. Explain "zone slippage" and give an example of where it probably occurs.

10. Explain how "isostatic adjustment" operates.

11. Discuss the possible effects of zone slippage upon man's environment.

12. Do you think it possible that geophysical studies of the earth's interior will one day be basic to very long-range weather forecasts? Explain.

EXERCISES

(Answers are given in the answer section at the back of the book.)

1. The specific gravity of crustal rock is about 2.8 while that of nearby mantle rock is 3.3. How many pounds does a cubic foot of each weigh? Water weighs 62.4 pounds per cubic foot.

2. It was stated in this chapter that if moving pictures of moving objects were taken at about six times the normal speed and then projected at normal speed that the "up-and-down" rates of movement would be very much as if the objects were on the moon. From this statement what do you deduce to be the ratio of the earth's gravitational pull upon an object on its surface to the moon's gravitational pull upon the same object on the moon's surface?

3. Many of the world's large mountain systems trend in a general

north-south direction. Do you think that this fact could be intimately related to the west-east rotation of the earth? Explain your answer.

4. One of the few regions where even small earthquakes apparently do not occur is the continent of Antarctica. From this statement and from material in this chapter, would you be inclined to say (a) that Antarctica will probably never have earthquakes, (b) that Antarctica will probably begin to have a series of small earthquakes, or (c) that Antarctica is probably due for a major earthquake?

5. Sketch a cross section of the probable interior structure of the earth as presented in this chapter, showing the crust, the mantle, and the inner and outer cores. Show respective densities and dimensions. Indicate the solid and liquid portions.

6. Assume that a mass of solid crustal rock of specific gravity 2.8 is floating in molten mantle rock of specific gravity 3.3 and that the mantle rock solidifies. What volume of the crustal rock is below the surface of the mantle? (See Problem 3, Chapter 12.)

7. In one region of the Alps the top of a large mountain is about 5.5 miles above the top of the mantle and the mountain "roots" directly beneath are about 36.5 miles below the top of the mantle. What volume of a vertical column through the center of the mountain "block" is below the surface of the mantle? Check this value with that obtained in Problem 6. What would this seem to indicate as to the correctness of the assumption that crustal rocks are plastically "floating" in denser rock? (Also see Problem 3, Chapter 12.)

8. It is known that slippage is taking place in the earth's crust in various places at the relative rate of about 2 inches per year. One of these places is the portion of California west of the San Andreas Fault. Los Angeles at a latitude of about 34° N is west of the San Andreas Fault and at present has a Mediterranean climate. Assuming that the northern boundary of the Mediterranean climate in this region is 38° N, and that the block to the west of the fault is moving due north while the block to the east is motionless, in about how many years would Los Angeles "slide" out of its present Mediterranean climate?

9. If points on the earth's surface can be located by astronomical means to within 25 feet of their true position, on the average, about how many years would have to elapse between a set of astronomical observations to definitely determine if some continents are actually pulling away from each other? Assume the supposed rate of drift to be 2 inches per year.

10. The thickness of the earth's crust, in miles, can in many regions be roughly approximated by the formula $T = 19 + 7H$. For example, for a place whose elevation is $\frac{1}{4}$ mile above sea level, the earth's crust at that point may be: $T = 19 + \frac{7}{4} = 21$ miles, approximately. This formula is very inaccurate for some regions but is notably a good approximation for others. (a) Assuming that your region is one where the formula applies, what is the thickness of the earth's crust where you live? (b) What is the thickness of the earth's crust below the ocean where it is 2¼ miles deep? (H = −2¼) (c) Considering your answer to (b), why would the Mohole, the hole drilled through the earth's crust to the mantle, be drilled in the ocean floor rather than on the continent?

CHAPTER 21

Introduction to Landforms; Topographic Maps

Geomorphology is the study of the origin of landforms and of their modification by natural forces. Landforms rank among the most influential and most noticeable features of man's environment. To a large extent, landforms such as mountains, plains, and valleys determine where people live, where they grow food, where they work, and where they can travel on land. As was seen in previous chapters, certain landforms also play important roles in climate and weather. The study of landforms is therefore a major area within the study of physical geography. The chief tools in the study of landforms are *topographic maps.*

Landform Classification

Major Landforms. The largest topographic features of any continent are its mountains, plains, and plateaus. These constitute the three major groups of landform study.

Mountains are naturally raised portions of the earth's surface whose smallest verticle cross section approximates an inverted V. The point of the V may be considerably modified. Some of the Big Horn Mountains of Wyoming, for example, have flat meadowland as nearsummit features. The summits of mountains may differ widely in elevation.

Hills are small mountains. The difference between a hill and a mountain is popularly one only of local comparison and word usage. What are called hills in one area might be known as mountains in another region. For instance, the Black Hills of South Dakota and the Allegheny Mountains of the eastern United States are of the same height. Among geographers, the commonly accepted dividing line in height between mountains and hills is 1000 feet.

Plains are level or nearly level surfaces of wide expanse. Plains are generally lower than their surroundings. The majority of the world's plains regions are less than one thousand feet above sea level. Plains whose elevations are greater than two thousand feet above sea level are usually called *high* plains. The Great Plains of the United States, ranging from 2000 to 5000 feet in elevation, are high plains.

Plateaus are tablelands. Their elevations are usually greater than ½ mile above sea level. Unlike plains, plateaus are generally higher than the bulk of their surroundings. However, some high-altitude plateaus, such as plateaus in the Andes of South America, are surrounded by mountains. A plateau may become dissected by streams, to form a *dissected plateau*. The Catskill Mountains of New York were formed by the dissection of that portion of the Allegheny Plateau.

Minor Landforms. Valleys, canyons, ridges, alluvial fans, and sand dunes are only a few examples of minor landforms. Students are often puzzled by the fact that features like the Mississippi River Valley and the Grand Canyon are called "minor" landforms. Large as each of these is, each is superimposed upon a major landform. The Mississippi River cuts across the Central Plains and the Gulf Coastal Plain. (See Figure 74.) The Grand Canyon is a result of partial dissection of the Colorado Plateau. Contrasted with the vast extent of

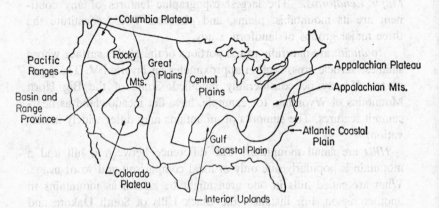

Fig. 74. Major land regions of the United States.

the two Plains regions and of the Colorado Plateau, any valley or any canyon, large or small, is still a relatively minor feature.

Origin and Modification of Landforms; the Erosion Cycle

Landforms in general result from a gigantic, slow battle which is continuously going on between internal forces in the earth and external forces on the earth's surface. As landforms in one area are being eroded, the amazing balancing process in the earth's crust, isostasy, discussed in some detail in Chapter 20, is forcing parts of the earth's crust upward in several areas. As a result of isostatic adjustment and the tremendous forces associated with crustal deformation, large blocks of the earth's crust are uplifted to eventually become *initial landforms* such as mountains and plateaus.

As these initial landforms are thrust or folded higher and higher, they will be under increasing attack from erosion agents such as rain and wind. Some of the eroded material will be deposited at lower elevations to make *landforms of deposition*. The landforms from which the eroded material came must now contain *landforms of erosion*. To illustrate: deltas are landforms of deposition. Material in the deltas comes from the main river valleys, the tributary valleys, gullies, washes, etc. These are landforms of erosion.

Landforms of erosion and of deposition are called *sequential* landforms, both being of later sequence than the formation of the initial landform.

Most of the material eroded from an initial landform, say a plateau block, will eventually be deposited in the ocean. There the particles may consolidate into rock. These rocks, containing the particles from the ancient plateau, may someday be slowly thrust high into the air, perhaps to form giant mountains. The mountains will in turn be eroded to form sequential landforms. These latter will themselves disappear, fragment by fragment, into the ocean again as millions of years pass. So the cycle continues.

It must be emphasized that the battle between the earth's internal forces and the forces acting upon its surface is a slow, continuous one. The processes involved are *uniform* as opposed to *catastrophic*. It was formerly thought that such features as great mountains and deep canyons resulted from sudden, violent natural catastrophes which may have taken place in a few days. Now it is realized that, with very few exceptions, any major natural changes in topographic relief result from the action of slow but never-ceasing processes on and below the earth's surface.

General Erosional Characteristics of the Three Main Rock Types

One of the most valuable abilities possessed by geographers and geologists is that of being able to determine at a glance the basic rock composition of a nearby or distant landform. To the casual observer, such ability often seems to border upon the miraculous. Actually what few general erosional characteristics do exist for each of the three main rock types—sedimentary, igneous, and metamorphis—can easily be learned and used by the average person. Such knowledge adds considerable interest to travel, in addition to being a very important aid to studying landforms more formally.

Erosion of Sedimentary Rocks and Resulting Topography. Sandstone and *conglomerate* are in general fairly resistant to chemical weathering because of the high percentage of silica in the form of a cement or in the form of quartz grains or both. A river cutting through silica-cemented sandstone accomplishes relatively little erosion by chemical weathering. Rather, it literally tears and knocks grains apart. Wind and rain have much the same effect, although accomplished much more slowly. The result is that a typical sandstone exposure is a ridge which is often jagged on top and which has many steep cliffs. Due to its porosity and resulting moisture content, sandstone may have considerable vegetation including good-sized trees growing in its soil.

Much of the cementing material in many *conglomerates* is calcium carbonate, and conglomerates of this composition weather out in humid regions as rounded hills while the same type of conglomerate forms cliffs in arid or semi-arid regions.

Siltstone may also erode in several ways. In arid or semi-arid regions it commonly forms sandy cliffs while in more humid regions it may be in the form of rounded hills or valleys.

Shale is extremely vulnerable to mechanical weathering but, as it is usually made up of already decomposed material, it is affected very little by chemical weathering. Shale is therefore found both in hills and in lowlands. It can form steep cliffs while particles of the same shale may also be spread out in a valley below, to become "gumbo" mud when it rains. Stream valleys often adjust their courses to run over beds of weak shale.

Limestone is extremely susceptible to chemical weathering as calcium carbonate is affected by even very weak acids as may easily be demonstrated by placing a drop of lemon juice on a piece of limestone and noting the resultant effervescence due to release of carbon dioxide. In humid climates limestone typically occurs in low rounded hills or in rounded valleys. This effect is even more pronounced in warm, moist regions. In arid or semi-arid regions, limestone often forms highland and steep cliffs, the formation of the cliffs being aided by a block-like jointing in limestone, and a resulting cliff as blocks disintegrate and fall. In moist regions this block-jointing aids in the circulation of water through the limestone and speeds up chemical weathering of the rock.

Erosion of Igneous Rocks, and Resulting Topography. It was brought out previously that the feldspar in *granite* is rather easily chemically weathered. As the most prevalent single mineral in granite is feldspar it might be expected that granite would weather and erode rather easily in a moist climate. This seems logical, but granite is also a very compact rock with a considerable proportion of resistant quartz. The result is somewhat intermediate in that granite in moist regions typically forms mountains and ridges which are considerably rounded.

The weathering and erosion of igneous rocks other than granite is usually complex. It can be said that, in general, igneous rocks tend to form mountains and ridges but there are some instances where igneous rocks have eroded faster than have surrounding sedimentary rocks, thus forming stream valleys. Few general rules can be given to cover the weathering and erosion of igneous rocks in general. On the other hand an observer who is skilled in igneous geology can many times go into a region and, on the basis of topography, vegetation types, and whatever rocks are visible, make a very good and quick appraisal of what igneous rocks are forming hills, which are in the valleys, etc. Such appraisals are usually materially aided by aerial photographs of the region.

Erosion of Metamorphic Rocks, and Resulting Topography. *Quartzite,* the metamorphic equivalent of sandstone, usually being mainly silica with little pore space, is highly resistant to both chemical and physical weathering. Quartzite therefore tends to form high, steep ridges, even more so than does sandstone.

Marble, the metamorphic equivalent of limestone, weathers and erodes much like limestone; that is, in moist regions it tends to form lowlands; in arid or semi-arid regions it tends to form highlands and cliffs. *Dolostone,* containing magnesium, is generally more resistant to both types of weathering and therefore to erosion than is limestone.

Slate, the metamorphic equivalent of shale, resists both chemical and mechanical weathering and often forms cliffs. These cliffs commonly parallel the "slaty cleavage" which, as previously explained, commonly develops at angles to the bedding planes of the original shale.

The erosion of metamorphic rocks formed from igneous rocks presents a more difficult problem than does the erosion of igneous rocks. Metamorphic structures are in general more complex than original structures and, in addition, the forces which brought about the changes usually alter the original resistance to both physical and chemical weathering to varying degree. As a very broad generalization, folded metamorphic rocks tend to occur in highlands and to be relatively unaltered by weathering and erosion except in regions subject to frost wedging. In this case, as for example in some New England states, large cliffs often develop along planes of "slaty cleavage." Where they occur in river valleys, folded metamorphic rocks commonly form steep sides, even in moist regions, a common reason for this being the development of more or less vertical planes of slaty cleavage during metamorphism.

Topographic Maps

Showing Relief on Maps. *Topographic maps* picture the relief of the earth's surface and are therefore indispensable to the detailed study of landforms. The configuration of the earth's surface can be shown on maps in a number of ways. *Altitude tinting* indicates elevation by assigning one particular color to a certain range of elevation. *Plastic shading* and *hachures* are both forms of *shading. Contour maps* are drawn with horizontal *contour lines* to show topography. (See Figure 75.)

Except for some road maps and except for display and other nontechnical purposes, plastic shading and hachures are seldom used alone to denote relief on maps made in the United States. The major

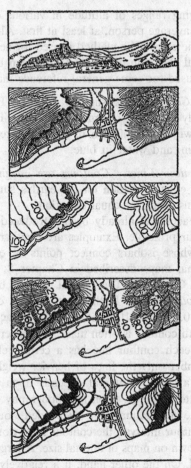

Fig. 75. The terrain topography in the upper diagram can be shown on a map by hachures, contour lines, hachures and contour lines combined, or by contour lines and plastic shading combined. Drawn by E. Raisz. (Courtesy of John Wiley & Sons, Inc., from A. Strahler's *Physical Geography,* 2d edition, 1960)

drawback to both methods is that relatively few precise elevations can be shown. Also some of the shading is doubtless more pleasing artistically than it is correct technically.

A major disadvantage to the method of altitude tinting stems from identification of certain natural features with certain colors. Most people link yellow with deserts, brown with soil, green with vegetation, etc. A map showing ranges of altitude in various colors is usually misleading to the average person, at least at first. Altitude tinting has advantages in some cases. The method is used for aeronautical charts so that the general elevation of an entire area can be quickly determined. It is also used for some general reference maps.

Contour Maps. *Contour maps* such as shown in Figure 75 are by far the most widely used type of topographic map. The contour lines are shown in brown, works of man in black and red, vegetation (if indicated) in green, and water in blue.

Contours and Contour Lines. *Contours* are imaginary lines which connect points of equal elevation on the earth's surface. A *contour line* on a map joins points of equal elevation.

Actually the reader has already been introduced to maps which employ the contour principle. Examples are weather maps described in Chapter 11, whose isobars connect points of equal barometric pressure; isothermal maps described in Chapter 8; and the isohyet maps described in Chapter 9. The vertical distance between contours is called the *contour interval.* In the United States common contour intervals are 10, 20, 50, and 100 feet. In order to facilitate reading of the map, every fifth contour is often made of heavier weight than the others. Although each contour line has a certain elevation, general practice is to number only the lines of heavier weight.

The choice of a contour interval depends upon the purpose for which the map is to be made, upon the topography of the area, and upon the size of the finished map. If a steep-sided mountain is mapped with a 10 foot contour interval, the contour lines would appear to be a solid mass of brown on maps of normal size. A larger contour interval would be used. On the other hand, if a relatively flat valley floor is mapped with a 10 foot contour interval, much of the detail between contour lines is lost. A 5 foot or even a 2 foot contour interval might be used. On some maps two contour intervals are necessary.

Hachured contour lines represent *depression contours* of minor landforms which are natural depressions. (See Figure 76.) The hachures of each line point toward successively lower elevations.

Characteristics of Contour Lines (Refer to Figure 75):

1. Contour lines do not touch or cross. If they did this would mean that the same point has two different elevations. The only exceptions to this rule are in the rare cases of caves, overhanging cliffs, etc.

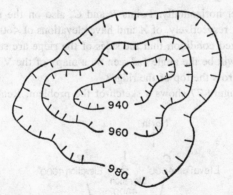

Fig. 76. Hachured contours are used on maps to represent depressions. The depression shown has fairly uniform side slopes.

2. A given contour must "close" upon itself but not necessarily within the bounds of a particular map.

3. The steeper a slope, the closer together will be the contour lines on the map. On a gentle slope shown on the same map, assuming the same contour interval, the contour lines will be a greater distance apart on the map.

4. Contour lines spaced approximately the same distance apart on a map indicate a slope of approximately constant grade.

5. Contour lines crossing streams or valleys form Vs which point upstream or up-valley. The Vs will approach Us in shape as the vertical cross sections of the valleys themselves vary from V to U shapes.

6. Contour lines crossing ridges of any kind form Vs which point *down* the ridge line to lower elevation. The shapes of the Vs may be modified as in the case of valleys, above; that is, the Vs will approach Us in shape as the vertical cross sections of the ridges vary from V to U shapes.

7. The sharpness of the point of a V or of the curve of a U, where a contour crosses a valley or ridge depends upon: (a) the gradient of the ridge line or valley bottom and (b) the gradients of the side slopes of the valley or ridge.

The reader should now review the above seven points and "Graphical Solutions" in Chapter 2 before proceeding with the examples given below:

Problem: Point *A* has an elevation of 4800 feet above sea level and is on top of a ridge which slopes due south at the rate of 20 feet vertically for

every 100 feet horizontally. Points B and C, also on the ridge, are 250'
east and west, respectively, of A and have elevations of 4600 feet. Assuming the idealized condition that the sides of the ridge are smooth, straight
planes, what will be the angle (as seen on a map) of the V of the contour
lines as they cross the top of the ridge?

Solution: Figure 77 shows a sketch of the problem. Remembering that

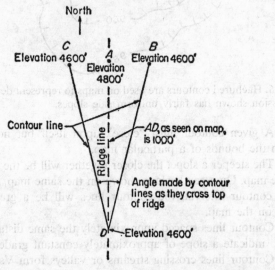

Fig. 77. The sharpness of the Vs as contour lines cross a ridge or valley
depends upon the gradient of the ridge line or valley floor and the gradients of the side slopes of the ridge or valley.

a contour line is a line of equal elevations, the first step is to locate a point
on the ridge line whose elevation is 4600. Obviously this point will be south
of point A. This new point is 4800 − 4600, or 200 feet lower than A. Its
horizontal distance from A may be solved by proportion: $\dfrac{20}{100} = \dfrac{200}{x}$;
$x = 1000$ feet. Point D is thus located, to scale, 1000 feet south of A. The
lines BD and DC are now drawn and the angle BDC is measured. (As the
sides of the ridges are assumed to be planes in this example, all other contour lines will have the same angle at the Vs.)

Problem: Points A and B are on the same straight slope. The points are
800 feet apart horizontally and have a difference in elevation of 340 feet.
What is the angle of slope, in degrees? (The angle of slope is the angle between a horizontal line and the line representing the slope.)

Solution: See Figure 78.

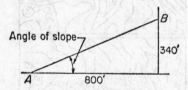

Fig. 78. Showing the relationship between slope, map distance, and the difference in elevation between two points.

Problem: A certain map has a scale of 1:600. The contour interval is 10 feet. Calculate the horizontal distance, in inches, between contour lines as seen on the map for: (a) a slope of 20°; (b) a slope of 50°.

Solution: See Figure 79.

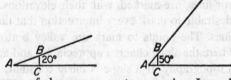

Fig. 79. Influence of slope upon contour spacing. In each diagram, BC represents the contour interval of 10 feet and AC represents the distance between contour lines as seen on a map. If BC is made $\frac{1}{5}$ inch $\left(\frac{10 \times 12}{600}\right)$, AC in inches is the map distance between contour lines on a scale of 1:600.

Topographic Profiles

A common problem in geographic reconnaissance or exploration is to determine, from a map, just what kind of topography will be encountered along the way if a field party takes a certain proposed route. A closely allied problem often faced by surveyors, mappers, and military personnel is to determine from a map whether two given points on the ground are intervisible. In each case, a sketch called a *topographic profile* is helpful.

Referring to the map of Figure 80, let it be supposed that the profile between A and B is required. A piece of paper is held with the top edge along the line AB. The points A and B are marked on the edge of the paper, with their respective elevations marked near the

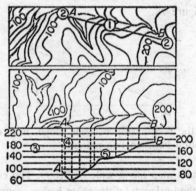

Fig. 80. Suggested steps in drawing a topographic profile. (Adapted from the Department of the Army)

edge of the paper. Next, the points where the edge of the paper intersects key contour lines, are marked, with their elevations. It is neither necessary nor desirable to mark every intersection that line *AB* makes with contour lines. The points to mark are valley bottoms, streams, ridges, points where the slope changes appreciably, and any other major "breaks" in topography. If a slope is fairly constant, two or three points on it are sufficient.

The paper can now be removed from the map. Lines representing contour elevations are drawn parallel to the edge of the paper as shown. The vertical scale is "exaggerated," as indicated, in order to bring out the details of topography along the route. Notice that points *A* and *B* are almost intervisible.

How Contour Maps Are Made

Contour maps are made by three main methods: The *photogrammetric* or *aerial photography* method; the *plane table-alidade* method; and the *transit-stadia* method. The photogrammetric method is now by far the most important method. The great majority of the topographic maps made by national, state, and local governments, and by large companies, are made by photogrammetric methods.

The Photogrammetric Method. After sufficient primary horizontal and vertical control has been established by procedures similar to those outlined in Chapter 5, horizontal positions and elevations of supplementary points can be determined by further surveying. Some points are usually marked on the ground or otherwise identified before flying so that they can be located on the aerial photographs. Typical "picture" points are trail intersections, identifiable rock outcrops, etc. Other points may be determined after the photographs are taken.

A plane now flies the area on specified flight lines and at altitudes consistent with the required average scale of the photographs. Figure 81 illustrates the simple relationship between altitude of flight, focal

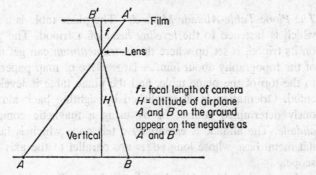

Fig. 81. Scale of aerial photograph under idealized conditions: $\dfrac{f}{H} = \dfrac{A'B'}{AB}$.

Therefore, scale of photograph $= \dfrac{f}{H}$. If focal length is 3 feet and altitude is 15,000 feet, scale $= \dfrac{3}{15,000} = \dfrac{1}{5000}$. Details of lens position, focal length, etc., are generalized in this diagram.

length of the camera, and approximate scale of the photographs. Vertical photographs are taken in such a manner that they overlap each other by certain percentages. This insures complete coverage and also provides "stereo-pairs," pairs of photographs which will give a three-dimensional effect when properly viewed together. It is by means of this three-dimensional effect that contours are determined, using the points whose elevations have been determined by surveying means as control.

The vertical positions of contours can be located by photogrammetric means to within $\frac{1}{2000}$ of the flying height, under good conditions. This means that if the plane flies at an average height of 4000 feet above the ground, a particular contour could be located to within 2 feet.

Locating the true horizontal positions of details on the photographs is not as easy as it may first appear. Photographs are perspectives, not orthographic projections, like the finished map. (See Figure 81.) A special method of horizontal control, such as the *radial line* method, may be used to determine correct positions of key points. The radial line method is based upon the triangulation principle described in Chapter 5. The belief that a good planimetric map can be made by merely piecing aerial photographs together is in general completely erroneous.

The Plane Table-Alidade Method.   The plane table is a large board which is fastened to the *leveling head* of a tripod. The plane table, on its tripod, is set up where the *instrumentman* can get a good view of the topography about him. A large piece of map paper is fastened to the top of the plane table, and the plane table is leveled and oriented. Orientation is accomplished by sighting back along a previously determined course, or by using a magnetic compass in the *alidade*. The alidade is essentially a telescope which is fastened to a flat metal base whose long edges are parallel to the axis of the telescope.

A *rodman* holds a long board called a *stadia rod* or *stadia board* vertically on a topographically strategic, distant point. The board is graduated in feet and tenths of feet. The instrumentman keeps one edge of the flat metal base of the alidade over the point on the map which represents his present position. He rotates the alidade around this point, sliding the alidade across the map until he sees the stadia board lined up with the vertical cross hair of the alidade.

The instrumentman then draws a *sight ray* along the edge of the alidade's base. Next he observes the vertical angle to a point on the rod. By means of two fixed horizontal *stadia* hairs in the telescope he obtains a rod *intercept*. This, combined with the vertical angle, enables him to calculate the elevation of the distant point and its distance from him. Using an engineer's scale, he plots the point on the sight line and pencils the elevation near it. After a number of such points have been plotted, the instrumentman starts sketching the contour lines. Usually much *interpolation* is done. For example, the instrumentman, now sketching the 830 foot contour, say, has plotted few and possibly no points whose exact elevations are 830. However, the 830 foot contour would be interpolated as being halfway between an 824 and an 836 elevation, if the two points are on the same general slope. Similar interpolations between other points would be made.

The Transit-Stadia Method. The transit-stadia method is really the "notebook" equivalent of the plane table method of obtaining topography. The transit is a telescopic instrument which measures horizontal and vertical angles. Instead of drawing sight lines on paper to a distant point, the *transitman* records in a notebook the horizontal angle from another line, usually one determined by triangulation. As in the plane table method, the transitman observes a stadia intercept and a vertical angle to a rod held on a distant point. He calculates the elevation of each point and its distance from him as a check against possible error.

Both the transit and the plane table are also used to obtain supplemental control and information for maps made from aerial photographs. A typical example is where forest cover is so thick that aerial photographs show only the tops of the trees.

How to Use Contour Maps

Map scale, compass declination, and map grids and projections have been discussed in previous chapters. Contour maps usually have information pertaining to these essentials printed in the lower margin.

In using contour maps to study landforms, it is essential for optimum use of time that the characteristics of contours, as given in this chapter, be learned by the student. Also, maps will immediately become more meaningful if it is remembered that for every landform of deposition there must be one or more corresponding landform of erosion, usually at a higher elevation. An exception to this is in the case of landforms caused by wind. In this case, the source of the material is usually a tremendous area whose modification may not be apparent or plainly attributable to wind erosion. (See Chapter 28.)

Another consideration is that of whether the major landform of the area shown is in the mountain, plain, or plateau group. As will be seen later, certain minor landforms are associated with certain major landforms.

Any measurements made on a map, or any calculations based upon map data, cannot be expected to have an accuracy greater than the accuracy of the map itself. Obvious as that point may seem, it is often overlooked to the detriment of the best use of time.

Such things as the volume of material in a landslide are often reported by geography students as something like "25,263,456 cubic yards." The final four digits would all be doubtful in even the most precise of engineering calculations. In general, due to errors in the map and in reading the map, not more than three significant digits (see Chapter 2) would be used in reporting a result based upon data on a map of normal size. The above volume would therefore be reported as 25,300,000 cubic yards.

The real significance of this is that all map measurements and calculations should be regarded as being very approximate. Once this is realized, time will not be wasted on unwarranted precision in either measurement or calculation.

The above is not to imply that all information on contour maps is approximate. For example, survey points of known elevation called *bench marks* (abbreviated B.M.) are shown on contour maps. The elevations of bench marks are usually known to the nearest $\frac{1}{100}$ foot and are usually given on maps to the nearest foot.

Index maps indicating the extent of topographic mapping in the United States and its possessions can be obtained from the U. S. Geological Survey. The index map is useful in obtaining topographic maps of particular areas. Other index maps obtainable from the Survey indicate the extent of aerial photography, geologic mapping, horizontal and vertical control, etc., in the United States.

State, county, and city governments are other possible sources of maps and topographic and other map data.

REVIEW

1. Name the three groups of major landforms. Which one of the three major features do you live on or in? List some minor landforms in your area.

2. Explain why the Grand Canyon of the Colorado is a "minor" landform.

3. Are mountains a result of uniform processes or a result of catastrophic processes? Explain.

4. Distinguish between "contour" and "contour line."

5. Discuss the making of a contour map by photogrammetric means. Start with an explanation of how the vertical and horizontal control is obtained.

6. What is a bench mark?

7. Explain the relationship between accuracy of measurements on calculations and the accuracy of the map itself. Why is it important to apply the principle involved?

8. Assuming that you wanted topographic maps of a certain area, explain how you would obtain them, other than buying them in a local store.

9. State the general relationship between the contour interval of a topographic map and the steepness of slope.

10. Other than going into the field, would it be possible to study a given landform without the aid of a topographic map or aerial photographs?

EXERCISES

(Answers are given in the answer section at the back of the book.)

1. On the portion of a contour map shown in Figure 80 assume that points A and B are about one mile apart. What is the slope, in percent, of the stream valley which passes near A and B?

2. An airplane is taking vertical photographs of a plateau whose elevation is 5000 feet above sea level. The plane is flying at an elevation of 10,000 feet above sea level. The focal length of the camera is twenty-four inches. What is the approximate scale of the photographs?

3. If the photographs of the above exercise are 9 inches by 9 inches in size, how much ground area in square miles is shown on each photograph?

4. A certain mountain slope is such that points A and B, 520 feet apart horizontally, have a difference in elevation of 340 feet. Using scale, straight-edge, and protractor, what is the angle of slope in degrees? (The angle of slope is the angle between a horizontal line and the slope.)

5. Hold your index fingers, tips together, about one foot in front of your eyes and at the same elevation as your eyes. Now focus your eyes on a more distant object, keeping your fingers near the center of your field of view. Now slowly pull your fingers apart. A small "sausage" will seem to float in air between your fingers. Can you explain this in terms of a principle demonstrated in this chapter?

6. A certain map has a scale of 1:1200. The contour lines on a certain regular slope shown on the map are spaced the same distance apart. If the angle of slope is 40 degrees and the contour interval is 20 feet, how far apart in inches are the contour lines as seen on the map? Use scale, straight-edge, and protractor.

7. The rocks in a certain humid area are principally limestone, sandstone, and granite. The limestone was deposited first, the sandstone next, and the granite—the youngest rock—intrudes into both the limestone and sandstone. The beds of limestone and sandstone are horizontal.

A valley has been formed by a river cutting into both the sandstone and the limestone. One side of the valley has been formed against the granite, the other side in the sandstone and limestone. Assuming an original 90° (vertical) slope for the granite, sketch a cross section of the valley as it would now appear, and explain various slopes, etc. Also indicate probable vegetation or lack of it on the various surfaces.

CHAPTER 22

Mass Wasting and Its Associated Landforms

Mass wasting is the downward movement of large quantities of rock or earth. (A name often used for any type of rock debris is *mantle*.) Mass wasting is basically a gravitational process which, once started, is controlled by such factors as rainfall, the composition and amount of the moving mass, and topography. The controlling factors of mass wasting determine the rate at which the wasting takes place. The amount of material available for mass wasting is largely dependent upon *weathering,* discussed in Chapter 17. The rate of movement in mass wasting can broadly be described as either slow or rapid.

Slow Movement of Rock and Earth

Soil Creep. The slow downslope movement of fine rock particles or soil is called *soil creep.* Such movement on slopes is often evidenced by trees, fences, telephone posts, etc., which have moved downhill and are now not vertical. Creep proceeds even under grass covers and thick sod.

Many factors combine to produce creep. Downslope movement of a solid is usually accomplished by either rolling or sliding, or by a combination of these actions. Anything which combines with gravity to cause rolling or sliding of a grain is therefore a factor of soil creep. The list of possibilities is virtually endless: the mechanical and chemical effects of subsurface water; temperature changes; differences in surface tension in the moisture between grains; wind; humidity; earth tremors; the disruptive effects of growing plants; animal life from insect size to that of burrowing animals; the size and shape of individual grains; molecular or electrostatic attraction between grains; and so on.

One of the most noticeable results of soil creep in some regions is the formation of so-called "sheep trails" on grassy slopes. These "sheep trails" are formed mainly by soil creeping and then stabilizing itself in the form of small shelves which may extend laterally for many feet before meeting other shelves. Grazing animals do use some of these "trails" as such and some "trails" have been widened and even started by animals. It is evident from agricultural statistics, however, that these "trails" in the main are only incidentally related to the presence of grazing animals and that they result from soil creep of some kind.

Talus Creep.   Rock material which weathers and falls from a cliff and comes to rest, usually on a slope below the cliff, is called *talus*. Many readers will recognize the smaller forms of talus as being *slide-rock*. *Talus slopes* are common in mountainous regions where temperatures drop below freezing. During the day, cracks in the cliff rock may fill with rain water or water from melting snow. At night, upon freezing, the water expands as it changes to ice and exerts tremendous pressure upon the rock, which may then split. This process is called *frost wedging*. The occurrence of talus is not confined to regions of high latitude or altitude, however. The only requisite for proper assignment of the term "talus" is that the rock fragments be in some kind of a pile which results from the natural fall and sliding or rolling of the fragments.

In cold regions, talus creep is accelerated by alternate thawing and freezing of water between the rock fragments. In both cold and warm regions, talus creep is increased by the action of water and, of course, by the addition and impact of new material falling and sliding onto the talus slope. The latter is a not inconsiderable factor as will be appreciated by anyone who has climbed or crossed a sliderock area and has seen firsthand how little it takes to dislodge the talus pile.

Solifluction.   When the upper layers of frozen ground thaw out, a type of creep known as *solifluction* may occur. Solifluction typically occurs in regions of *permafrost* where the ground is frozen from a depth of 2 feet to, in some cases, as in some areas of Alaska and Siberia, more than 1000 feet. More than ¼ of the land surface of the earth is covered by permafrost, hence its existence is of paramount importance from the standpoint of present and future usage and development by man.

As the frozen ground thaws, it assumes the characteristics of a thick liquid. The thawing, however, does not proceed more than a few feet downward and the thawed soil—essentially mud—rests on top of the frozen subsoil. The thawed soil, acting like any liquid when a container is tipped, tends to flow down any slope, no matter how slight. Vast quantities of material are moved in this manner in those regions of permafrost where thawing occurs.

Rock Glaciers.   A mass of rock debris which resembles a glacier in shape and movement is called a *rock glacier*. Rock glaciers typically follow smaller valleys and ravines and may extend for several miles in length.

The causes of the slow, glacier-like flow of these "rock rivers," as they are sometimes called, are not well understood but it is evident that many rock glaciers are subject to alternate thawing and freezing of the water between the various rock fragments. In general, water and ice particles seem to be important factors in the movements of most rock glaciers.

Rapid Movements of Rock and Earth; Associated Landforms

The distinction between slow and rapid movements of rock debris is, as might be imagined, an arbitrary one except for those movements which are obviously one or the other, as in the case of soil creep which is always slow. At the other extreme is the avalanche. In general, however, as a sort of rule of thumb, rapid movements of rock are those in which actual movement at the time of its occurrence is or would be readily apparent to the human eye.

Mudflows.   A moving mass of rock debris saturated with water to the general consistency of mud is called a *mudflow*. Contrary to what might be implied from their names, real mudflows are rare in very moist regions. Apparently one thing needed to start a mudflow is a large quantity of weathered material which has not appreciably changed its composition. To this material must be added an intense rain or a rather sudden and large addition of water from melted snow. Thus, mudflows occur in mountainous regions, and especially in mountainous arid or semi-arid regions.

A mudflow can be an awesome sight. They occur rather frequently in the Peruvian Andes where one mudflow may fill an entire valley, carrying trees, boulders, and dwellings along with it at a rate of only a few feet per second. One of the most noticeable features of these mammoth flows is the continuous grinding noise of large boulders as they come together in the narrowed portions of the valleys. These mudflows bring about some interesting highway engineering procedures in some countries. Many times, after a mudflow has gone over a highway which crossed a narrow valley, the solidified mud is 20 or 30 feet thick in the valley. Rather than attempting to uncover the former highway, it is much more feasible to rebuild the highway over the top of the solidified mudflow. The result is that portions of roads in many countries now go over little hills instead of, as formerly, down into small valleys and then up the other side.

A spectacular type of mudflow occurs with some volcanic eruptions. Perhaps the best-known example occurred in A.D. 79 when Vesuvius, in eruption, hurled tremendous volumes of water vapor into the air. Being hot, the vapor rose quickly, cooled, and changed into water, and a gigantic, terrible thunderstorm was born over Vesuvius. The ensuing heavy rains drove into the porous slopes of Vesuvius and mingled with the old and new volcanic ashes and cinders. Gigantic mudflows were created which swept down upon the town of Herculaneum and buried it, while Pompeii was being buried mainly by volcanic ash. It is primarily due to the sealing action of the mudflows that the buildings, art treasures, artifacts, etc., in Herculaneum were so well preserved.

Rockfall. The process of rock falling freely through the air is called *rockfall.* Rockfall, of course, is the immediate prelude to the formation of *talus,* discussed on a previous page in this chapter. The typical situation is that a talus slope lies below a cliff which supplies debris to the slope.

The position, shape, and construction of a talus mass on a slope depends largely upon the lengths of free fall of the individual pieces of talus, the sizes and weights of the particles, and upon the shape and inclination of the talus slope. Depending upon these factors, talus may be spread rather evenly over a slope, or it may be in the shape of one or more *talus cones,* cone-like masses of rock debris whose apexes are uphill from their bases. Rock material which falls in the same place or is channeled into the same place will, under the action of gravity, tend to assume cone shape. Assuming fairly dry material, the surface of the talus cannot exceed an angle of about 30° with the horizontal (the *angle of repose*) before surface particles start to move. Once surface particles start to move downslope, particles beneath them also are disturbed. Thus a talus cone is normally an exceedingly short-lived feature as far as specific component fragments are concerned.

Assuming that two fragments of the same type of rock falling from a cliff and from the same height have different masses, the one with the larger mass has the higher energy of motion. This usually means that upon impact it will roll and slide farther down the slope than the lighter material, before it comes to rest. Furthermore, the larger pieces will roll over any obstacles more easily than will the smaller pieces. Thus the apex of a talus cone commonly consists of smaller rock fragments while the base has larger fragments.

Landslides. A large volume of rock debris which slides down a steep slope is called a *landslide*. There are two main varieties of landslides: *rockslides* and *slumps*.

A rockslide occurs when large masses of bedrock move downslope, usually initially along a steeply sloping plane of weakness in the bedrock. Very often a rockslide plows into unconsolidated earth material and carries earth and trees along with it.

Slumps differ from rockslides in that, where rockslides soon become masses of rather thoroughly mixed rock debris, slumps more or less preserve their original *slump blocks* which move downslope as large blocks of rock or earth. It is commonly said that slump blocks "rotate backward" as they slide downward. This effect can be understood by holding a coin against the upper inside of a bowl or cup and then letting the coin slide slowly to the bottom until it is lying flat. It will be noticed that, in its journey, the coin actually does rotate backward about a horizontal axis; otherwise it would not end up in a horizontal position at the bottom. A slump block therefore rotates backward, moving down a typically curved slope.

Other than the primary requirement of a steep slope, a plentiful supply of water is necessary for movements which are properly termed landslides. Because of the high water content and subsequent slippage and plasticity, landslides always show one or more features of what is referred to as "landslide topography": hummocks, depressions, natural dams across valleys, sharply curving slopes, etc.

Earthflows. The principal difference between an *earthflow* and a landslide is that an earthflow, as the name indicates, involves a more fluid or flowing action than does a landslide. Where both landslides and earthflows are triggered because of water content in the earth or rock layers, earthflows more or less maintain their original characteristics because of the plasticity afforded by the high water content. This is in contrast to a landslide which, once it starts, is characterized by an obvious mechanical breaking up of large quantities of rock or earth. In an earthflow, the rock or earth is usually highly saturated with water. As might be surmised, where a landslide may begin and end within a few minutes, the progress of an earthflow is measured in hours or days.

REVIEW

1. Define mass wasting.
2. What are the evidences of soil creep?
3. What is talus? Describe a typical talus area.
4. What is permafrost? How much of the world's land surface is covered by permafrost?
5. What is rockfall? What is a mudflow?
6. Distinguish between "landslide" and "earthflow." What triggers the start of each, other than a steep slope and gravity?
7. What is a rock glacier? Describe the movement of a rock glacier.
8. What is solifluction? In what regions does it occur?
9. List the slow movements of mass wasting; list the rapid movements of mass wasting.
10. How would you determine if a particular example of mass wasting is a slow or a rapid movement?

EXERCISES

(Answers are given in the answer section at the back of the book.)

1. The talus cones on a certain slope consist of rock fragments of about the same size. The parent rock cliff is composed of a top white layer, a middle brown layer, and a bottom black layer. There are very few brown rocks in the talus. What color are most of the rocks in the bases of the cones?

2. Figure 82 is a contour map of an area in Colorado which illustrates several features and principles already discussed in this book.

(a) What is the gradient, in percent, of the stream which flows out of the larger lake in the center of the map?

(b) What feature is illustrated in the area bounded by the two western-most streams which flow slightly to the northwest? Notice especially the existence of a large "gully" and of a ridge below the "gully."

(c) The 9750 and 10,000 foot contours, in the area about 2½ miles east of the west edge of the map and about 1½ miles north of the map's southern edge, represent a sudden change in slope which is evident almost around the entire mountain. What causes this change in slope?

(d) Outline all major valleys, gullies, etc., in blue, and all major ridges in red.

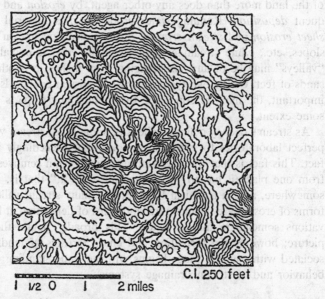

C.I. 250 feet

1   1/2   0   1   2 miles

Fig. 82. Topographic map illustrating several erosional and depositional features. (From *Photogeology* by Miller & Miller. Copyright, 1961. McGraw-Hill Book Company. Used by permission)

CHAPTER 23

Running Water and Its Associated Landforms

Running water in association with mass wasting changes the face of the land more than does any other agent, by *erosion* and by subsequent *deposition*. Running water erodes—carries material away—by *sheet erosion* and *stream erosion*. Sheet erosion occurs on ungullied slopes, etc., while stream erosion refers to erosion in valleys. The "valleys" may be of any size, ranging from inches in depth to thousands of feet. Of the two types of erosion, stream erosion is the most important, the main reason being that almost any slope is gullied to some extent.

As streams occupy defined valleys of some kind, stream valleys are perfect laboratories for studying a simple but exceedingly important fact. This fact is that whenever an agent of erosion removes material from one place it has to "do something with it," that is, deposit it somewhere, and in a typical form. So, in many stream valleys, landforms of erosion are balanced by landforms of deposition at lower elevations somewhere in the valley. This broadly paints the general picture; however the formation and characteristics of landforms associated with running water begins with an understanding of stream behavior and of stream drainage systems.

Fundamentals of Stream Behavior

The Origin and Maintenance of Streams. It was pointed out in Chapter 19 that most of the water immediately below the earth's surface comes from precipitation and that much of this underground water eventually goes into stream systems. A typical stream therefore contains water with two different post-precipitation histories: some of the water directly entered the stream system as *surface runoff* while other water first sank into and percolated through the ground before joining the stream.

A *perennial* stream flows the year round while an *intermittent* stream has one or more periods of dryness. Perennial streams can obviously be maintained by the melting of glaciers and the overflowing of lakes, etc. Many perennial streams do not have such sources of supply, however, and some do not even have good *watersheds,* large collecting areas near the stream heads where water drains in one general direction. In such cases it will usually be found that the bed of the perennial stream is cut well below the water table in one or more regions and that the saturated material below the water table is the nonfailing source of the all-year supply of water.

On the other hand—and this is typical of the more arid climates—some of the world's wildest and most unmanageable rivers in time of spring flood are some of the world's most docile and driest rivers in late summer. In these cases it is usually evident that the stream bed is above the normal water table. Therefore, when the bulk of the snow supply has melted and the winter rains have ceased, the stream bed is left literally high and dry, with no water in the form of runoff and little in the way of underground water seeping into the stream.

Stream Flow. Readers who performed the simple experiment outlined in Chapter 19 to illustrate the flow of underground water as it discharged into an area of lower pressure noticed that the lines of flow were *laminar,* or *streamlined.* Such streamline flow occurs when there is little friction to interrupt movement.

Consider, though, what happens in a stream. The water is continually hitting obstacles and being forced to go through many side-to-side and up-and-down gyrations. All of this results in *turbulent* flow in a stream. In terms of a phenomenon already discussed, turbulent flow of a stream is much like the turbulence which is always occurring in a thundercloud. Without friction to shape it, the cloud would be a solid mass instead of being of cauliflower appearance and composed of billowing smaller clouds, each of which is itself a complex structure of whirls and loops. Similarly, friction of water against rock and of water against water creates complex whirls and loops in streams, resulting in turbulent flow.

Stream Energy. In normally flowing streams, most of the energy is converted by friction into heat energy. It is during floods or near floods, therefore, that most streams accomplish the bulk of their geological work. It is therefore important to note at this time that most of the landforms of erosion made by streams are carved out for the greatest part when streams run well above normal in volume of water. It can also be deduced that the bulk of the material being carried by a stream in flood will be deposited when the above-normal velocity of the stream slackens. It is apparent, then, that most landforms of stream deposition, like most landforms of stream erosion, are essentially products of above-normal flow of water.

Stream Erosion and Deposition

Stream Erosion. The material carried along by a stream is called the stream's *load*. The load of a stream consists of solid particles being mechanically moved, and of material which is dissolved in the water.

Due to turbulence, a stream may tear out particles of rock from its channel by *hydraulic plucking,* the removal of rock by the force of water alone. It is readily seen that the possibility of such removal of rock particles is at a maximum under conditions of increased flow and velocity, as during floods.

Also due to turbulence, rock particles in a fast-moving stream are continually being tossed around in the stream and these tumbling particles are capable of *abrasion,* wearing away channel rock and dirt. Abrasion is actually a very complicated filing action in that the filing is done in a highly irregular fashion by the erratically tossing grains and stones. After a flood in a canyon, the complicated loops thus made by some stones can often be traced in the form of hieroglyphic-like scratches on the canyon walls.

Streams are also capable of taking some material into *solution.* Most of the dissolved material in streams, however, was brought there by underground water which finally entered the stream system. As an extreme example of each activity, some perennial streams in the western United States are unfit for drinking purposes because of their high concentration of poisonous or other salts.

Transportation is part of erosion. The transporting power of a stream depends mainly upon its volume of water, and upon the velocity of the water. As these increase, the sizes and numbers of the particles being moved by the stream also increase. For example, a certain normally flowing stream may be just able to move stones ½ inch in diameter. If the velocity is tripled as in flood, the stream can theoretically transport boulders 5 inches in diameter.

A measure of the volume of water in a stream, and its velocity, is given by the *discharge* of a stream. For example, if a stream is flowing at the rate of 5 feet per second at a given point where the cross-sectional area of the part of the stream channel being wetted is 600 square feet, then the discharge is 5×600, or 3000 cubic feet per second.

It should be noted that a value for discharge, in itself, does not indicate whether or not much geological work is being accomplished. A fairly large river can be discharging at the rate of 3000 cubic feet per second and be just barely flowing along. At the other extreme a small creek in flood, confined to a narrow canyon, can do tremendous geological work with the same discharge of 3000 cubic feet per second. In formula form, discharge = area × velocity $(D = AV)$. The discharge of a stream increases from head to mouth, due to the increasing tributary drainage as the stream continues in its course.

The *stream gradient,* the slope of the stream bed, governs stream velocity. Velocity is usually expressed in feet per second, as indicated, while the wetted area of the channel is expressed in square feet. A simple relationship for converting units of velocity is that 60 miles per hour equals 88 feet per second. As an example, a stream flowing 15 miles per hour would be flowing at the rate of $\frac{15}{60} \times 88$, or 22 feet per second.

Stream Channel Changes; Deposition.   Due to erosion a stream will normally cut both vertically and laterally into its channel. The noticeable effects of this cutting are that the width and depth of the stream channel both increase. This of course means that the cross-sectional area of the normal channel increases in times of flood, at least temporarily.

Profiles, or side views, of streams would show that streams are trying to attain a *profile of equilibrium* from head to mouth, a curve along which the stream can flow in near equilibrium. Actual equilibrium is, of course, never attained but the stream profiles, or *long profiles,* indicate how closely a stream approaches this ideal state. A long profile is shown in Figure 83.

After a stream deepens and widens its channel by *degradation,* the question then arises as to what happens to the removed material.

Fig. 83. The long profile of a stream. The solid line represents the actual profile and the dashed line the theoretical profile sought by the stream. Vertical scale is exaggerated.

Much of it contributes to the formation of recognizable landforms of deposition but some of it also is dropped right in the stream channel itself as the velocity of the water slackens. Typically, then a stream scours its channel to new dimensions and then reduces the size of the new channel by *aggradation,* or by depositing material in the channel.

Streams, Mass Wasting, and the Erosion Cycle

As an example of stream erosion, the Allegheny Plateau of the eastern United States is so dissected by streams that its original plateau characteristics are not apparent in many regions. The Catskill Mountains, as stated in Chapter 21, were formed by the dissection of part of the Allegheny Plateau by streams. Stretching into Pennsylvania and West Virginia, the Plateau is really a series of mountains and hills, the latter also having been formed by dissection by streams.

The Erosion Cycle. An important fact concerning such dissection by streams is that, just as the Allegheny Plateau is still being eroded, stream erosion of this kind is also continually at work over most of the world's land masses. Eventually many portions of many of these land masses will be eroded to or nearly to the level of the sea. Sea level—or *base level*—is therefore the theoretical end point of the *cycle of erosion,* the succession of erosional events by which a land mass is base-leveled.

Stream Erosion and Mass Wasting. Parts of what are major erosional and depositional events can be witnessed today as they happen, in stream valleys. No one who has seen a large river in flood can doubt, noting the turbidity of the water, that he is seeing a great erosional force at work. Anyone who has flown over a large river delta has seen at first hand a dramatic example of the tendency of land masses to reach base level.

A very important point here is that youthful stream valleys are, in general, V-shaped instead of having vertical sides. If streams by themselves were the only erosive agents acting upon land masses, a plateau such as the Allegheny Plateau would be characterized by canyons and mountains with almost vertical sides instead of by the much gentler topography now existent. Not only would the topography be different, but general erosion would be proceeding much more slowly. As a matter of fact, it is very doubtful that stream erosion, by itself, would ever base-level a landform of appreciable size. Further, even a combination of stream erosion and sheet erosion would not by itself bring about the general erosional sculpturing we see today.

The answer to this apparent problem is *mass wasting.* As a stream cuts into a landform, the valley sides are excavated essentially vertically. However, while some of the water on the surface of the ground, on either side of the stream, will run off into the main stream valley, some will also soak into the ground. The weakened sides of the stream channel then tend to *slump,* or fall into the stream channel, by mass wasting. Once this happens, small tributary streams can easily carry much of the material into the main stream, which then carries it away, in addition to the slumped material it received directly. In addition, *sheet erosion* and *rainwash* carry considerable material into the main stream. The youthful stream thus continues widening its valley at the top while it cuts its channel and valley deeper and the valley keeps approximating a V in cross section. Where the side of one valley is cut back so that it intersects or nearly intersects the side of an adjacent valley, a hill or a mountain is formed.

Geologic Age.   It will occur to some readers that the topography of the Allegheny Plateau is considerably more rounded and gentle than that of the Colorado Plateau, as exemplified by the Grand Canyon of the Colorado and by other canyons in that and other plateaus. Two reasons for the difference, of course, are differences in rock types and in climate. Whatever the causes for differences in relief, though, the Colorado Plateau is a region of *geologic youth* as compared to the more *mature* Allegheny Plateau. Note that the expression *youth, maturity,* and *old age,* as used in a geological sense, refer to topography and not necessarily to chronological age.

During its cycle of erosion, then, an *initial landform* (see Chapter 21), such as a mountain, goes through the various stages of geologic youth, maturity, and old age. As it does so, *sequential* landforms such as valleys and ridges develop. These in turn go through the stages of geologic age, hosting or contributing to the formation of other landforms of erosion and deposition which in turn go through the stages of geologic age, etc., etc. Finally, the entire region which the initial large landform once occupied is in geologic late old age and may approximate a *peneplain,* a large plane-like, eroded surface which has relatively little topographic relief. The actual or theoretical attainment of a true peneplain is probably impossible, due to counteracting factors such as isostatic adjustment and horizontal compressive forces in the earth's crust. At any rate, no perfect peneplains exist on the earth's surface today although the many references to peneplains in geological literature no doubt lead the casual readers to believe that "textbook" peneplains are fairly common surface features.

Features of Stream Drainage

The *drainage system* of a stream includes the stream and its tributaries. In general, the beds of tributaries enter the main stream at the level of the main stream, notable exceptions being in glaciated regions. This is discussed in Chapter 24.

Relationship of Tributaries to the Main Stream. The fact that the beds of tributaries enter the main stream at the level of the main stream in a geologically mature valley is another example of the way natural forces tend to balance each other and attain equilibrium. Imagine the mouth of a tributary stream which, for some reason, is about one foot directly above the level of the main stream, so that a small waterfall is formed. Due to normal stream erosion the tributary will keep cutting into the rock of dirt on the side of the main stream. Because of this cutting and due to mass wasting on the sides of the tributary, material will be moved into the main stream which carries the material away. Finally, the bed of the tributary will be at the level of the main stream.

Now what prevents the tributary from cutting its bed *below* the level of the main stream? The answer is that a tributary may, say, during flood, cut its bed below that of the main stream but this is only temporary. The main stream fills this gouge in its bed with rock material and this automatically brings the bed of the tributary back to the level of the bed of the main stream. If the main stream cuts its channel deeper, the tributaries follow suit because of increased gradients near the main stream. If the main stream suddenly aggrades, or raises, its channel in an area, tributary mouths in that area will also necessarily have their channels raised and the tributaries will still enter the main stream at the level of the main stream.

It is important to realize that, as a drainage system of a river includes its tributaries, any adjustment in one part of the river somehow affects the whole drainage system in general and the main stream and each tributary in particular. Conversely, any major change in an important tributary somehow affects the whole system. This intimate relationship in a drainage system is of great importance, especially in the case of a river like the Mississippi, whose drainage system extends well over ⅓ the area of the continental United States.

Watersheds and Divides. A *watershed* is a large area upon which water runs in one general direction. A *divide* is the line separating two watersheds. As an example, a valley side is a watershed. If two sides of two parallel valleys meet, the ridge separating the valley sides is a divide.

Drainage Patterns. The pattern of a drainage system as shown on a map is often a thumbnail sketch of the geomorphological history of the region. Of more importance to the geographer is the fact that drainage patterns reflect regional rock types and structures.

The *dendritic*—"tree-like"—pattern shown in Figure 84 is characteristic of regions whose rocks are not layered or, if they are layered, have not been tilted to appreciable slopes.

The *rectangular* pattern of Figure 84 typically occurs in regions whose rocks have been jointed or faulted, or where exposed planes of weakness of metamorphic rocks more or less control stream positions. As the figure shows, the streams tend to have right-angle bends.

The *trellis* pattern, illustrated in Figure 84, is often confused by students with the rectangular pattern, but the patterns are really very different. It should be noted that the tributaries of the trellis pattern are essentially parallel to each other and are long. Further, the tributaries of the rectangular pattern are *not* necessarily parallel to each other and may be relatively short in length. Trellis drainage patterns often occur where a main stream cuts straight across a series of folds whose rocks have varying resistances to erosion, although, many

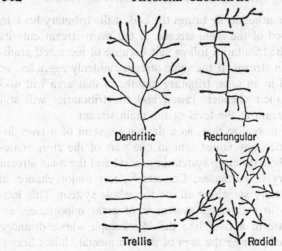

Dendritic   Rectangular

Trellis   Radial

Fig. 84. Stream drainage patterns.

times, the main stream itself has adjusted itself to flow along soft rocks and therefore may show abrupt bends. Tributaries often develop in the bottoms of the folds, in the softer rock, and therefore are at approximately right angles to the main stream.

A gap known as a *water gap* is formed where streams cut through folds. Water gaps and trellis patterns are fairly prevalent in some regions of the eastern United States, an example being the Appalachian region.

A *radial* drainage pattern is usually associated with dome mountains, volcanic mountains, etc. It is illustrated in Figure 84.

The Growth of a Drainage System. It seems to be a more or less popular belief that stream valleys lengthen, in a down-slope direction; in other words, that a stream valley grows downhill.

The fact is that stream valleys normally grow *headward,* or toward the heads of the streams. As the valley deepens and steepens near the stream head, erosion automatically preserves a balanced long profile, and the stream valley grows uphill, past its former head.

A given watershed covered by streams will start moving its divide back as soon as most of the streams of that watershed have their heads on the divide. In such a case, a stream on the "moving" watershed often *captures* the headwaters of a stream on the opposing watershed, as illustrated in Figure 85. As the figure shows, this often

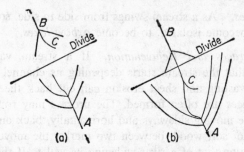

(a)   (b)

Fig. 85. Stream *A* in the lower part of the diagram helps carve the divide back to (b) where stream *A* "captures" part of stream *B*'s channel and tributaries, the latter "barbed." *C* represents the abandoned segment of stream channel *B*.

results in reversed or "barbed" tributaries for the pirate stream, and in an abandoned length of channel in the drainage system which was *pirated*.

Landforms of Stream Erosion

Stream Valleys. It has been pointed out that stream valleys result from a combination of mass wasting, sheet erosion, and stream erosion. Figure 86 shows the stages of development of a typical river valley in a humid region during an erosion cycle.

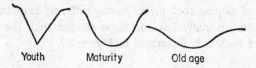

Youth   Maturity   Old age

Fig. 86. The cross section of a stream valley in various stages during its erosional cycle.

Meanders and River Plains. As a stream carves out its valley, it tends to form *meanders,* or large curves, as the valley matures. The stream cuts steep bluffs on one side of a curve, and deposits material on the other side. Few people who see this common phenomenon—a wide, flat, gravelly expanse on one side of a river curve, with a steep bluff opposite—realize that in the gravelly expanse they are looking at the birth of a river plain whose width may some day be measured in hundreds of miles.

Oxbow Lakes. As a stream swings from side to side, some meander loops may become isolated, to become *oxbow lakes.*

Stream Terraces and Rejuvenation. If a stream valley is *rejuvenated* so that the stream starts deepening its channel much faster than mass wasting and sheet erosion can cut back the valley sides, *stream terraces* are often formed. The process may roughly be likened to a file moving sideways and horizontally, back and forth over a flat piece of soft wood, between two marks, the movement of the file representing that of a river widening its valley. If the file is now moved rapidly back and forth in a direction paralleling its long dimension, a relatively deep channel will result, and the former floor of the "valley" forms a terrace on either side of the new channel. The new movement of the file represents rejuvenation of the region which is caused by an increase in energy of the stream. Such an increase in energy could be caused by regional or local uplift of land masses.

Incised Meanders. If meanders are well established in a valley before rejuvenation, the main stream may stay in the meander loops despite its increased vigor, and cut, or *incise,* the meanders into the rock below. In such cases, the topography presents the seemingly anomalous combination of meanders, representing maturity, in youthful canyons and gorges.

Cuestas and Hogbacks. A *cuesta* is an asymmetric ridge formed by the erosion of sloping rock layers having differing resistances to erosion. A cuesta normally has one slope steeper than the other. The formation of cuestas is illustrated in Figure 87.

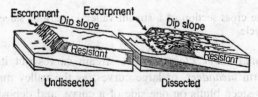

Fig. 87. How a cuesta develops in arid or semi-arid regions (left) and in more humid regions (right). (Modified from *Elements of Geography*, 4th edition, 1957, by Finch et al. McGraw-Hill Book Company)

If the initial slope of the rock layers is greater than about 12°, the ridges formed will be more symmetrical and pointed, and are then properly termed *hogbacks*. Hogbacks are therefore commonly formed in regions where former mountain building activity is evident while cuestas are characteristic of plains underlain by gently sloping rock layers.

Pediments.   A *pediment* is a sloping erosional surface cut into bedrock at the base of a mountain or mountain range. Pediments are associated with weathering in arid climates and are probably largely a result of erosion by running water. Normally, pediments have a relatively thin cover of alluvium although some are exposed over large areas.

Pediments seem to defy certain accepted principles of weathering in that they make distinct angles with the sides of the mountains, rather than gradually merging into them. Pediments are apparently formed by several forms of erosion associated with running water, including shifting back and forth of streams, and subsequent erosion over a wide area. In some regions, the formation of pediments is obviously greatly influenced by rock type, by inclination of rock layers, and by joint and fracture systems in the bedrock.

Landforms of Stream Deposition

Braided Channels.   Consider a stream in an arid or semi-arid region which is carrying a considerable amount of *alluvium* or stream-transported material in its main channel. As the velocity of the water appreciably slackens, alluvium is deposited in the channel in the form of a *bar*. During the next period of high water, the stream is commonly swung to either side of its original channel by the bar and new channels now spread out from the site of the bar. As the flow of water subsides, these channels will also have bars deposited in them and, during the next period of high water, more channels will be formed. In this manner, a stream in arid or semi-arid regions often forms an intricate series of curving channels which curve, meet, and even cross one another. Such a pattern is called a *braided pattern*. A braided stream channel is, of course, indicative of aggradation in that part of the channel.

The braided channel pattern is common in streams whose discharges vary considerably throughout the year, hence braiding is characteristic of streams in arid or semi-arid regions. In general, streams in such regions are subject to periods of dryness punctuated by discharges of flood proportion due to thunderstorms, and, in some cases, melting snow in the spring.

Alluvial Fans. Where a stream gradient is abruptly lessened, as when a mountain stream meets a valley floor, the stream's alluvium often spreads out from the stream mouth in the form of a cone. The shape of such a cone, typical of intermittent streams of arid or semi-arid regions, can be approximated in miniature by holding a piece of cardboard at an angle of about 20 degrees to the top of a table, and then trickling a substance like salt or granulated sugar onto the cardboard in the same spot until a cone is built up. It will be seen that varying the slope of the cardboard will change the shape of the cone, but that the apex of the cone will always remain somewhere on the slope.

The building of an alluvial fan is more complex than this simple experiment indicates. For example, many alluvial fans are several miles wide, some of the most recently deposited alluvium being around the base of the cone. Obviously, water must have somehow carried the material to that position.

Study of alluvial fans generally shows a braiding pattern. Channels choke up by bar formation, and new channels are cut. Alluvium is moved through each of these new channels which fan out from a more or less common area, at a rate dependent upon the net energy of the water in a particular channel. When the transporting power is not enough to carry the alluvium farther, the material is dropped and a bar is formed which, during the next high water, causes the formation of new channels, and the extension of the alluvial fan continues by braiding. Where large alluvial fans coalesce, *piedmont alluvial plains* may be formed.

Alluvial Fill. Many streams are now cutting through considerable thickness of alluvium which the streams apparently once deposited in the valleys. The streams, now degrading, were once aggrading, otherwise the alluvium would not have been deposited.

The problem as to what causes a stream to deposit alluvium to thicknesses of sometimes several hundred feet or more has a simple general answer: the transporting power of the stream was reduced in that region. Specific causes for such reduction are not so easily determined but among possible causes the following named may be listed: temporary damming by landslides, volcanic flows, or glacial debris; downdrop or uplift of the surface, resulting in a gentler long profile; reversal of drainage due to mountain building activity or faulting; a local increase in the hardness of the rock being eroded, bringing about a flattening of the long profile.

Alluvial Terraces. A stream which has partially filled its valley with alluvium and is now running on top of the alluvium will, if its energy is now increased, encounter little resistance to either downward or lateral movement. As a result the stream cuts down fairly rapidly and also tends to swing from side to side, in effect slipping sideways from one side of the valley to the other, working down to lower elevation. In this manner, *alluvial terraces* are formed on either side of the valley. Because the stream was at different elevations on different sides of the valley, no two alluvial terraces in a valley will normally be at the same elevation in a given cross section of the valley. This is not true of regular stream terraces, described previously, which result from rejuvenation.

Flood Plains and Natural Levees. During flood, a stream may enter the *overbank* stage, water pouring over the sides of the channel. Alluvium is also moved laterally out of the channel in this manner and some may deposit as ridges, or *natural levees,* on the channel sides. Towns on the banks of large rivers are commonly built upon natural levees which were deposited by the stream when younger.

Large rivers in flood, in a wide valley, pour water out onto the *flood plain,* that part of the valley floor which is subject to flooding. In so doing, rivers deposit alluvium throughout the flood plain. The result is that some of the world's most fertile soil is found in flood plains. The obvious drawback is that fertile *bottom lands,* below the natural levees in elevation, are flooded time after time unless artificial levees or other devices prevent such flooding.

Deltas. A *delta* is commonly formed where a stream enters a standing body of water. Although the name "delta" indicates a triangular-shaped construction, many deltas are modified to other forms by current action, extreme changes in stream velocity and load, etc.

Viewed from overhead, the classic, triangular delta looks much like an alluvial fan, part of which has been deposited under water. As a matter of fact, all types of deltas commonly exhibit a braided pattern of channel formation in their landward parts. In profile, however, a delta is much less steep than an alluvial fan. One main reason for this is that the standing body of water temporarily buoys up the material being discharged into it. Thus, whereas the material in an alluvial fan is almost abruptly dropped in its channel, material making up a delta is carried for a longer distance. While settling, the material sorts itself by weight and volume, hence deltas are typically composed of more or less definite graded layers sloping into the standing water.

Stream Adjustment and Types of Streams

A stream is a good example of nature's tendency to follow the paths of least resistance. Given enough time, the streams of a drainage system would probably *adjust* themselves so that they all flowed on the inherently weakest, most easily eroded rocks, or along regions of structural weakness such as fault zones, rock joints, and planes in sharply compressed metamorphic rocks. So, a drainage pattern is in the main dependent upon the slope of the ground, or upon the characteristics of the rock material over which it flows, or both.

A stream which, in general, follows the existing slope of the ground, and whose drainage pattern is not appreciably affected by rock types is a *consequent* stream. The drainage pattern of a consequent stream is usually *dendritic,* or tree-like. (See Figure 84.)

The *trellis* pattern (see Figure 84) is characteristic of some *subsequent* streams, streams which flow along softer and more easily eroded rock. As brought out previously, softer rocks tend to occur in lowlands, not because of folding in itself, however, but because of subsequent erosion. Therefore streams occupying the bottoms of such folds will eventually run in softer rock after having eroded whatever harder rock is on the surface. All *subsequent* streams do not exhibit a trellis pattern, the only requirement for proper use of the term "subsequent" being that the stream flows in or along weak rock. Again, the weakness of the rock may be inherent or it may be due to faulting, jointing, etc.

An *antecedent* stream is one which has enough energy to cut through folds, etc., which are rising along its course, without being greatly deflected from its original direction of flow. Antecedent streams typically show water gaps and a trellis pattern. If a stream fails to cut across a fold in its path and its course is therefore altered, the stream is *deflected*.

The above is far from being a complete summary of stream classification based on stream adjustment to slope and rock type. The determination of stream history, more often than not, is a complex study involving history within history. The above descriptions, however, in conjunction with the portion of this chapter dealing with drainage patterns, will give the reader a basic working knowledge of drainage features. From this, in many instances, a major part of the geologic history of a region and considerable information about the underlying rock structure can quickly be deduced from even simple maps, such as road maps.

Cultural and Economic Aspects of Streams and Their Associated Landforms

Other than the important fact that streams distribute and supply fresh water, man's most basic need, streams play other very important roles in man's culture and economy. Some of these roles are outlined below.

Streams and Settlement. Man cannot live without water, hence the world's human population patterns have always been largely determined by the availability of fresh water. Great civilizations have arisen in regions of plentiful water supply and many of these civilizations abruptly disappeared when the supply of water failed.

Today some countries are facing water famine within the next generation. As stated in Chapter 1, by 1980 the United States must increase its water supply to double what the supply was in 1960. The problem would be a serious one even if the potential sources of the water were relatively pure. As it is, however, radioactive, industrial, and natural wastes are polluting our water at an alarming rate. It seems almost certain, unless changes are made, that future population patterns in many regions of the United States will largely reflect local technological triumphs in the mass purification of highly contaminated water from streams.

Streams and Economic Development. In many regions of the world, agriculture has developed along the quiet stretches of large rivers while manufacturing industries have developed where the same streams plunge over falls furnishing power. Good examples are the northern half of the eastern United States, and the Pacific coast.

In addition to the simple relationship between streams and manufacturing, industry, and agriculture, stream valleys have often been major routes of exploration which have later developed into highways of travel and commerce. Highways and railroads are located in stream valleys because stream erosion has already done what would be impossible or unfeasible for man to do all over the world. Stream erosion has removed many million cubic miles of rock to make major travel possible over what would otherwise be impassable terrain. Further, many cities were located along or near water courses, not because of drinking water and power supply alone, but also because mature stream valleys are natural routes of overland commerce. In many regions, river boat transportation, along with highways and railroads, has played and is still playing a major part in commerce.

The backbone of America's general development prior to the Civil War was almost literally its stream systems. For example, after the War of 1812 the Mohawk Valley of New York State was settled by veterans who had been given land grants. In many places, falls on the Mohawk River furnished power for industries. In 1825 the Erie Barge Canal, passing through the Mohawk Valley, was opened. The West was now connected by water to New York City via the Mohawk and Hudson rivers and by 1850 New York City had become the country's leading city in commerce and manufacturing. Without the stream valley of the Mohawk, New York City would not have become the economic and cultural colossus it now is, and New York State would not have had the distinction which it held until recently of being the most populous state in the United States.

Stream Deposits and Economics. Some of the world's greatest agricultural regions are located in wide river valleys such as the Valley of the Nile in Egypt, the lower Mississippi River Valley of the United States, and the Po River Valley of Italy. In each case, the fertile soil is alluvium, or stream-deposited material.

Stream deposits are also important in other than agricultural regions. Streams concentrate valuable minerals such as gold, tin, tungsten, diamonds, and semiprecious stones into *placer* deposits, in many regions of the world. Less appreciated, but of far more importance, are stream concentrations of raw building and construction material such as sized stones for concrete; and sand for concrete, glass-making, and for the ceramics industry in general. In turn, the ceramics industry, by virtue of its refractory products, is basic to the steel industry. All in all, if it were not for natural concentrations of many minerals and stones by streams, it is certain that cultures and economics in the more advanced areas of the world would be far different than they now are.

REVIEW

1. Discuss the origin of streams and the maintenance of their flow.

2. Distinguish between turbulent flow and streamlined flow. What is laminar flow?

3. What comprises the "load" of a stream?

4. What is the "long profile" of a stream? What is a "profile of equilibrium"?

5. Define "erosion cycle."

6. What is a peneplain? Are they prevalent on the earth's surface?

7. Explain how a youthful stream enlarges its valley.

8. Show, by means of examples, why tributaries normally enter the main stream at the level of the main stream.

9. Distinguish between dendritic, rectangular, and trellis drainage patterns. Also, discuss these patterns in terms of underlying rock structure.

10. Discuss the headward growth of streams and the attendant modification of their valleys and long profiles.

11. Discuss the deposition of valley alluvial fill, and the formation of alluvial terraces.

12. What is stream "braiding"? Name two landforms where it is of importance.

13. Distinguish between consequent, subsequent, and antecedent streams.

14. Explain how cuestas are formed. What is the difference between a cuesta and a hogback?

15. Discuss the cultural and economic aspects of streams.

EXERCISES

(Answers are given in the answer section at the back of the book.)

1. A stream is flowing at the rate of 10 miles per hour. The area of the wetted part of its channel is about 2000 square feet. What is the stream discharge, in cubic feet per second?

2. Excluding friction, etc., the energy of any stream is directly proportional to the square of its velocity. A certain stream flows along one part of its course at 10 miles per hour. At the base of a falls farther down-

stream, the water reaches a velocity of 30 miles per hour. How much
has the energy increased?

3. Draw sketches illustrating dendritic, rectangular, and trellis drainage
patterns. Label each one. Draw typical contour lines on each, numbering
the contours. Show a water gap, by means of contour lines, on the trellis
drainage sketch.

4. Draw long profiles for a hypothetical stream in (a) geologic youth,
(b) geologic maturity, (c) geologic old age.

5. In general, hard rocks tend to form ridges while soft rocks tend to
form valleys. Make a sketch illustrating how it is possible for just the reverse to occur.

6. Draw a cross section of a valley whose terraces are (a) alluvial terraces, (b) terraces caused by rejuvenation.

7. What is the largest river near where you live? What part, if any, did
the river play in the development of the region? What part, if any, is it still
playing in the economy of the region?

8. Figure 88 is a topographic map of an area in Canada. Stream *B*
once flowed along the length of the wide north-south valley shown but
was captured at *A* by the other stream. The top of the map is north.

(a) In what direction does stream *B* flow?
(b) In what direction does stream *D* flow?

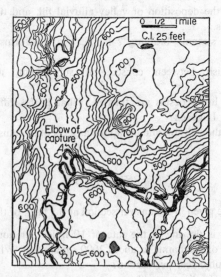

Fig. 88. Topographic map of an area of stream capture and diversion.
(From *Photogeology* by Miller & Miller. Copyright, 1961. McGraw-Hill
Book Company. Used by permission)

(c) What formed the peculiar "hook" at *A*? What are the "loops" in stream *B* called?

(d) How wide is the valley floor of stream *B*? stream *D*?

(e) If you were to farm this region, where would you buy, assuming that all land has not been worked before and is the same price?

(f) Draw a profile along a line extending from the lower left to the upper right corner.

(g) In the lower right section of the map, the stream shows a rather abrupt change in direction. What could cause such a change in direction?

CHAPTER 24

Glaciation and Its Associated Landforms

Formation of Glaciers

Types of Glaciers. Glaciers are large, slowly moving masses of ice. Most of the important glaciers of the world may be described as being either *valley* glaciers or *continental* glaciers. Valley glaciers are also known as *alpine* glaciers. Continental glaciers are also called *ice sheets* or *ice caps,* depending upon their size, ice sheets being larger than ice caps.

How Glaciers Originate. As their name indicates, valley glaciers form in mountains and move down usually already existent valleys. Valley glaciers are in general, therefore, direct products of local precipitation, usually snow, at high elevations. Latitude is secondary to elevation as a control in the forming of valley glaciers. For example, a number of large valley glaciers at high elevations lie almost athwart the equator in various parts of the world.

On the other hand, continental glaciation is associated with cold climates which extend over large areas. As in the case of valley glaciers, continental glaciers are formed where snow is trapped by mountain topography.

Glacier Structure. Glaciers, whether of the valley or continental type, commonly exhibit three fairly well-defined layers. The top layer is snow, the middle layer is intermediate between snow and ice, and the bottom layer is ice. The sequence illustrates the ultimate conversion of snow into ice, in glaciers, by alternate thawing and freezing, and compaction.

Valley Glaciers

Movement of Valley Glaciers.   When a valley glacier is a few hundred feet thick it will normally start to flow down the stream valley whose head it occupies. The ice flows plastically while the general movement of the glacier is resisted by contact with the valley sides and bottom. One result is of course that glaciers move slowly. Even the fastest moving valley glaciers travel only about ⅕ of a mile per year.

How Valley Glaciers Erode.   An effect far more important than rate of glacier movement, but associated with it, is that a typical valley glacier necessarily must accomplish considerable erosion in its valley. The stream valley in which a valley glacier starts to form usually has a youthful V cross section in its upper reaches. One common reason for this is that if the altitude of the head of the valley is high enough to receive snow, the stream valley is probably geologically youthful, in its high elevations at least, with a V cross section.

The fact that ice as usually seen is much more brittle than rock and apparently should not be able to erode rock is of little importance when the high confining pressures in a glacier are considered. Consider a cubic foot of ice 500 feet beneath the surface of a glacier, and assume that this particular cubic foot of ice is pressing against the rock wall of a valley. The forces involved are tremendous. Due to the weight of the ice above it, alone, this single cubic foot of ice exerts a force of 30,000 pounds in all directions upon the rock. Most rock in the earth's crust is fissured and cracked to considerable extent and, in regions where glaciers form, these cracks and joints have been farther expanded by freezing water. The resulting fracture system often outlines blocks of rock which can be relatively easily sheared off and "quarried" by moving ice which is under a pressure of thousands of pounds per square foot.

The quarrying process described above is called *plucking* and is the most important kind of glacial erosion from the standpoint of the amount of geological work done. In addition to plucking, glaciers perform a certain amount of *abrasion*. A glacier is almost literally a moving file, its largest "teeth" being ice-embedded rock which originally fell onto the glacier or which was plucked. The "teeth" in glaciers commonly vary from the size of small pebbles to huge boulders the size of small houses. Finer rock material in glaciers results from abrasion and from the collecting of wind-blown dust. Although the geological effects of abrasion are interesting and often striking as will be outlined when continental glaciers are discussed, abrasion compared with plucking performs only a small fraction of the tremendous changes in topography which are brought about by glaciation.

Landforms Made by Valley Glaciers

Landforms of Erosion.   The birthplace of a valley glacier is a *cirque,* a natural amphitheater which the growing glacier carves out by frost wedging and plucking. Where eroding cirques eventually work themselves close to each other, sharp ridges known as *arêtes* are formed. A low area among glaciated peaks is a *col.* A *horn* is formed where cirques come together to form a peak such as the Matterhorn in the Swiss Alps.

A glacier, mainly because of its plucking action, considerably modifies the valley down which it moves. The original V shape of the valley cross section is commonly changed to a U shape by glacial erosion. Tributary valleys are often thus left "hanging" above the main valley as *hanging valleys* whose streams become *falls* as they plunge into the main valley. Ridges in the main valley are cut back by glacial erosion and form *truncated spurs* whose cross sections are rough, inverted Vs. Other common erosional features of glaciated valleys are *tarns,* or glacial lakes, characteristically found in or just below the cirques.

Fjords are formed when glaciers scour the mouths of river valleys to depths below that of sea level. As such a glacier melts in its lower reaches, the sea enters the trough, creating a fjord, a long, narrow arm of the sea. Fjords are common sights on the Norwegian and Alaskan coasts. Actually, fjords are fairly common. It is probably not too well known, for instance, that the coast of Maine is essentially one fjord after another, and that the lower Hudson River Valley is also a fjord.

Landforms of Deposition Made by Valley Glaciers.   It is evident that much of the rock debris carried by a glacier is near the valley walls where it either fell onto the glacier or was plucked from the walls. Many valley glaciers therefore carry these side or lateral ridges of loose rock along with them as *lateral moraines*. Where two valley glaciers come together, terminal moraines merge to form a *medial moraine*.

Rock debris is commonly also concentrated at the lower end of the glacier by plucking, and by some melting of ice which allows the rock debris to settle down onto the valley floor. As a valley glacier moves at a slower rate near the valley walls because of resistance, the pile of material at the lower end of the glacier—an *end* or *terminal* moraine—is commonly curved convex down valley.

If a valley glacier melts faster than it forms ice, and this is typical of many valley glaciers in their lower elevations, the glacier is said to *retreat*. Actually, the term "retreat," although part of the vocabulary of geological literature relating to glaciology, is misleading in that many readers apparently get the impression that glaciers somehow start pulling back up their valleys when they "retreat." The only process involved of course is melting, which brings about the subsequent exposure of a formerly ice-covered part of a valley and the deposition of the various types of moraines onto the valley's floor and lower sides.

Continental Glaciers and Their Landforms

The Problem of Continental Glaciation. Unlike valley glaciers whose formation is often due to more or less local climate conditions, the massive continental glaciers require widespread colder climates. Portions of the world have been through several periods of continental glaciations but at the present time there are only two true ice sheets and they occur on Greenland and Antarctica, the great bulk of each sheet being well within the arctic and the antarctic zones, respectively.

Some former ice sheets, however, extended far south of the Arctic Circle. Over one million years ago, for example, in the Pleistocene epoch, the first of four periods of continental glaciation in the northern hemisphere began. In the United States, during the last period of glaciation, ice moved as far south as 37° N. At that time, and until about 30,000 years ago, ice covered all of New England, most of New York State, much of Pennsylvania, and all of North America north of the Ohio and Missouri rivers. In Europe the southern edge of the ice roughly approximated the latitude of 50° N.

The big problem of continental glaciation is this: what causes a temporary but widespread lowering of temperature over a considerable portion of the world? Closely associated with this problem are such facts as the one that Antarctica, now the "icebox of the world," must have enjoyed a much warmer climate about 250 million years ago as evidenced by the ages of coal seams in Antarctica.

Various hypotheses have been advanced to explain the cause of large-scale temperature drops to bring about glaciation over a large area. These hypotheses include those of reduced receipt of solar radiation, a change in the carbon dioxide content of the atmosphere, thus reducing the "greenhouse effect" of heat entrapment (see Chapter 8), a possible slipping of some zone of the earth, resulting in a migration of continents (see Chapter 20), a change in the earth's orbit or in the inclination of its axis (see Chapter 6), and changes in the movements of warm ocean currents (see Chapter 12). The occurrences at the same time of reduced solar radiation and many mountains is favored by some earth scientists as a possible explanation of continental glaciation.

The fact is, though, that even the most carefully thought out explanations of the cause of continental glaciation are at best only intelligent guesses, and most of them are based upon the presumption of former major changes in certain natural phenomena. Such changes, in general with the exception of slippage in the earth's crust, cannot be proved to have actually occurred in times past and evidence of such major changes going on today, except again for slippage in the crust, is largely lacking. Attention is called to Exercise 1 at the end of this chapter, which outlines a possible hitherto unpublished line of investigation concerning this problem which may be of interest to some readers.

Movement of Continental Glaciers.   Whereas a valley glacier moves like the river of ice it is, the general movement of continental glaciers is more like a slow oozing outward from a central core. It is not necessary that the bottom ice of the glacier be moving toward lower elevation. As a matter of fact, some of the most striking effects of continental glaciation have resulted from lower portions of continental glaciers moving uphill. As long as the central area of glaciation is high in elevation, the addition of more ice to that area keeps the ice front advancing by a squeezing process over even awesome obstacles.

The question naturally arises as to why continental glaciers do not extend their ice far out to sea. Although such *ice shelves* are fairly common, they are of limited areal extent because of the continual *calving,* or falling, of large masses of ice into the sea to form *icebergs.* (See Chapter 12.) Motion pictures of such calving often show that the blocks of ice plunging from the glacier front seem to be leaning backward. Evidently the fractures which initiate the calving must be near the bottom of the ice rather than near the top. (This fact may easily be demonstrated by contrasting the manner in which, say, the slices of an apple drop away when cuts are made in a downward direction and then in an upward direction. The original fractures are apparently formed at the base of the ice by melting of the ice by the sea water, and by increased buoyancy due to tidal action.

Landforms of Erosion Made by Continental Glaciers.   As in the case of glaciation by valley glaciers, the plucking done by continental glaciers is by far the most important type of erosion accomplished. Abrasion by continental glaciers, however, leaves some striking effects in the form of polished and *striated,* or grooved, bedrock.

Minor landforms of continental glaciation include *roches moutonnées,* "sheep rocks," large pieces of bedrock which commonly have a smoothly polished and striated slope and a rough, angular slope. *Roches moutonnées* are extremely interesting in that they illustrate both types of glacial erosion, and indicate the direction of flow of ice. The ice moved in the direction from the abraded *stoss* side toward the steeper *lee* side where, possibly because of a dip in topography, the moving ice plucked blocks of rock, rather than continuing abrading. The process described is analogous to running a file under heavy pressure along the edge of a piece of wood (abrading) until a corner is reached where, if the same heavy pressure is maintained, splinters may separate (plucking) on the "lee" side.

The amount of erosion done by continental glaciers in even relatively flat country is almost unbelievable in itself, yet that erosion seems to pale in comparison with continental glaciation erosion over an area containing valleys. In such areas the ice literally acts like a gigantic plow, especially if the bedrock is strongly jointed or fractured, and moves through the valleys, inexorably gouging out millions upon millions of tons of rock. Like valley glaciers, continental glaciers eroding in this manner characteristically leave U-shaped valleys behind them. The basins of many of the world's most important and most scenic lakes were created by glaciation of valleys by continental glaciers. For example, some of the Great Lakes basins were apparently formed in this manner, as were many lake basins in the northern United States, in Canada, and in northern Europe.

Just as valleys are made U-shaped by glaciers, hills and mountains which have been buried under moving continental glaciers typically have rounded appearances and are generally low in height above their surroundings.

Although not glacial erosional features as such, it should be remarked here that the present courses of the Missouri and Ohio rivers were largely determined by the southernmost position of the ice in Pleistocene times. The ice front acted as a wall along which the drainage systems of the Ohio and the Missouri adjusted themselves to flow into the Mississippi.

Landforms of Deposition Made by Continental Glaciers. Rock material carried by and deposited by glaciers is called *drift*. The name is a holdover from the days when it was believed that such rock obviously foreign to a given locality had been carried across ancient seas by icebergs, and then deposited, after so "drifting."

Drift is either *stratified drift* or *till*. Till is not stratified and consists of unsorted and ungraded drift. As is probably evident, stratified drift is stratified through the action of water. Till in general is not subjected to flows of water capable either of causing stratification or of carrying the till into a pond, or lake, or river where stratification might take place.

Terminal moraines are formed by continental glaciers pushing rock material ahead of them and then, upon retreating, leaving the piles and rough deposits of rock debris which roughly outline the former edge of the ice. To the rock debris pushed ahead at the ice edge is added the considerable debris which continental glaciers normally carry in their forward parts in the ice which, upon melting, deposits the widely scattered debris over a large area. The result is that terminal moraines formed by continental glaciers, instead of being essentially wide piles of debris as in the case of those made by valley glaciers, usually cover many square miles of up-and-down topography made up of almost innumerable small hills and depressions, some of which commonly hold ponds or small lakes. The depressions, many of them apparently caused by the melting of blocks of ice surrounded by rock debris, are called *kettles*. The formation of kettles can be approximated in miniature by completely covering an ice cube with sand or other granular unsoluble material, and then letting the ice melt to form a "kettle." A type of typically kettle-dotted moraine called a *recessional moraine* is often formed where the retreating edge of a melting ice sheet is for some reason halted or slowed down long enough so that concentrations of debris are deposited along the general vicinity of the glacier's front.

It might be expected that deposits made by continental glaciers would characteristically be spread out in all directions and in relatively undefined form. This is true for the general deposits of drift in the United States which vary from about 15 feet in thickness in New England to 100 or 200 feet in the glaciated parts of the Central states.

A glacier, however, is also capable of doing some fairly intricate shaping of some of its transported debris as it deposits it. An example of this is a *drumlin,* a hill which viewed from overhead looks as if it has been roughly streamlined, as actually it has. Like a falling raindrop, a drumlin has a blunt end and a sharper end. Also as in a raindrop, the blunt end of a drumlin is made blunt by a resisting force acting upon it. In the case of raindrops the force is air resistance; in the case of a drumlin the force is exerted by the advance of the glacier. Thus the long axis of a drumlin parallels the direction of flow of the glacier, at least as it was in that area, while the sharper end of a drumlin points like an arrow in the direction of glacier movement.

Drumlins are usually less than 100 feet in height and usually less than ¾ mile long. They are composed mostly of till which contains a high percentage of clay, which probably makes possible the molding into a streamlined shape. Drumlins are prevalent in some glaciated regions, there being about 7000 drumlins in New York State alone. One of the most unusual occurrences of drumlins is in Boston Bay, Massachusetts, where drumlins dot the bay as islands.

A melting glacier usually develops tunnels which carry off the *meltwater*. Rock debris is therefore deposited in these tunnels and, upon total melting of the glacier in an area, appears as long, winding ridges called *eskers*. Eskers are commonly from 20 to 60 miles long—some are more than 100 miles long—and may be 100 feet high, or more. Eskers often show a braided structure in various places along their courses, along with rough stratification. They are therefore *glaciofluvial* deposits, glacier deposits stratified by water. Eskers have been identified in Canada, Illinois, Michigan, Minnesota, Wisconsin, New York, and other places.

Much of the rock material carried by the streams in the glacier's tunnels is swept out past the edge of the glacier, onto the *outwash plain.* Here, extreme braiding takes place and the drift is distributed over a large area, much as material is distributed throughout an alluvial fan. Southern Michigan, as an example, is noted for its outwash plains.

As the glacier retreats, the upper limits of its outwash plain is often marked by a terminal moraine with its ridges and depressions. Some of these depressions quickly become ponds or lakes as they fill with meltwater. Material being moved out of the glacier's tunnels is now checked by the terminal moraine and piles up into a hill or ridge to form a *kame.* Material discharged into a glacial pond or lake is thereupon sorted and stratified and may build a *delta kame.* Kames in general are of several types and can be formed in several different ways in addition to those described. They are usually fairly well stratified, at least in some parts of their structures.

Cultural and Economic Aspects of Glaciation

Manufacturing and Settlement. The pattern of manufacturing and settlement in the northeastern United States still strongly reflects the fact that water power largely determined that pattern. Going back still further, we find that it was the drift from continental glaciation which blocked then existent stream valleys and forced most of the larger streams in the northeastern United States out of their valleys and across rough terrain. So, these streams now plunge over falls after falls in their new courses. It was at the larger falls, with their water power, that industries and settlements grew.

Agriculture. Some of the best agricultural land in the United States is found in Ohio, Indiana, Illinois, Iowa, Minnesota, Nebraska, South Dakota, and North Dakota. These states, with the exception of the latter three, were, with minor exceptions, totally glaciated. The eastern eighth of Nebraska was glaciated as was, roughly, the eastern half of South Dakota. All of North Dakota, with the exception of the southwestern quarter, was glaciated. The important result of the glaciation in the above named eight states was the development of outwash plains and extensive plains of till. It is on these fertile plains of glaciation that much of the agricultural economy of the United States is based. In effect, the ice sheets plowed the land, buried many of the large stones, distributed the soil minerals by meltwater, and then left, leaving behind great flat expanses of some of the world's richest and most easily worked soil.

Also, during Pleistocene times, the waters of a mammoth lake were impounded between a crustal block in west-central Minnesota and the edge of the ice sheet which was then far into Canada. The lake extended westward into North Dakota. The ancient lake is known as Lake Agassiz, named for Louis Agassiz, the originator of the theory of continental glaciation. Sediments formed on the bottom of the great lake are now the soil for the famous Red River Plains wheat growing region. Lake sediments also formed excellent soil in areas in other states such as in western New York, eastern Michigan, northern Ohio, northeastern Illinois, and eastern Minnesota. In these cases, however, the sediments were laid down in former extensions of some of the Great Lakes.

Whereas the prairie ground was fairly easily worked, many early farmers in Wisconsin, New York State, and in some New England states were experiencing the same difficulties: hilly land composed of drift almost impossible to till because of glacial boulders. The soil itself was rich enough and, like most glacial drift, held an appreciable amount of water. Lush grass grew on these hills. If plows couldn't get between the rocks animals could, and they could live on the grass. Thus originated the important "Dairy Belt" of the United States, stretching from Wisconsin eastward into the New England states.

In the above ways, among others, glaciation has determined the agricultural patterns in many areas of the United States. And, today, in the northeastern states, dairy cows dot steep, green hills formed by ice sheets while in the plains regions machines work the great flat expanses which were formed by the same ice sheets.

Commerce.   One of the most outstanding examples of the effect of glaciation upon the development of a region occurs on the east coast of the United States. During the Pleistocene epoch, a large moraine was deposited in what is now largely ocean, and the remnants of the moraine, as formerly pointed out, now comprise such features as the long arm of Cape Cod, Nantucket, Martha's Vineyard, and the Elizabeth Islands. The moraine overlies cuesta structures in those regions.

The same general moraine structure crosses New York Bay. Between Staten Island and Long Island, both essentially parts of the glacial structure, the moraine was cut by a channel due to the strong flow of the Hudson River. This resulted in the present situation of the Upper Bay, with its narrow entrance and protecting seaward morainal hills (Forest Hills, for example), being one of the finest harbors in the world, a considerable factor in the development of New York City in particular and of the United States in general. Other effects of glaciation upon commerce include the location of major highways and railroads across well-graded drift plains and, of course, the many extensive commerces of and on the glacier-associated Great Lakes, themselves.

Recreation. Many of the most popular recreation areas in the world are glaciated areas. Consider, for example, Wisconsin and Michigan with their total of 20,000 lakes, New York State with its 8000 lakes, and New England with its 7500 lakes. All of these regions have important summer recreation and tourist-associated industries largely because of the many scenic lakes, most of them of glacial origin. Other areas feature more spectacular glacial scenery, notably Alaska, Glacier National Park, and Yosemite National Park. The popularity of the latter area has grown to such proportions that the portion of the Yosemite Valley floor near the government center is one of the most densely populated areas in the United States during the summer months.

Other Effects of Glaciation. Many towns and cities gained their first water supply from glacial lakes or from water impounded in thick glacial till. An astonishing number of municipalities still get an appreciable amount of water from glacial deposits, and other towns and cities have created huge reservoirs from systems of small glacial lakes and their rivers.

It was mentioned in Chapter 23 that stone and sand suitable for construction is often found in old stream beds. Some of the best and most extensive deposits of such stone and sand occurs in old stream beds which once flowed on an outwash plain below a glacier. There, the constant back-and-forth braiding of channels resulted, many times, in well-washed cobbles, gravel, and sand which was graded vertically and, to considerable extent, horizontally.

REVIEW

1. Name the two main types of glaciers. Describe the origin and movement of each.

2. Define: cirque, col, arête, horn. Discuss the formation of each.

3. Discuss the formation of lateral, medial, and terminal moraines by valley glaciers.

4. What is meant by the "retreat" of a glacier?

5. State the essentials of three hypotheses relating to the cause of continental glaciation.

6. Why do not ice shelves of continental glaciers extend far out to sea?

7. Explain formation of the *roche moutonnée* structure.

8. What are the two main kinds of glacial drift?

9. Discuss the formation and appearance of eskers and drumlins.

10. Explain how certain agricultural patterns in some parts of the United States were determined by glaciation.

11. Explain the relationship of glaciation to New York Harbor, and thus to the general development of the United States.

EXERCISES

(Answers are given in the answer section at the back of the book.)

1. (Suggested as a term project or as the subject of a term paper.) Develop a hypothesis explaining the cause of continental glaciation. The following listed points are suggested as sequence for research:

(a) The earth's magnetic poles are known to be continually shifting. At the present time the earth's north magnetic pole is about 550 miles west of Greenland and the south magnetic pole is over the coast of Antarctica. Greenland and Antarctica are the sites of the world's present two greatest ice sheets.

(b) Is the earth's magnetic field related to weather phenomena? Could a change in position—and probably also an induced change in the character—of the magnetic field bring about a lowering of about 5° F in average temperatures over large areas? As stated in Chapter 20, certain changes in the earth's magnetic field are apparently related to changes in relative rotational velocity of the outer core.

(c) Why do auroras in the earth's magnetic field center at high latitudes?

(d) There is some evidence that solar flares affect the course of the major jet stream. It is known that much radiation from the sun is trapped in the outer Van Allen belt of the magnetic field. It therefore seems likely that changes in the earth's magnetic field might have some effect upon the jet stream.

(e) The jet stream is apparently related to several weather phenomena, such as the southward extension of very cold weather for abnormally long periods of time, etc.

(f) Contrast the general curve of the jet stream shown in Figure 57 of Chapter 10 with the general curve outlined by the Missouri and Ohio rivers as shown on a map of the United States. The courses of these rivers closely approximate the southernmost extent of continental glaciation in the United States.

(g) Does it seem possible that the average position of the jet stream or of some part of it over a number of years is associated with continental glaciation of the United States? Consult sources of meteorological data and compare the average curve of the jet stream in Europe with the curve of the southernmost limits of continental glaciation in Europe.

(h) After thoroughly researching the above and other points, state a hypothesis to explain the cause of continental glaciation, assuming that the indicated line of research does lead to a valid speculation.

2. Figure 82 of Chapter 22 is a map of glaciated terrain. The principal feature is a large mountainous mass of igneous rock which has been sub-jected to glaciation by valley glaciers. On Figure 82:

(a) What feature is represented at the head of the stream on the left side of the map?

(b) What are the geological names of the two lakes?

(c) What feature is represented on the sharp ridge, somewhat to the left of the smaller lake?

(d) What is the feature about halfway between the right and left edges of the map, and two miles from the southern boundary of the map?

(e) What is the feature between the two lakes?

CHAPTER 25

Oceans and Their Associated Landforms

The effects of the oceans upon climate were discussed in Chapter 12. This chapter describes the erosional and depositional work done by oceans, and the resulting landforms.

Ocean Currents, Waves, and Wave Action

Ocean Currents. In addition to the kinds of ocean currents described in Chapter 12, local currents of much smaller magnitude occur in oceans, especially near land. Such currents are often capable of both erosion and deposition over considerable distances.

Tidal currents can transport appreciable amounts of sediments where incoming tides or ebb tides cause river-like movement of water through narrows such as occur in some bays, river mouths, etc. Some incoming tidal currents cause local high water of 50 feet or more. More important, from the standpoint of geological effects, some such currents are known to scour ocean floors which are as deep as ¼ mile below the surface.

Longshore currents, or at least their effects, are well known to surf bathers. Typically, after some time in the surf, bathers start toward the beach only to find that they have been moved along the shore and are now some distance from the point at which they entered the water. The longshore current which moves them is a result of the waves approaching the shore at an angle other than a right angle. As the waves "break," some of the water travels more or less parallel with the shore, as a current.

Rock particles swept up onto the beach by incoming water perforce follow paths more or less parallel with the direction of the rushing water. This direction is rarely at exact right angles to the shore. As the water flows back, however, it must follow the steepest inclines, bringing the rock particles with it until a breaking wave again sweeps the particles up onto the beach. The result is that particles tend thus to migrate in zigzag fashion along the beach by *beach drifting*. It should be emphasized that the term "beach" as used here refers to the entire surf zone.

Waves and Wave Action.   It seems to be a fairly popular belief that a given ocean wave consists of water which has traveled in that wave for what may have been considerable distance. The fact is that, except for currents, upwelling, surf action, etc., ocean water does very little apparent traveling. A given particle of water in a wave system will seldom advance more than a few hundred feet before returning to, or very nearly to, its original position, even in wave systems generated by other than intense storms.

Wave action occurs when wind blowing across the surface of the water forces water particles forward and upward into ridges whose particles of water are then pulled downward by gravity. This results in an oscillatory pattern whose waves are due to each particle of water describing approximate vertical circles whose diameters and actual completions as closed loops depend upon the character of the waves being generated by the wind. If the circle is not quite completed, some water *drifts* in the direction of the wind. This may occur during stormy weather, to varying extent. With such exceptions, however, each particle of water describes a near-perfect loop and it is the rising and falling of the particles as they sweep around the loops which give the effect of continuing forward movement of the waves. It is not a particular wave of *water* which keeps moving forward; it is the wave *form* which moves.

The generation and apparent travel of a wave can be graphically demonstrated by placing a coin tangent to a ruled line on a piece of paper. Holding a pencil point on the paper against the point of tangency, slowly rotate the coin counterclockwise and at the same time slide the coin fairly briskly to the right so that it remains tangent to the line. The pencil point, held firmly against the same point on the coin, moves on the paper as the coin moves. By the time the pencil point returns to the ruled line, a "wave" will have been traced on the paper. It should be pointed out that the described experiment actually portrays waves "moving" from right to left. It will be seen that the actual shape of the wave and the distance between crests depends upon the relative amounts of rotation and movement along the ruled line. In nature, these effects are governed by the strength and duration of the wind, and by the distance the wind travels over the open ocean.

The above experiment also clearly shows that the height of a wave is equal to the diameter of the circle of travel of a water particle. Suppose, however, that the coin is now rotated fairly rapidly while it is moved very slowly along the line. It will now be found that the pencil is describing a counterclockwise loop which is trying to close upon itself to the left. This represents a slowing up of the wave velocity. Just as the penciled curve now breaks downward, toward the left, ocean water similarly "breaks" because the now faster moving water particles are thrust higher and higher into the air and are also thrust ahead of the advancing wave front. There literally being nothing below these particles to support them, the wave breaks. By that time the original vertical circles of particle motion have been deformed into ellipses whose heights may be several times that of the original waves.

Surf, and Its Work

After a wave breaks, its motion is a composite of wave motion and of running water. Surfboard riders, for instance, ride downhill on the water which slides down the shore side of the advancing wave front. Beneath the surface, the water particles in a particular loop are either hitting bottom or are agitating deeper water against the bottom. The result is that the ocean bottom is continually being scoured in the surf zone. Many rock particles are thrown obliquely up onto the beach and are then pulled straight back, the process being continuously repeated, to cause beach drift, as already explained. Considering the scouring activity, the beach drifting, and the great hydraulic energy finally released in the surf, it probably is clear that most of the erosional work done by ocean water is performed in the zone of the surf.

As in the case of stream erosion, the two principle methods of wave erosion are by *hydraulic action* and *abrasion*. Hydraulic action relates to the work done by the surf itself, while abrasion occurs when rock particles carried in the surf abrade the coastline rocks and beaches. Also as in the case of stream erosion, erosion by waves is at a maximum during high water. This occurs in the surf zone because of storms or infrequently because of so-called *tidal waves*, actually the result of submarine earthquakes.

Wave Refraction

One of the most striking ocean shore phenomena is that of *wave refraction,* the change in direction of a wave so that before it breaks, it is roughly parallel to the shore. No matter how oblique to the shore the deep-water waves are, the surf waves are usually nearly at right angles to the slope of the beach, a fact which has been noticed by many observant visitors to ocean shores.

Wave refraction is of considerable importance in erosion. A wide promontory, for example, is thus often eroded on all beaches by surf which pounds away at almost right angles to each beach. On the other hand, the erosional work of the surf in inlets and bays is spread out in fan fashion, rather than being concentrated. The result is that whereas points and promontories tend to be relatively quickly eroded, indentations in a coastline tend to remain relatively unchanged over a period of years, considering wave erosion alone.

Wave refraction occurs because a wave approaching shore at an oblique angle hits bottom or near-bottom at different times along its length. The first part of the wave to slow its forward velocity is of course the shoreward section. This same change in forward velocity occurs successively along the entire wave front until the wave has turned so that the water particles in all loops are moving at about the same speed. This will occur only where the water is approximately the same depth along the wave front which in turn means that the entire wave is moving straight up the slope of the beach.

Wave refraction can be demonstrated by an experiment whose underlying principles approximate those involved in wave refraction: Hold a piece of preferably rough-surface paper so that it makes an angle of about 30° with a table top. The paper represents a sloping beach, and the table top represents the ocean. Now, swiftly roll a pencil (a "wave") across the table top toward the paper, but at an angle so that the pencil will start to roll obliquely up and not straight up the paper incline. The pencil will "refract," or swing around, as it moves on the incline until it is going nearly straight up the slope. (This particular experiment also illustrates the main actions involved in the already explained *beach drift* wherein a rock particle is swept up onto the beach at a slight oblique angle and is then pulled straight down the beach slope by the retreating water.)

Landforms of Ocean Wave Erosion

Sea Cliffs. *Sea cliffs* are commonly carved out of land which originally sloped fairly steeply to the sea. Hydraulic action, due to the force of the surf as it pounds away at the land, is of far greater importance than is abrasion in the making of a sea cliff.

The surf first laboriously carves a very low cliff but as soon as the cliff is about as high as the average wave dashing against it, the cliff starts to retreat shoreward relatively rapidly. As it does so, it becomes higher because of the slope of the land toward the sea.

The formation of a sea cliff is considerably speeded up by the presence of joints and cracks in the rock which allows the surf to remove whole blocks of rock. An important factor is that depressions, holes, and caves in the rock are filled with air which, when tons of water are hurled against the rock, becomes compressed. As the air is trapped in this manner and compressed, it must finally either be compressed to the extent where it will resist further forward motion of the water or it must force itself into the surrounding rock. It does the latter, through joints and cracks, and in this manner further weakens the rock until the surf finally removes blocks which have been effectively outlined and loosened by the compressed air.

It is obvious that the actual cutting of the cliff takes place only where the surf hits it near its base. Yet, many newly formed sea cliffs are vertical or even tend slightly to overhang the beach. Such retreat of the whole cliff is due to the *notch,* cut into a cliff's base, being overhung by the rest of the cliff. (See Figure 89.) Finally, the rock will progressively shear off above the notch, in much the same manner as

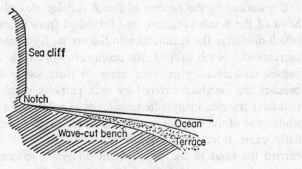

Fig. 89. Ocean shore features.

an iceberg plunges off a glacier after the ice is undercut by the ocean water, and the cliff retreats.

Finally a sea cliff is cut back to where the surf accomplishes very little more erosion on the base of the cliff. All that is left now is for the overhanging parts of the cliff to fall down. By then the character of the ocean floor offshore from the cliff, in and somewhat beyond the zone of the surf, has been considerably changed from its original form. This change is discussed next.

Wave-Cut Benches and Terraces. As sea cliffs are being formed, the ocean floor in the surf zone is also being carved into a new slope. In addition to the purely hydraulic action of the surf upon the ocean floor, rock masses and particles from the cliffs and from the surf zone are carried back and forth across an *abrasion platform* or *wave-cut bench.* (See Figure 89.) Such rock benches are fairly common sights along some coasts, at low tide. In other places, the benches are covered to varying degree by sediment whose seaward extensions are called *terraces.* In some regions, several wave-cut cliffs and benches can now be seen far above sea level, showing that sea level in that particular region has successively dropped in relation to the land since the cliffs and benches were cut.

Landforms of Wave and Current Deposition

Beaches. A *beach* is actually that part of the ocean floor within the surf zone, although in popular usage "the beach" is that part of the surf zone which is shoreward of the temporary high water mark.

The sediments on beaches, such as sand, are continuously worked and reworked by the process of *beach drifting,* described previously. Most of the beach sediments are furnished from inland, by streams which discharge the sediments into the ocean. By means of longshore currents and beach drifting, the sediments work their way along the coasts, concentrating in some areas to form sandy beaches. Such beaches are therefore covered by rock particles which for the most part have traveled many, often hundreds of miles. Most of the famous white sand of the beaches on Florida's east shore, for example, originally came from other coastal states to the north. There, rivers carried the sand to the ocean where longshore currents and beach drifting then transported the sand southward. Thus most of the sand on the described Florida beaches was once part of the Appalachian Mountains.

Spits.   Ridges of sand or other small size rock material which project into the ocean are called *spits*. Spits build up as material which drifts along a beach and past a headland and is deposited in deeper water, below the influence of near-surface drift. Spits therefore commonly form at the mouths of bays. (See Figure 90.) There, only short dis-

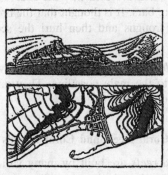

Fig. 90. Shoreline features. Drawn by E. Raisz. (Part of Fig. 75) (Courtesy of John Wiley & Sons, Inc., from A. Strahler's *Physical Geography*, 2d edition, 1960)

tances from the headlands, the water is usually considerably deeper because the shoreward limits of the shallow surf zone along a headland, extended into open water, is seaward of the bay's surf zone. A spit often has a "hook" which curves shoreward because of wave action, such as the hook on the northern end of Cape Cod.

Bay Bars.   Bay bars, or *bay barriers,* are ridges which close the mouths of bays. It is apparent that most bay bars have been formed by extension of spits.

Barrier Islands.   Barrier islands, or *offshore bars,* are islands whose long axes are more or less parallel to the coastline. Some barrier islands lie miles offshore. They commonly occur in regions where coastal waters are shallow far to seaward, such as in some areas along the Atlantic shore of the United States. While some barrier islands are evidently the remains of former spits, others are probably formed by the quick succession of wave scour and deposition in the surf zone. Still other barrier islands seem to have been formed by a combination of these methods. Coney Island is one of many barrier islands on the Atlantic coast. When barrier islands close off a bay mouth, a *lagoon* is formed.

Longshore Bars.   *Longshore bars* may be thought of as being small submerged barrier islands and, in many cases, may actually be barrier islands in the making. Longshore bars are also apparently formed by a quick succession of wave scour and deposition, as they are usually flanked by troughs which are evidently the source regions of the material in the longshore bars. It is thought that the breaking waves probably scour out the troughs and then hurl the sediments into ridge form.

Tombolos.   A *tombolo* is a ridge which connects two islands or which connects an island to the main coastline. They are evidently caused by drift action of some type.

Coral Reefs and Coral Islands

Coral Reefs.   *Coral reefs* are built by many varieties of marine organisms living together in colonies. Actually, coral polyps commonly contribute less to the building of a reef than do other organisms such as algae, hence the term "coral" popularly lends more romanticism than realism to the consideration of many reefs and islands. Many colonial marine animals and plants secrete lime and, as the old organisms die, the younger ones build their communal edifices on top of the old dead colonies. The three main types of coral reefs are believed to be formed by subsidence of the island around which the coral is growing or by a rise in the level of the ocean, or by both. The supposed sequence of events is as follows:

First, a *fringing reef,* fairly close to shore, is formed. Next, while the island slowly sinks, the coral reef keeps growing and a *barrier reef,* some distance from shore, is formed with a lagoon between the reef and the island. Finally, with continuing upward growth of the colonies as the island sinks, and final complete subsidence of the island, an *atoll* results.

Colonial coral and other colonial marine animals which build reefs thrive in warm, clear, shallow water. Reef-building coral, for example, will not live in water which is much colder than 67° F or which is more than 200 feet deep. So, throughout the fringing reef-barrier, reef-atoll sequence, the actual or relative sinking of an island automatically spells the doom of the old colonies and forces new colonies to build on top of the old in order to be in warm, shallow water.

Coral Islands.   *Coral islands* can usually be recognized as parts of recognized coral reef systems. Again, the word "coral" is extremely misleading in that many "coral" islands are built up in large part from the skeletal remains of marine organisms other than corals.

Shoreline Classification

Shorelines are often largely classed as being either shorelines of *submergence* or shorelines of *emergence*. A "shoreline of submergence" indicates that a particular coastline was relatively drowned as the sea pounded away at it, while the term "emergence" indicates that a coast was relatively lofty during attack by the ocean. A "submerged" coast would therefore show numerous bays and inlets due to drowning of river mouths while an "emerged" coast, being made up of youthful, undisturbed strata just risen from the ocean, would be fairly straight. Recently, however, a new system of classification has been developed, principally for the reason that with the melting of the great Pleistocene ice sheets and other Pleistocene glaciers, most coasts became coasts of submergence. Today there are very few shorelines of emergence. The new system of shoreline classification describes shorelines in terms of whether the chief landforms being, and to be, attacked by the ocean are landforms of deposition or landforms of erosion.

The Cycle of Erosion along Coasts

Figure 90 depicts part of a typical shoreline which is being eroded by the ocean, and which provides an excellent base for studying the erosional cycle of a coastline.

As the headland in the right-hand part of the diagram is cut back, the sea cliff will increase in height, and the spit, moving back with the cliff, will finally become a bay bar. The former bay will now silt up with material from the stream and will become a *tidal flat* or a *tidal marsh*. Whatever sea cliff erosion was still proceeding on the headland to the left will now cease as the bay bar migrates shoreward with the developing sea cliff on the right.

Finally, the headland on the right will have been cut back to a position where its cliffs are roughly in line with the inner shore of the former bay. By then, the tidal marsh or flat will have been destroyed and the coastline in this region will be essentially straight, consisting of an irregularly eroded headland to the left, a drowned river mouth, and a headland to the right with sharp ocean cliffs.

If further ocean erosion proceeds the shoreline will move back, with some development of sea cliffs on the headland to the left, and with further expansion of the sea cliffs on the headland to the right. In this manner, even highly irregular shorelines all eventually become shorelines which are nearly straight.

An irregular shoreline, such as the one described, is therefore one of early youth while a regular shoreline, if formed in the above manner, is one of maturity. Various gradations of geologic age lie between, in shorelines of intermediate character. The cycle of erosion of a coast is an extremely interesting phenomenon in several ways. Among other things, it illustrates, on a grand scale and with many easily studied examples of the various stages of erosion, nature's attainment of near-equilibrium over extreme and varied obstacles.

Cultural and Economic Aspects of Landforms of Ocean Erosion and Deposition

The relationship between indented coastlines with their many harbors, and regional developments of the shipping and fishing industries has been evident throughout history. Also, over the past three centuries the number and kinds of harbors possessed by a country often largely determined its position in world trade.

Formerly the closer a ship could get to the buyers and sellers of its cargo, the cheaper it was for all concerned. This resulted in ships sailing far into estuaries, to river ports. The establishment of these busy ports spurred the growth of inland industry and agriculture which in turn materially helped the railroad industry to boom. With railroad main and spur lines finally reaching to the coasts, it was now cheaper to abandon the inland ports, use the bays as harbors, and there load and unload the cargoes from trains to ships, and *vice versa*. In the meantime, although the ports were on their way toward moving seaward, the railroads had effectively tied a country together. It is apparent that the "submerged" type of shoreline has been and remains a controlling factor in the economies and resulting cultures of many countries.

It should also be mentioned that the recreation and tourist industries are intimately concerned with landforms of ocean erosion and deposition. The barrier island called Coney Island previously mentioned in this chapter is world famous as are many true beaches. Many of the world's most famous ocean bathing areas are noted for wide, gently sloping beaches and scenic sea cliffs. Contrasting with these mature shorelines are the younger shorelines with their coves and bays which harbor millions of small pleasure craft such as sailboats, emblematic of the tremendously fast-growing recreation of boating which in the United States alone is figured in terms of over a billion dollars annually.

REVIEW

1. What is a longshore current? Explain "beach drift."

2. Discuss waves and wave action, explaining the apparent motion of ocean water for a considerable distance.

3. What is "wave refraction"? Of what significance is it in erosion?

4. Discuss the formation of a sea cliff.

5. Explain how wave-cut benches and terraces are formed.

6. Define "beach." Where does most of the sand, etc., on beaches come from?

7. Explain how spits and bay bars are formed.

8. What is a barrier island; a longshore bar; a tombolo? Explain how each is formed.

9. Are all "coral" reefs and islands built primarily of coral? Explain.

10. Discuss the cycle of erosion along a coast, starting your discussion by assuming that the ocean is eroding a deeply indented coastline with bold headlands and many bays.

EXERCISES

(Answers are given in the answer section at the back of the book.)

1. Perform the experiment of "wave refraction" described in this chapter. What effect, if any, does increased slope of the "beach" seem to have upon refraction? What effect, if any, does increased velocity of the "wave" seem to have upon refraction?

2. In what direction is the longshore current flowing, in Figure 90?

3. Suppose, referring to Figure 90, that the level of the sea suddenly

338   PHYSICAL GEOGRAPHY

rises 100 feet. Make a sketch of the resulting shoreline. Contour interval is 20 feet.

4. If the headland to the right in Figure 90 is cliffed back to a position where the resulting cliff is in line with the most shoreward side of the bay shown, how high will the cliff be at its highest point? Contour interval is 20 feet.

5. Suppose, referring to Figure 90, that the level of the sea suddenly dropped so that the area shown in the figure is completely land. Describe the appearance of (a) the spit, (b) a delta, where the stream enters the bay, (c) the former sea floor, oceanward from the cliff on the right, (d) the floor of the former bay.

6. It is a common practice for sightseers, picnickers, amateur photographers, etc., to use the tops of overhanging sea cliffs and river bluffs for their activities. It is apparent to anyone who has studied physical geography or geology that these cliffs and bluffs were largely formed by thousands of similar overhangs suddenly plunging to the base of the cliff or bluff.

What precautions does your state take, in regions of appreciable tourist travel, to insure that such scenic vantage points are either safe or are closed to public entry?

CHAPTER 26

Crustal Rock Movements and Associated Landforms

When crustal rock moves it is usually either *tilted, bent* or *folded, faulted,* or subjected to a combination of two or more of the above listed movements. *Tilted* infers that rock has been inclined from a former position. *Bent* means that rock has been broadly curved or *warped. Folded* describes rock which has been forced into wave-like form while *faulted* means that rock has moved along a fracture. The basic causes of such movements are only incompletely understood but the relationships of these movements to certain resulting landforms are well known. As will be seen, landforms associated with large-scale movements of crustal rock are of extreme importance in our daily living.

Rock Tilt and Coastal Plains

The coastal plains of the world are outstanding examples of tilting without related major faulting or folding. The strata underlying coastal plains were once part of continental shelves where the strata formed. In some cases crustal forces slowly thrust parts of the continental shelves above sea level to form *newly emerged* coastal plains whose parts are subjected to erosion as soon as they emerge from the ocean. In other instances, coastal plains apparently emerge largely because of a falling of sea level, such as occurs during continental glaciation when large quantities of water are withdrawn from the ocean to become ice on land. In still other cases, coastal plains apparently emerge during some combination of large-scale crustal movement and great change in volume of water in the ocean basins. In all instances, at least some crustal movement probably takes place.

Erosion of Coastal Plains. If crustal movement increases the original tilt of strata in a coastal plain area, that area becomes more and more subject to increased stream erosion. Even with such increased tilt, the slope of coastal plain strata is not normally more than one degree or so, and erosion of a coastal plain area to the point where the area is well drained by stream systems is a long process.

The first streams formed on coastal plains are *consequent* streams following the slope, and *subsequent* streams whose courses are influenced by weak rock. These stream types were discussed in Chapter 23, as were various drainage patterns, and the formation of *cuestas,* erosional ridges whose long axes are roughly at right angles to the slope of the strata. Cuestas are typical of eroded coastal plains and are found on the Atlantic and Gulf coasts of the United States. The glacial debris of Long Island, for example, overlies part of a cuesta formed by erosion of Atlantic Coastal Plain strata.

The existence of such cuestas near present shorelines infers, of course, that considerable erosion of the coastal plains area has taken place. Therefore it would be expected that those parts of coastal regions featuring such cuestas would be fairly well drained, and in general this is true. For example, the Atlantic coast from Maine to Virginia has the cuesta described above, in addition to several more, and in general is well drained. This portion of the Atlantic Coastal Plain is a region of relatively old emergence. From Virginia through the Carolinas, Georgia, and Florida, however, evidence of cuesta formation is lacking, and so is general good drainage. That part of the Atlantic Coastal Plain is of such relatively new emergence that drainage is virtually nonexistent in some regions, resulting in swamps such as the Dismal Swamp of Virginia and North Carolina, the Okefenokee Swamp of Florida and Georgia, and the Florida Everglades.

Economic and Cultural Aspects of
Coastal Plains of the United States

It was previously pointed out that most present shorelines are really shorelines of submergence because of the melting of glaciers toward the end of the Pleistocene epoch and the rise of sea level. At that time vast areas of newly emerged coastal plains must have been inundated as the water rose over gently tilted strata.

From the standpoint of geologic time, only a few years have elapsed since the end of the Pleistocene epoch, and many present landforms are not much more eroded now than they were then. This is especially true of some coastal plains areas which, because of their low angles of slope, are not easily modified by erosion. So, the erosional features visible on a coastal plain are often duplicated on the continental shelf where the submerged portion of the eroded coastal plain lies. This fact is of great importance in considering the cultural and economic aspects of some of the world's coastal plains. The cultures and economies of many coastal regions are intimately associated not only with the coastal plains proper, but also with their drowned extensions, portions of the continental shelves. The Atlantic Coastal Plain, shown in Figure 74, is a good example of the foregoing statement.

The Atlantic Coastal Plain. At first glance there seems to be little if any relationship between the existence of the Atlantic Coastal Plain and cultural and economic patterns along the seaboard. An Atlantic Coastal Plain cuesta, however, previously mentioned, extends beneath the surface of the ocean from Nantucket to Newfoundland to form the mammoth fishing banks of America's eastern seaboard, one of the world's four most important fisheries. Cape May, which half closes the mouth of Delaware Bay, is part of the same cuesta as is Cape Charles which is seaward of Chesapeake Bay. Thanks in large part to the bays' being protected by the two giant capes resulting from erosion of the cuesta, the general Delaware Bay–Chesapeake Bay area is particularly well suited to transoceanic and coastal ocean commerce. The present status of the area as one of the greatest industrial regions in the United States is a logical development which was considerably aided by the fact that the coastal plain in that region was fairly well eroded before being partially submerged. This resulted in the deeply indented bays surrounded by land of low elevation, a fairly rare combination which is extremely amenable to many kinds of development.

The Gulf Coastal Plain. With the exception of the coastal region itself, the Gulf Coastal Plain (see Figure 74) is well eroded and exhibits many cuestas and intervening lowlands which combine to give the region a belted appearance when seen from the air or on a map. For this reason this area is sometimes called the *belted coastal plain.* The region is humid, hence the cuesta ridges are typically of sandstone while the lowlands, containing some of the country's most fertile soil, have been carved out of the more soluble limestone.

The Gulf Coastal Plain is rich in mineral resources associated with sedimentary rocks, notably *petroleum, sulfur,* and *soft coal.* Methods of extraction are interesting in that they reflect the extremely simple geological structure of most coastal plains regions. Sulfur, for instance, is extracted by forcing hot water and compressed air down three concentric pipes, a fourth pipe returning the sulfur in melted froth form to the surface.

Testifying to the shallow depth of ocean water and the shallow depth of the petroleum occurrence, offshore oil drilling rigs are common sights along the coastal areas of the Gulf Coastal Plain. Although some folding of strata in the Gulf Coastal Plain has resulted in concentrations of oil, much of the petroleum occurs in depositional traps formed during deposition of the coastal plain strata.

Alaska's Coastal Plain.   A coastal plain also exists along much of Alaska's northern coastline. The coastal plain is characterized by expanses of swampy and marshy ground which is frozen during most of the year. As in the Gulf Coastal Plain, Alaska's coastal plain, known as the Arctic Plains, contains petroleum deposits.

Bending and Folding of Crustal Rock

Soft material, cloth for example, can assume a series of wrinkles or folds because of its structure, but the explanation of rock bending and folding is far less simple. For one thing, the source of the great compressive pressures needed to force layers of rock (their combined thicknesses often totaling hundreds and thousands of feet) into huge folds is not known. Rock folds are often demonstrated in the laboratory by compressing horizontal "strata" of varying colors of clay between end blocks which are kept sliding toward each other on a table, but where are the equivalents of the corresponding end blocks in nature, and what makes them move? This comprises one of geology's greatest unsolved mysteries. One thing seems certain, however: if folding of rock began to take place near the earth's surface, the rock being folded upward and thrust above the earth's surface would fracture instead of bending because of the differences in pressure. Folding of rock therefore is probably done well beneath the surface of the earth, under *confining* pressures.

Whatever their source or sources, these pressures in the earth's crust do bend and fold rock. The bending can be permanent or temporary. When the bending becomes so accentuated that the rock can be said to be folded, the rock has undergone plastic flow and deformation and will never return elastically to its former shape. It has been permanently deformed.

The meanings of the terms "elastic" and "plastic" as used in earth science to describe rock movement must be understood first if the student is to understand the bending and folding of rock. "Elastic" means that rock is capable of resuming its original shape and dimensions after deformation. "Plastic" means that *slip* of minerals has taken place within the rock so that the rock will never return to its original shape or dimensions. This brings up the point that rocks which are folded rather than being bent into broad warps must suffer plastic action and are therefore permanently deformed.

This can be strikingly illustrated by holding a paperback book along the binding with one hand, and firmly clamping the opposite edges together with the other. Now try to bend the book. It will be found that only a slight bend can be made. If the grip on the unbound edge is now relaxed, though, so that the pages slip past each other, the book can be sharply folded. Similarly, when rock is folded, slippage within the rock must occur. If rock is merely bent, it can often regain its former shape and measurements if the deforming forces are removed.

As an illustration of the last statement, it will be found that although the book in the above illustration could be only slightly bent when no slipping occurred, it is easily brought back to its former condition by maintaining the same pressure but in reverse. This represents a release of the deforming pressure and an elastic return to former condition. Let the leaves slip again, however, until a fold is formed. Now firmly clamp the open edges together with the hand and try to "bend" the fold out. The interesting new folds which are developed in this manner have their counterparts in nature, because trying to take out the fold while holding the slipped pages firmly together in this manner is analogous to forces acting upon already deformed rock. Unlike elastic deformation, plastic flow is a no-return operation in rock because, once it has occurred, a new internal rock structure has been formed.

The fact that rock can exhibit actual elasticity is of far more than academic interest. Rock which was bowed under the tremendous weight of continental glaciation in North America is now springing back elastically at such a rate that within a few thousand years the

entire drainage of the Great Lakes may be into the Mississippi
River system. Of more immediate concern is the fact that earthquakes
are apparently generated by sudden elastic rebound of rock masses,
a subject to be discussed more fully later in this chapter.

Structures Associated with Bending and Folding of Rock

Crustal Warping. A *crustal warp* is a gentle bend in rock. If the
bending is upward from a point, a *structural dome* has been formed;
if downward, a *structural basin* has been formed. Examples of such
broad warping are the state of Michigan which for the most part
occupies a structural basin, and the Paris Basin of France which is
noted for its outlying cuestas formed by erosion of the basin structure.
The Weald Uplift of England is a structural dome as are the Nash-
ville Dome of Tennessee and the Bluegrass Region of Kentucky.

It must not be assumed that structural domes and basins are now
all topographic uplifts and depressions, respectively. As a matter of
fact, many of these structures are now represented on the surface in
plains and other flat regions only by a series of roughly circular and
concentric rings which are the eroded strata. Flying over these eroded
structures often gives one the impression of flying over gigantic bull's-
eye targets which have been somewhat erratically painted on a plain.
(A dome structure which tends to remain as a dome despite erosion
may form a *dome mountain.*)

Anticlines and Synclines. When rock is folded into wave-like form,
the crests of the folds are called *anticlines;* the troughs of the folds
are called *synclines*. Anticlines and synclines can vary in size from
microscopic to gigantic folds measured in thousands of feet. Anticlines and synclines are very evident in most mountain structures, to
the point where some young mountains are essentially huge anticlines
while deep young valleys are on synclines. As an example of the
sizes which these structures can attain, Florida is the above-sea-level
portion of a great anticline composed, for the most part, of limestone.

Erosion of Anticlines and Synclines. If a piece of paper is loosely
folded once so that it makes a V when viewed from the end, the
crease represents the *axis,* and the two paper slopes represent the
sides, or *limbs,* of the structure. If the paper is held so that the "axis"
is parallel to a table top (sea level), it can be seen that horizontal

erosion of such an anticline, or syncline, will result in a series of more or less parallel strata. Such erosion can be quickly performed on the paper structure by a pair of scissors, the cuts being made parallel to the table top. (The actual field structure of course is full of strata while the paper represents only one layer of folded strata.)

If the crease of the folded paper is held at an angle to the table top, this represents a *plunging* structure, one whose axis is not horizontal. Upon "erosion" now by scissors, the cut being made across both "limbs," and parallel to the table (sea level), it will be found that the eroded "strata," viewed from overhead, form a V. In the field the V shape varies to a U shape depending upon several things, including the shape of the structure and the degree of plunge, or slope, of the axis. Figure 91 is a map showing an eroded, plunging anticline which has been faulted. In this particular example and as

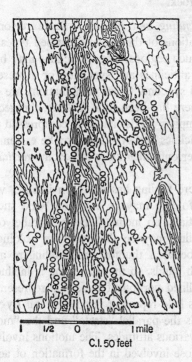

Fig. 91. An eroded, plunging anticline. Top of diagram is north. (From *Photogeology* by Miller & Miller. Copyright, 1961. McGraw-Hill Book Company. Used by permission)

often happens, more resistant strata have formed ridges which out-line the V shape.

Figure 91 also shows, contrary to what might be expected, that the eroded anticline has largely become a depression in the earth's sur-face. This is interesting in that it indicates that this particular anti-cline has experienced several stages of erosion. It no doubt was once a topographic ridge but, after erosion exposed weaker rocks near the axis, the stream system adjusted themselves to the weaker rocks and carved out a topographic depression. It is very common for anticlines thus to form topographic depressions, while domes are commonly reduced to almost flat surfaces as, many times, are the inner portions of structural basins. Synclines usually form valleys in geologic youth and while many synclines also form valleys in geologic maturity and old age, many others form ridges due to adjustment of streams onto belts of weaker rock.

Variations in Bending and Folding. Some regions are noted for complex combinations of the above described types of rock bending and folding. In such regions, large anticlines may be composed of a series of smaller anticlines and synclines, or a present anticline may be an overturned syncline. Other combinations are common.

Even where there has been little faulting, the geology of a folded region can be complex. Folds can be so compressed that they become *closed* folds. Anticlines and synclines may be extremely distorted and may be thrust over onto their sides to become *reclining* or *recumbent* folds.

In regions where folding has not been intense, very simple types of bending and folding may be common. One such structure is a *monocline,* essentially an incline between parallel or nearly parallel strata. A monocline may be illustrated by holding the ends of a stretched string between thumbs and forefingers and then moving one hand, or both hands, so that the string is inclined to its original position. The inclined portion of the string represents the monocline while the portions held represent parallel strata. By varying the posi-tions of the hands the parallel "strata" and the "monocline" can be made to assume various attitudes. The motions involved are probably very similar to those involved in the formation of actual monoclines.

Cultural and Economic Aspects of Bending and Folding of Rock

The influence of topography controlled by rock folding upon population and transportation patterns is well illustrated by the Appalachian region of the United States. There, where possible, roads follow the long valleys and go through water gaps or wind gaps in getting to other valleys. Towns and cities and large farms rest in the valleys while the steep, forested ridges provide some of the most striking scenery in the world. Where simple anticlines and synclines were formed, the ridges and valleys are parallel. Where the axes of the folds dip, or where other complex action has occurred, the ridges and valleys often come together to form extremely irregular topography. These regions, of course, are sparsely settled as are the areas where sharp folding and subsequent erosion has resulted in steep slopes, narrow valleys, and knife-edge ridges. Another good example of linear ridges and valleys is seen in the Coast Ranges of California.

Rock folds and bends are intimately associated with much of the world's mineral wealth. Consider coal, to start. The first stages in the formation of coal occur in swamps where plant material is processed by bacteria to the *peat* stage. Upon deposition of more plant material, the peat becomes more compressed, the effect being that some water and gas are literally squeezed out, and the peat becomes *lignite,* a brown coal. Upon further deposition and compression, the lignite similarly changes into another grade of coal, and so on.

Although bituminous coal is commonly found in essentially horizontal layers which would seem to indicate little bending or folding, it is very doubtful that the large coal fields of the world could have been formed without bending of rock somewhere. In order that layer after layer of coal be formed, it is necessary that the swamp sink and when this happens, rock beneath the swamp must bend or fracture. In the case of fracture plus actual folding, *anthracite* coal is often formed. This type of coal is discussed in more detail in the next chapter.

Much of the world's petroleum and natural gas has been trapped in subsurface structures such as anticlines, synclines, and domes. Oil tends to migrate from the original rock—the *source* rock—in which it formed. If the pore spaces of the surrounding rock are small, the oil will migrate upward due to capillary force, and may be found on the

limbs of an anticline or dome. If the pore spaces are large or if faulting has been prevalent, the oil may flush out and finally end up in a
synclinal structure. It is no exaggeration to say that the oil and natural gas industries are literally vitally concerned with rock bends and
folds.

As another example, take iron. Some of our greatest iron ore
deposits were formed in large synclines—geosynclines—and are sedimentary in origin. The Clinton iron ore, extending from New York to
Alabama, was formed in this manner as, partly at least, were the
great iron ore deposits of the Great Lakes region.

Other important examples of sedimentary mineral deposition in
geosynclines include iron ores in Canada and France, salt and gypsum
deposits in many areas of the world, and manganese deposits in
Russia.

Faulting of Crustal Rock

A *fault* is a fracture along which there has been appreciable movement. Faults are often astonishingly regular in form in that their
opposing surfaces are commonly, for all practical purposes, flat
planes. A typical fault appears as if its rock had been sheared and
most faults have apparently been formed by shearing action.

This explains the flat faces of fault planes and the occurrence of
parallel faults in many regions in that shearing stresses develop only
at certain specified angles under given conditions. As for their origin,
shearing stresses develop when rock is under straight compression or
tension, or is attempting to bend. Study of a fault can therefore often
lead to a good understanding of the structural history of a particular
region, especially of the magnitudes and directions of the crustal
forces, present and past, in the area.

Fault Structures.   There are several types of faults but the geographer is more interested in how faults affect topography than in the
mechanics of faulting. The essential fact of faulting is that *fault
blocks* are formed, just as when a block of wood is sawed in two the
cut represents the fault plane between two fault blocks. The effect of
faulting upon topography therefore depends upon the movement of
the fault blocks.

Blocks may rotate or otherwise move to form *fault block mountains,* the steep face of the block being called a *fault scarp.* The Basin

and Range Province (Figure 74) in the western United States is another outstanding example of faulting, being composed of thousands
of fault blocks, the valleys between these "ranges" being called
"basins."

Some of these ranges were formed in great part by upthrusts
rather than by simple rotations, to form upraised blocks called
horsts. Downdropped blocks are called *grabens,* and when the blocks
are of considerable size, this action forms *rift valleys,* such as the
Rift Valley of Africa. Other such downdropping largely produced
the Scottish Lowlands, Death Valley, part of the Rhine Valley, the
Dead Sea Rift, and has contributed in varying degree to the formation of many more of the major valleys and depressions on the earth's
surface.

Earthquakes. If two fault blocks are moving with respect to each
other, considerable friction will be developed. If a strong, thick giant-
sized steel cable were imagined to be placed across the fault surface
and fastened on both sides, it would deform and stretch and would
roughly represent what is happening everywhere on the fault surface:
due to friction, the rock is being bent more and more elastically in
the direction of movement. Finally, the rock will "snap," as a
stretched rubber band snaps, as the rock suddenly and elastically
regains its former shape, or close to it. Just as the end of a formerly
stretched, suddenly released rubber band stings a hand, so the elastic
rebound of the deformed rock will release energy to the surrounding
bedrock. The suddenly released energy travels through the earth in
the form of waves, some of which, near the earth's surface, throw
surface layers into wave form. It is in this manner that earthquakes
are believed to originate.

Earthquakes are therefore the causes of widespread movements in
the earth's upper layers, rather than being the results of such movements. They are extremely important in that they represent never-
ceasing adjustment in the earth's outer layers. Every minute two
earthquakes occur somewhere in the world. Although earthquakes
tend to occur principally in well-defined earthquake "zones," it is
probable that very few areas in the world have never been host to
the *focus,* or heart, of a quake. For example, in the United States,
California is known for its high number of earthquakes, yet every
state has had at least one earthquake. The earthquakes of probably
highest intensity in the United States, incidentally, occurred in Mis-

souri in 1811 and 1812. During one of those earthquakes, the course of the Mississippi was changed in several areas.

Cultural and Economic Aspects of Faults

In addition to the fact that faults modify and sometimes control topography, which in turn largely controls population and transportation patterns, faults are of immediate interest to those who live in the world's earthquake regions. The earthquake belts of the world coincide strongly with the volcano and mountain belts of the world. This is because mountain regions are regions of crustal weakness and change. Molten rock material makes its way to the surface more easily through fractured rock than, say, rock underlying plains regions, resulting in volcanoes in mountain regions. It is logical to expect many earthquakes to originate in the more highly fractured and unstable regions in the earth's crust, such as the mountain zones.

The effects of earthquakes upon environment are only too well known by the many thousands of people who have witnessed the destructive power of an earthquake which, in one minute, may exceed the energy in 10,000 early-type atom bombs. The tremendous force released is usually due to the fact that large masses of crust, under tremendous stress, are strained until they attain near-equilibrium by a sudden release and rebounding action. As already pointed out, the action is not unlike that of stretching a rubber band and suddenly releasing it. As a matter of fact, the energy built up and released in such elastic straining and rebounding can be demonstrated by vigorously stretching and releasing a thin rubber band about ten times and then holding it against the bottom of the lower lip (which is very sensitive to heat). The increased warmth of the band indicates its gaining and release of energy.

When submarine earthquakes occur, *tsunami* or *seismic sea waves* are often generated and sweep across the ocean at speeds up to 500 mph. Where they crash onto coasts these waves, which have caused great destruction and loss of life, are commonly called *tidal waves,* although their origin and their effects have nothing to do with tides, unless they happen to coincide with a period of high tide.

From the standpoint of the economic activities associated with earth sciences, the most important thing about earthquakes is that, as previously stated, earthquake data constitute our most valuable source of information concerning the earth's interior.

Some important mineral deposits are associated with fault zones because the original solutions carrying the ore minerals found routes of travel along the fault planes. In general, very large faults are not well mineralized, one reason being that many of the world's large faults formed after the last major world-wide mountain building activity and therefore mostly after the introduction of mineral-bearing igneous material into the mountain systems.

Water-carrying strata is often either sealed off or exposed to the surface by faulting. In the latter case, some springs in an area often occur in almost a straight line as when viewed on a map. The reason for this is that the water-bearing strata has been exposed along the straight fault face. Examples of this type of spring are the Arrowhead Springs and the Palm Springs of California.

REVIEW

1. Explain the meanings of the terms "plastic" and "elastic" as they relate to rock deformation. Give an example of rock deformation involving elasticity. Give an example of rock deformation involving plastic action.

2. Place the following: (a) the Dismal Swamp, (b) the Okefenokee Swamp, (c) the Everglades.

3. Discuss the relationship of fishing banks of the Atlantic seaboard to the Atlantic Coastal Plain.

4. Define "structural dome" and "structural basin." Give two examples of each.

5. Define "anticline" and "syncline." Discuss the cultural and economic aspects of bending and folding of rock.

6. What is a fault? How is a fault formed?

7. What are fault block mountains? Give two examples of such faulting.

8. What is a graben? Give four examples of famous regions associated with grabens.

9. Explain the generation of an earthquake.

10. Why are the earth's earthquake, mountain, and volcano belts practically synonymous?

EXERCISES

(Answers are given in the answer section at the back of the book.)

1. The topographic map of Figure 91 shows an eroded, plunging anticline in a sand dune area. The top of the map is north.

(a) How far apart are the main ridges about 1½ miles north of the southern boundary of the area shown?

(b) What is the approximate slope (the *dip*) of the westernmost main ridge?

(c) Two faults are indicated on the east ridge. How far are they from the southern boundary of the area shown?

(d) An intermittent stream is shown near the bottom center portion of the map. What is its gradient in feet per mile?

(e) Movement along the northernmost fault on the east ridge has displaced a block of the ridge in a general east-west direction. About what distance has the block been displaced?

2. Assume that a certain coastal plain is inclined one degree with the horizontal. If sea level rose 150 feet (as during melting of glaciers), how far inland would the sea advance in miles, assuming that the coastal plain extended this far?

3. In an eroded structural dome, as seen from overhead, are the outside strata older or younger than the inside strata? In an eroded structural basin, as seen from overhead, are the outside strata older or younger than the inside strata? Sketch typical cross sections of both structures, showing several strata to check your answers.

4. Sketch an anticline which is made up of smaller anticlines and synclines.

5. Assume that an anticline is a perfect V shape in cross section and that the angle between the sides of the V is 60°. If the anticline "plunges" at an angle of 15° with the horizontal, at what angle will the strata meet on a horizontal, eroded surface? (That is, what is the angle between the sides of the Vs made by the contours, as seen on a map? See Chapter 21.)

CHAPTER 27

Igneous and Metamorphic Activity; Associated Landforms

Igneous Rock

As explained in Chapter 17, igneous rocks are those of "fiery origin" and they result from the solidification, or freezing, of molten rock material called *magma*. The solidification of magma can occur on the surface as an *extrusive* rock or it can take place beneath the surface as an *intrusive* rock. Hence, igneous rocks occur either in igneous *intrusions* or in igneous *extrusions*.

The types of intrusions and extrusions to be discussed in this chapter are those which strongly affect man's environment and are therefore those igneous structures of great size. It is stressed at this time that the terms "intrusive" and "extrusive" refer to the original position of rock as it solidified and not necessarily to its present position in relation to the surface. For example, much granite is now seen on the surface of the earth, due to erosion, but all granite is intrusive, having been formed at least ½ mile beneath the surface. As another example, many original extrusions have been covered by sediments or by other extrusive rocks, but they are still extrusive in that they solidified on the surface.

Igneous Intrusions and Associated Landforms

Batholiths and Stocks. The largest known igneous intrusions are called *batholiths*. A batholith is a large intrusive igneous body with no known base and whose map area is more than 40 square miles. A *stock* has the same description except that its map area is less than 40 square miles. Both batholiths and stocks are commonly roughly circular in map view. Both often cut into and across the structure—bedding and shear planes, folds, particular rock types, etc.—of the original bedrock. Batholiths and stocks are therefore often *discordant* as opposed to being *concordant* where original bedrock is, for the most part, merely shoved aside *en masse* by the expanding intrusion instead of being further cut into. Batholiths and stocks are composed of granite or granite-like rocks. Although the size of a stock is limited, batholiths are often of tremendous proportions. The exposed area of the gigantic Idaho batholith is more than 16,000 square miles, but it seems almost dwarfed by the Coast Range batholith of western Canada which is 1200 miles long and up to 100 miles wide. Another example, the Sierra Nevada, formerly mentioned as being a fault block 400 miles long and about 60 miles wide, was faulted out of the massive Sierra Nevada batholith.

Laccoliths. A *laccolith* is a lens-shaped intrusive igneous mass which usually domes overhead rock upward rather than cutting through it. A laccolith is therefore *concordant*. (See Figure 92.)

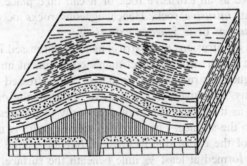

Fig. 92. Diagram of laccolith, an intrusion that has raised the overlying strata. (Adapted from *The Principles of Physical Geology* by Victor Monnett and Howard Brown. 1950. Ginn and Company)

Laccoliths are rarely more than a few miles in diameter but are often more than ¾ mile thick. A typical laccolith, then, looks something like a great inverted spoon bowl. Mountains of laccolithic origin are fairly common in some regions, an example being some of the Henry Mountains of Utah. Laccoliths are usually granitic in structure.

Dikes and Sills. A *dike* is an intrusive, tabular mass which cuts across the structure of the original bedrock. Dikes commonly weather out to form ridges although some dikes weather to form valleys. Most dikes are probably formed by magma filling fissures and then freezing in the fissures. Dikes are composed of basaltic rock.

A *sill* is an intrusive, tabular mass which is usually parallel to the layered structure of the original bedrock. Like dikes, sills are also composed of basaltic rock.

Dikes and sills vary from microscopic to huge size. One dike in Africa is 300 miles long and up to 40 miles wide. The palisades sill (the Palisades), exposed along the west side of the Hudson River for many miles, is from 800 to 900 feet thick.

One of the outstanding features of the Palisades sill is the *columnar jointing* which has developed, giving the effect of vertical columns weathering out of the sill. This type of jointing is frequent in sills and dikes and results from stresses set up as the rock cooled. The joints and therefore the columns are always at right angles to the major cooling surfaces.

Volcanic Necks. A *volcanic neck* is a solidified plug which fills the main vent of a former volcano. Shiprock, New Mexico, a tourist attraction, is a volcanic neck. Shiprock's rough, craggy appearance and the dikes radiating from the volcanic plug are typical features associated with the erosion of the cone type of volcano.

Cultural and Economic Aspects of Igneous Intrusions

With the possible exception of some laccoliths, the cultural and economic aspects of igneous intrusions depend upon to what extent intrusions have been uncovered and eroded and have been made a part of our environment. Igneous intrusion is almost synonymous with mountain building activity and igneous intrusions are responsible for much of the present topography and textural qualities of the world's land surfaces. Igneous intrusions are thus seen to be closely associated with population patterns and transportation patterns.

The wealth—and cultural effect—associated with igneous intrusions is tremendous. The great hard-rock mining districts of the world are in regions of mammoth igneous intrusions such as the Idaho batholith, the Boulder batholith of Montana, the Sierra Nevada batholith, the several Andean batholiths of South America, the gold "reefs" of South Africa, the igneous intrusions of the Kalgoorlie district of Australia, those of the Great Bear Lake region of Canada, and many others. In many mining regions the varied mineral wealth is geographically banded according to respective electrical conductivity in a rough lead-zinc-copper-silver-gold sequence. It is not unusual for ore minerals of a dozen or so elements to be mined in the same district. It should also be pointed out that the world's greatest primary diamond deposits occur in volcanic necks.

Sills are sometimes important sources of rock used in construction, while many types of gem stones are found in coarse-grained "pegmatite" dikes. These dikes also furnish large supplies of minerals such as mica, and strategic elements such as beryllium which is used for hardening copper and in nuclear reactors.

Perhaps the most important role of igneous rock is an ancient one which is often overlooked: that of being the parent material of all water and of all soil on earth, assuming that the earth was once nothing but igneous in constitution. Without the gases of hydrogen and oxygen in the original magma, water would not have formed. Without water or without the exact present mineral content of the earth's magma, our present soil would not have formed as it has. Life, if it had started at all, would be in far different form than it now is.

Igneous Extrusions and Associated Landforms

Volcanoes.   A *volcano* is a vent in the earth's surface through which molten rock material and gases escape. Volcanoes occur in a wide variety of sizes and shapes, from flat-surfaced vents only a few inches in diameter to mountains thousands of feet high. The structure built up by a volcano is called the volcanic *edifice*. There are three main kinds of edifices:

The *pyroclastic cone* (see Figure 93) is mainly built up of ejected

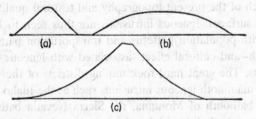

Fig. 93. The three main classes of volcanic edifices. Note that the composite cone (c) is a composite form of the pyroclastic cone (a) and the shield volcano (b).

cinder material. Being angular, the fragments lock onto each other and a steep-sided cone may result.

A *shield volcano* results from the generally slow outpouring of magma—now *lava*—onto the ground. In this way, rounded mountains may be built up around the main vent or vents. The great height of some of these shield volcanoes is often not recognized by the viewer due to the volcanoes' extreme lateral dimensions. The summit of Mauna Loa, the Hawaiian volcano, is almost 14,000 feet above sea level, a fact which first-time visitors to Hawaii often find hard to believe.

Composite cones, as the name indicates, combine some features of pyroclastic cones and shield volcanoes. Composite cones are often of great size and almost perfect symmetry. Their sides are gently convex toward their bases. Mt. Hood in Oregon is a composite cone as are Mt. Fujiyama in Japan, Vesuvius in Italy, and Mayan in the Philippines. There are many more composite cones than there are of the purely pyroclastic or shield types. The shape of a composite cone apparently results from the alternation of explosive eruptions with the quieter eruptions characteristic of shield volcanoes.

When a volcano erupts, gases and rock products are ejected. The chief gas erupted is steam. Some carbon dioxide is always present in volcanic gas, along with various other gases such as sulfur dioxide, and the gaseous forms of some acids, like hydrochloric acid, for example.

Ejected rock may be in either molten or solid form, some volcanoes first spewing solid, crusted-over lava and then ejecting molten lava. Molten lava solidifies quickly if hurled into the air in incandescent clots and more slowly if extruded upon the surface as part of a flow. Contrary to popular belief, more lava commonly breaks through the side of an erupting steep-sided volcano than is ejected at the top. The reason for this is that a steep-sided volcanic edifice is largely built of cinder material which is fairly easily breached by lava.

Volcanic eruptions are classified according to the type and sequence of material ejected and how it is ejected. The *Hawaiian* eruption is the quietest of the four types, the lava merely pouring over the sides of the edifice. In the *Strombolian* type of eruption the lava does not crust over between the frequent eruptions. The *Vulcanian* type of eruption is characterized by crusted-over lava being blown out first, followed by molten lava. Stromboli and Vulcano are Mediterranean area volcanoes.

The *Pelean* eruption takes place because of a plugging up of the main vent in a volcano's upper reaches. The volcano then literally blows its top, the explosions sometimes pointing straight down the slopes of the volcano. Such explosions typically hurtle great fiery clouds called *nuées ardentes,* and huge rocks down the slopes. It was such an explosion in 1902 on the West Indian island of Martinique which killed 28,000 people in a matter of minutes and destroyed the entire town of St. Pierre. Similar eruptions are believed to have destroyed a great volcanic edifice in Oregon, and to have formed the basin of Crater Lake in the enlarged crater, or *caldera,* of the inwardly collapsed structure.

One of the most interesting phenomena attending violent volcanic eruptions is that of induced rainstorms. Many times the steam being ejected in such an eruption rises so swiftly that clouds form over the site. Apparently, volcanic ash not only acts as nuclei for the ensuing rainfall, but also as tiny capacitors for the temporary storing of electrical charges. At any rate, violent volcanic eruptions are often capped by correspondingly violent thunderstorms and heavy rainfall. Such a storm was generated in 79 A.D. when Vesuvius erupted and destroyed the towns of Herculaneum and Pompeii. A resulting mudflow swiftly covered much of Herculaneum's lower levels and effectively sealed off priceless artifacts, many of which have since been recovered, some of them in almost perfect condition.

The "smoke" emptying from a volcano is not smoke at all but is composed of fine rock particles which are hurled out of the volcano either in solid form or as tiny liquid clots which almost immediately freeze in the air. The smallest fragments are *ash,* the next larger are *cinders,* while fragments more than 1¼ inches in diameter are called *bombs.* Some bombs of more than fifty tons in weight have been found. The terms *ash* and *cinders* are holdovers from the days when volcanic eruptions were believed to result from great subsurface combustions of some kind.

Fissure Eruptions.   When lava pours onto the earth's surface through a long fracture, or fissure, the eruption is called a *fissure eruption.* Such fissures are often tens of miles long. The material extruded in fissure eruptions is often some form of basalt which, due to its high melting point (about 1100° C at atmospheric pressure), stays molten longer than a light-colored extrusive rock does. As lava from a fissure eruption then stays molten for a considerable length of time, it can travel a long distance before solidifying. In Iceland, whose rocks are essentially all basalt, lava flows of over fifty miles in length have been mapped.

Lava flows from fissures have formed *plateaus* in several parts of the world. The Columbia Plateau which covers the greater portions of Oregon and Washington, and smaller portions of Idaho, California, and Nevada, is about 200,000 square miles in area. The vast Deccan flows of India cover almost 300,000 square miles in area. Other large plateaus have been formed by basalt in Africa and South America. Smaller basaltic flows occur in Mexico.

Cultural and Economic Aspects of Volcanoes

Despite their earned reputations as killers and destroyers, volcanoes furnish an amazing number of products necessary to our economy and welfare.

Basalt and other kinds of lava are used in road construction and as stone for concrete. *Pumice,* "rock froth," is used as an abrasive and in cleansers. It is also used as an insecticide carrier for dusting crops from the air. *Perlite,* a glassy volcanic rock, is much used for insulation. *Obsidian,* volcanic glass, has long been used by Indians for arrowheads and spearheads, and it is also used in some optical instruments. *Bentonite,* altered volcanic ash, is used in the oil industry as a drilling mud, in the metallurgical industry as a conditioner for molding sand; it is used in construction work, in the ceramic industry, in detergents, in the paper and rubber industries, and in several other industries.

Erosion of Volcanoes

Pyroclastic cones are structurally weak because their loosely consolidated cinder slopes are extremely subject to erosion. The rock of composite and shield volcanoes is often resistant to erosion in itself, but the truncated cone shape of a volcano more than compensates for such resistance by forming, in effect, a steep non-ending watershed. The streams on volcanoes form easily recognized *radial drainage patterns,* appearing on maps to radiate from common central areas.

The erosion of a pyroclastic cone or composite volcano finally reaches the stage where a volcanic neck with radiating dikes is left. The erosion of an area of shield volcanoes results in greatly varied topography, especially if some of the volcanoes are quiescent or extinct, while others are still active. Such a situation exists in the Hawaiian Islands which are essentially such a group of shield volcanoes.

Metamorphism and Its Economic Aspects

Metamorphism of rocks can be accomplished by heat, by contact with solutions or gases, by pressure, or by some combination of these agents. The weathering of metamorphic rocks into landforms has been discussed in Chapter 17.

The formation of anthracite coal from bituminous coal is perhaps the classic example of metamorphism which involves both pressure and heat. The chemical constitutions of bituminous and anthracite coal indicate that at least some heat is needed to complete the metamorphism from soft to hard coal. The chief agent, in the case of much anthracite coal, is pressure, as evidenced by the occurrences of the larger anthracite fields in strongly folded regions. In such metamorphism, heat drives off some substances, speeds up the action of the remaining molecules which forces them farther apart, and pressure molds the weakened structure into a new form. The above explanation is somewhat oversimplified but is essentially what happens in many pressure-heat metamorphisms.

Heat present during metamorphic activity may result from friction of rock layers, from proximity to an igneous intrusion, from heat due to depth, or from a combination of the above. The heat due to depth is defined by the *geothermal gradient,* the earth's increase in temperature with depth. Its average value is about 1° F per 60 feet of depth, but this can vary widely. The source of the heat is assumed to be in the breakup of radioactive minerals in the earth's crust. The geothermal gradient therefore applies only to the earth's crust, as far as is known. Obviously the continuation of the gradient to the earth's center would result in a fantastically high value for the temperature of the earth's core.

Metamorphism plays an important part in the formation of some important mineral deposits. Some tungsten minerals, for instance, are formed by the interaction of minerals in sedimentary rocks and gases from nearby igneous intrusions. Several large lead-zinc deposits have resulted from the metamorphism of carbonate rocks by lead and zinc solutions, an example being the lead-zinc region of Missouri and Oklahoma. Similar metamorphism has resulted in the formation of industrial and strategic minerals, such as some beryllium minerals and corundum. The metamorphism of shale to slate has already been outlined. (See Chapter 17.)

Complex Landforms

From what has been said about the temperatures associated with metamorphism, it is probably apparent that igneous intrusions and extrusions must always bring about some metamorphism of older, adjacent rock. It has already been explained that the pressures in the earth's crust which are great enough to cause folding also cause permanent changes in rock. Similarly, at least some metamorphism must occur along any fault zone.

On a larger scale, many areas of the earth have been directly subjected to intense periods of intrusion, folding, and faulting, and are characterized by folding, faulting, and metamorphism of all types of rocks, including metamorphic rocks themselves. Such areas and structures are termed *complex*, and the erosion of these areas and structures also tends to be complex. As may have already been surmised by the reader, some of the world's most rugged topography is found in these regions of complex geology.

REVIEW

1. A certain lava, once extruded upon the surface, is now buried by hundreds of feet of sediments. Is the lava now considered to be extrusive or intrusive?

2. What is a batholith? What is the main difference between a batholith and a laccolith, other than size?

3. Describe a dike; a sill.

4. What is the economic importance of many batholiths?

5. Describe the four types of volcanic eruptions. Why do thunderstorms sometimes form over violently erupting volcanoes?

6. What is the "smoke" which billows out of erupting volcanoes?

7. What is a "fissure eruption"?

8. List the general uses of volcanic rocks.

9. What are the possible sources of heat present during metamorphic activity?

10. What are "complex landforms"?

EXERCISES

(Answers are given in the answer section at the back of the book.)

1. In a certain dike, the columns formed by cooling are inclined 30° from the vertical. At what angle is the *dike* inclined to the *horizontal*?

2. Sketch the profiles of the three main kinds of volcanic edifice.

3. Excluding Alaska and Hawaii from consideration, can you think of a valid reason why the economically most advanced countries do not, in general, have many volcanoes?

4. The melting (and freezing) point of basalt at atmospheric pressure is about 1100° C. Express the melting point of basalt in degrees Fahrenheit.

5. A certain vertical dike (A) cut its way through limestone. Subsequent erosion smoothly planed off the upper parts of the dike and the limestone, and then sandstone was deposited on the erosional surface. A second dike (B) then cut across dike A, the limestone, and the sandstone and the whole sequence is now exposed in a road cut. Describe how you would be able logically to reconstruct the series of events in chronological order. Assume that both dikes caused noticeable alteration, such as baking effects, of the older rock they intruded.

6. Everyday living involves the use of things made from or with the help of igneous and metamorphic minerals. For example, writing with pencil on paper demonstrates one use each of a metamorphic mineral and a volcanic product: the graphite in pencils is metamorphosed carbon, and altered volcanic ash is used as a filler for paper. As another example, a piece of furniture is made by using metal tools and is polished with volcanic abrasive. Even the plastic industry depends upon machines and molds made possible by igneous minerals. Can you think of any manufactured object or material whose manufacture or present composition does not involve the use of either igneous or metamorphic minerals?

CHAPTER 28

Wind and Its Associated Landforms

Wind Erosion

Kinds of Wind Erosion. There are two main kinds of wind erosion: *deflation* and *abrasion.* Deflation is the removal of large quantities of material by the wind, while abrasion refers to the filing action of wind-carried material. Of the two, deflation is much more important in landform formation and erosion, at least at the present time. Although extreme aridity is not needed for deflation, the amount of deflation in a region of given size is proportional to the dryness of the top layers of soil, to the lack of vegetative cover, and to the size of rock particles on the surface layers.

Deflation Basins and Desert Pavement. In desert regions, *deflation basins* are formed by the wind taking up material and transporting it, so that a shallow basin is excavated. These basins may range up to several miles in lateral dimensions but are generally very shallow. Shallow deflation basins are represented on contour maps by depression contour lines. (See Chapter 21.)

In many desert regions, finer particles have been removed to the extent that pebbles and sometimes even cobbles have moved close together to form a *desert pavement,* or *deflation armor.* The migration of the pebbles and cobbles finally to form a closely joined "armor" is apparently caused by combinations of undercutting, rolling, and sliding.

How the Wind Picks Up Material. At first glance the raising and moving of sand and dust by the wind appears to be a very simple process: the wind stirs up the particles and then carries them away.

As a quick summary of deflation, the above description is probably as good as any other, but it is not an explanation. For one thing the fact that rock material in the form of dust is often carried miles above the surface of the earth by the wind demonstrates that "horizontal" wind motion is actually turbulent, with vertical eddies and drafts, otherwise the dust would not have been carried aloft. Probably the only near-streamlined natural movement of dust in wind occurs in "dust devils," towering, twisting columns of dust which wind slowly over the land in response to the formation of very localized low pressure areas and subsequent cyclonic spiraling on a minor scale.

It is interesting that wind itself can bring about low pressure which can cause dust to rise into it. The principle behind this action has been known for many years and is the reason for aerodynamic lift as in airplane flight. The action itself may be demonstrated by placing a piece of lightweight paper on a table, with about one fourth of the paper overhanging the edge. If a vertically-held hand is now vigorously swept across and just above the overhanging section, the paper will start to lift. The movement is somewhat similar to that of a large sheet of paper rising high into the air just after an automobile has passed over it. From the above illustrations it is apparent that the greater the velocity of the wind, the higher a given quantity of dust will rise, the reason being that the decrease in pressure is proportional to the wind velocity. Furthermore, the quantity of dust thus raised and carried away is proportional to the wind velocity. Just as parts of airplane wings are of several slope designs for varying lift and flight situations, so do the slopes of the land being traversed by the wind determine to some degree how much dust will rise and be transported by the wind.

The lifting effect of the wind is therefore capable of making particles rise into the wind but it is probably obvious that a combination of loosening and then lifting of the particles would result in much more material being lifted into the wind and carried away. Such a loosening is believed to be accomplished by sand grains which, hurled against each other near the surface of the ground by the wind, then bounce into the air. Coming down, these sand grains stir up the finer material, hit other sand grains, bounce into the air again, hit other sand grains, and so on. This process is called *saltation*. Also contributing to the resulting deflation are turbulent eddies set up on the now roughened ground surface. These eddies are much like those in fast moving streams which flow over rocky beds.

How the Wind Transports Material.   It is logical to expect that wind would lift finer particles to greater heights than it does coarser and heavier particles. Study of wind action confirms this. During a windstorm, sand travels along within a few feet of the ground by saltation, while dust particles are actually carried aloft and forward in the wind. The lifting effects due to reduced pressure and eddy currents are both increased by increase in wind velocity. Some "dust storms" therefore tower to heights of a few miles above the ground. Particle size normally decreases from the earth's surface upward in dust storms, while the wind velocity increases with height. Therefore the finest particles in a given storm are usually carried the farthest, all particles being deposited at distances from the beginning of their journey which are inversely proportional to their size.

Abrasion. So far, very little has been said in this chapter about wind abrasion. Although wind abrasion seems to be of relatively small general importance when compared with deflation, in performing geologic work, its effects in some regions are often very noticeable. Sand-abraded narrow canyon sides are fairly common in some areas as are *ventifacts,* many-surfaced stones whose waxy luster and facets show that the ventifacts were carved under desert conditions by abrasion.

Maximum abrasion is usually confined to a few feet above the ground, where sand particles and larger silt particles are the abrasives. An exception to this occurs in the previously mentioned canyons where the funneling action of the wind often piles the larger windborne particles up to considerable height.

It can be said that important effects of wind erosion at the present time are almost entirely due to deflation. It should be mentioned, however, that in times past, under vastly different conditions of wind and weathering than are now present on the earth's surface, abrasion may have been of much more importance than deflation in some regions.

Wind Deposits of Sand

Formation and Structure of Dunes. A *dune* is a wind-deposited mass of sand. A dune, then, forms because of an interruption in the movement of sand by the wind but the actual causes of all such interruptions are not known.

It is known, however, that some dunes form over and around obstacles and other irregularities in the land surface. Conceivably a bush, or a dead animal, or even a slight change in the slope of the ground could act as a nucleus for dune growth. Probable nuclei of this nature have been found in dunes but other dunes reveal no evident cause for their formation.

As a dune grows, sand grains pushed by the wind travel up the *windward* face of the dune and then tumble down the *leeward* face, or *slip* face, of the dune. The leeward side of a dune is the steeper side, usually making an angle of about 30° with the horizontal. Heights of 100 feet or so are common for sand dunes and some former dunes are known to have attained heights of approximately 1000 feet. Dunes having heights of about 750 feet occur in some places in Africa.

If sand keeps moving up the windward slope and down the leeward slope of a dune, the dune will either elongate parallel to the wind, "move," or both. If the only appreciable source of sand is the dune itself, then removal of sand from the windward to the leeward side will cause "moving" or *migration* of the dune without much change in size. Depending upon grain size, wind velocity, and type of sand material, dunes tend toward *cross-stratification* as erosion is predominant over deposition, and *vice versa*. In cross-stratification, layers of sand are at angles to other layers.

Kinds of Dunes. There are many kinds of sand dunes but those with definite form are members of one of four major classes: *transverse, barchans, U-shaped,* and *longitudinal* dunes, or *seifs.* (See Figure 94.)

Transverse dunes are sand ridges whose long dimensions are perpendicular to the direction of the wind. They are common in very

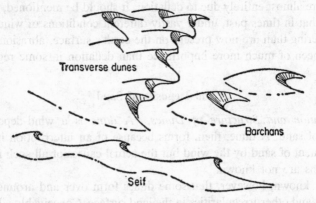

Transverse dunes

Barchans

Seif

Fig. 94. Sand dunes. Prevailing direction of wind that formed these dunes is from left to right. (Adapted from *Elements of Geography,* 4th edition, 1957, by Finch et al. McGraw-Hill Book Company)

sandy regions and vary in height from ridges a few inches high to structures which are several hundred feet in height. Transverse dunes usually have sharp leeward slopes of about 30° while their windward slopes are often about 10°.

Barchans, as seen on a map or from overhead, are crescent-shaped dunes. The "horns" of the crescent point to leeward. Barchans are commonly spaced widely apart on hard, flat desert floors. Barchans therefore largely furnish their own sand for migration and, being unhampered by other dunes, ridges, and topography in general, travel rapidly for sand dunes, moving as much as 150 feet per year in some instances. Barchans often attain heights of 100 feet or more and have sharply-defined leeward slopes. Due to the natural shelter afforded on the leeward side of a large barchan, these dunes are often used as revetments for airplanes in desert regions, and for desert camp sites.

U-shaped dunes look like poorly-formed barchans, except that the points of the crescent are to the windward side. The slip face, however, is on the leeward side as in the case of transverse dunes and barchans. U-shaped dunes are sometimes evidently formed by vegetation stabilizing the horns-to-be of a dune as the central portion of sand moves forward.

Longitudinal dunes, or *seifs,* are ridges of sand which parallel the direction of the wind. Why these ridges form parallel to instead of at right angles with the wind direction is very incompletely understood except in a few instances. One of these instances occurs in the vicinity of narrow canyons where it is obvious that the wind sweeping through the canyons has literally extruded the sand in ridge form onto the desert floor. Many longitudinal dunes are, however, found in the central portions of deserts, far from canyons or other possibly parental topography. Some longitudinal dunes in Australian deserts are over 100 feet high and over 100 miles long.

Sand dunes can easily be duplicated in miniature by spreading out one cubic inch of salt to form a ridge about 3 inches long and ¼ inch high on a dry surface and then gently blowing across the surface, at various places, at right angles to the long axis of the ridge. A transverse "dune," with a noticeably steep leeward slope and gentler windward slope will form.

To form a barchan, deliberately try to form a crescent shape from the original ridge by varying the direction of blowing. The miniature barchan formed will have a steep leeward side and a gentler windward side. The result of this experiment suggests that barchans are at least sometimes formed in this manner in regions where the direction of the "prevailing" winds shifts during the year.

A U-shaped dune may be made by again forming the flat ridge, wetting each end of the ridge with one drop of water, and blowing toward the center of the ridge. The U-shape will almost immediately form and, with careful, gentle blowing a steep leeward slope and gentler windward slope can be obtained. (Obtaining the U-shape in miniature in this way is about the same thing as having the ends of a real ridge stabilized by vegetation as the wind blows transverse to the entire ridge.)

Loess

Loess (lûs) is fine, wind-blown material composed mainly of silt. Loess deposits are found in many regions of the world and have been derived from either glacial drift or from deserts. Typically, loess is yellowish in color. Its presence in quantity gives the Yellow River and the Yellow Sea of China their names. The loess deposits in northern China, the world's largest known concentrations of loess, were derived from deflation in often far-distant Asian deserts. The loess in China is more than 150 feet thick in some areas, and many Chinese in these areas, following centuries-old custom, live in caves which have been made in the soft cliffs. Examination of loess reveals that it is mechanically disintegrated and but little weathered chemically, hence the loess of China makes extremely fertile soil as its original minerals are virtually all present.

The North American and European loess deposits resulted, for the most part, from the drying out and subsequent deflation of the finer particles of glacial drift. A major source of the glacial loess was, no doubt, *rock flour* made by the grinding action of rocks carried and pushed along by the glaciers. Extensive glacial loess deposits have been mapped in the "corn belt" of the United States, along the Missouri and Mississippi rivers, and in eastern Oregon and Washington. Large deposits of glacial loess have long been recognized as such in other areas, including the Rhine Valley of Germany. It has probably already been recognized by some readers that the word "loess" is of German origin, from *löss* or, broadly, "loosened."

Economic and Cultural Aspects
of Wind Erosion and Deposition

The most striking effects of wind erosion and deposition in the United States are seen in the "dust bowl" years when repeated periods of drought on the plains culminate in the huge dust clouds composed of fine particles of soil. Such periods of drought and deflation have been among the most disastrous, economically and culturally, that this country has passed through. The process of such large-scale deflation is almost terrifying in its simplicity: the top soil reaches a certain aridity, the wind blows at more than ten miles per hour, and the fertile plains regions are literally blown to dust.

On the credit side of wind erosion and deposition, loess is an almost perfect parent material for soil. In the United States, corn is grown in Iowa, Illinois, and Nebraska on soil derived in large part from loess, and wheat is grown in loess soil in Nebraska, Kansas, and southeastern Washington. Argentine Pampa soil is largely loess-associated, as are rich, productive wheat-growing soils of central Germany, Poland, and the Ukraine of southern Russia.

REVIEW

1. What are the two kinds of wind erosion?

2. Explain in detail how the wind picks up silt and dust.

3. How does the wind transport sand? How does the wind transport dust? What is the relationship of grain size to distance of transportation? Why?

4. Explain how sand dunes in general may start to form.

5. How high are sand dunes commonly? How high do they get in some regions?

6. How does a dune "migrate"?

7. What are the four major classes of sand dunes?

8. What is loess? What are the two main sources of loess?

9. Discuss the cultural and economic aspects of wind erosion and deposition.

EXERCISES

(Answers are given in the answer section at the back of the book.)

1. Sketch map views of the four main kinds of dunes. Show wind directions. Place four contour lines on each sketch of a dune.

2. Perform the experiments described in this chapter to make miniature dunes. Can you make a longitudinal dune in similar manner? How do you think most longitudinal dunes are made by the wind, remembering that the long axes of these dunes parallel the direction of the wind?

3. Sand on the leeward side of a dune is often on a 30° slope while the sand on the windward side is often on a 10° slope. What are these slopes, respectively, in terms of percent slope?

4. Deposits of loess in Nebraska, Iowa, Washington, etc., can be explained by their proximity to the outwash plains of continental glaciation. However, extensive loess deposits on the east side of the Mississippi River go as far south as Mississippi. How can you explain these particular deposits?

Bibliography

The books cited below are examples of the many excellent, less-technical references readily available to the general reader.

Size and Shape of the Earth

Flanagan, D., ed. *The Planet Earth*. New York: Simon and Schuster, 1950. See "The Shape of the Earth" by W. A. Heiskanen.

Hosmer, G. L. *Geodesy*. New York: John Wiley and Sons, 1930. 2d ed.

Jacobs, J. A., R. D. Russell, and J. T. Wilson. *Physics and Geology*. New York: McGraw-Hill Book Co., 1959.

Maps and Map Projections

Davis, R. E. *Elementary Plane Surveying*. New York: McGraw-Hill Book Co., 1955. 3d ed. See Chapters 14 and 19.

Deetz, C. H., and O. S. Adams. *Elements of Map Projection*. Special Publ. 68, U. S. Dept. of Commerce, Coast and Geodetic Survey, Washington, D. C.: U. S. Government Printing Office, 1945.

Greenhood, D. *Down to Earth: Mapping for Everybody*. New York: Holiday House, 1951.

Raisz, E. *General Cartography*. New York: McGraw-Hill Book Co., 1948.

Earth-Sun and Earth-Moon Relationships

Gaposchkin, C. (Payne) *Introduction to Astronomy*. Englewood Cliffs, New Jersey: Prentice-Hall, 1954.

Mehlin, T. G. *Astronomy*. New York: John Wiley and Sons, 1959.

Struve, O., B. Lynds, and H. Pillane. *Elementary Astronomy*. New York: Oxford University Press, 1959. (Recommended for readers with strong science backgrounds.)

Wylie, C. C. *Astronomy, Maps, and Weather*. New York: Harper and Brothers, 1942. See Chapters 5, 6, 13.

Weather

Blair, T. A., and R. C. Fite. *Weather Elements*. Englewood Cliffs, New Jersey: Prentice-Hall, 1957. 4th ed.

Koeppe, C. E., and G. C. DeLong. *Weather and Climate*. New York: McGraw-Hill Book Co., 1958.

Lehr, P., R. Burnett, and H. Zim. *Weather*. New York: Simon and Schuster, 1957.

Taylor, G. *Elementary Meteorology*. Englewood Cliffs, New Jersey: Prentice-Hall, 1954.

Climate

Blumenstock, D. *The Ocean of Air*. New Brunswick, New Jersey: Rutgers University Press, 1959.

Critchfield, H. *General Climatology*. Englewood Cliffs, New Jersey: Prentice-Hall, 1960.

Hambidge, G., ed. *Climate and Man*. U. S. Department of Agriculture, Washington, D. C.: U. S. Government Printing Office, 1941.

Trewartha, G. T. *An Introduction to Climate*. New York: McGraw-Hill, 1954.

Rocks and Minerals

Fenton, C. L., and M. A. Fenton. *Rocks and Their Stories*. New York: Doubleday & Co., 1951.

Hurlbut, C., Jr. *Dana's Manual of Mineralogy*. New York: John Wiley and Sons, 1959. 17th ed.

Pough, F. H. *A Field Guide to Rocks and Minerals*. Boston: Houghton Mifflin Co., 1955.

Wade, F., and R. Mattox. *Elements of Crystallography and Mineralogy*. New York: Harper and Brothers, 1960.

Soils

Bennett, H. *Elements of Soil Conservation*. New York: McGraw-Hill Book Co., 1955. 2d ed.

Hambidge, G., ed. *Climate and Man*. U. S. Dept. of Agriculture, Washington, D. C.: U. S. Government Printing Office, 1941.

Kellogg, C. *The Soils That Support Us*. New York: The Macmillan Co., 1944.

Stefferud, A., ed. *Soil*. U. S. Dept. of Agriculture, Washington, D. C.: U. S. Government Printing Office, 1957.

Landforms

Atwood, Wallace W. *The Physiographic Provinces of North America*. Boston: Ginn and Co., 1940.

Lobeck, A. K. *Geomorphology: An Introduction to the Study of Landscape;* New York: McGraw-Hill Book Co., 1939.

Lobeck, A. K. *Things Maps Don't Tell Us*. New York: The Macmillan

Co., 1956. (Outstanding analyses of landform developments explained in nontechnical manner.)

Loomis, F. *Physiography of the United States*. New York: Doubleday & Co., 1937.

Miller, V., and C. Miller. *Photogeology*. New York: McGraw-Hill Book Co., 1961. (Excellent for the study of landforms, etc., by means of aerial photographs and contour maps. Contains good explanations of the processes involved.)

Shimer, J. *The Sculptured Earth: The Landscape of America*. New York: Columbia University Press, 1959.

Thornbury, W. *Principles of Geomorphology*. New York: John Wiley and Sons, 1954.

Water

Kuenen, P. *Realms of Water*. New York: John Wiley and Sons, 1956.

Lane, F. *The World's Great Lakes*. New York: Doubleday & Co., 1958.

Stefferud, A., ed. *Water*. U. S. Dept. of Agriculture, Washington, D. C.: U. S. Government Printing Office, 1955. (Contains articles on surface and subsurface water.)

Tolman, C. *Ground Water*. New York: McGraw-Hill Book Co., 1937.

Wisler, C., and E. Brater. *Hydrology*. New York: John Wiley and Sons, 1949.

Glaciation

Coleman, A. *The Last Million Years: A History of the Pleistocene in North America*. Toronto: University of Toronto Press, 1941.

Cotton, C. *Climatic Accidents in Landscape-making*. New York: John Wiley and Sons, 1948.

Flint, R. *Glacial and Pleistocene Geology*. New York: John Wiley and Sons, 1957.

Leet, L., and F. Leet, eds. *The World of Geology*. New York: McGraw-Hill Book Co., 1961. See pp. 101–135.

The Oceans

Carson, Rachel. *The Sea Around Us*. New York: Oxford University Press, 1951.

Kuenen, P. *Marine Geology*. New York: John Wiley and Sons, 1950.

Shepard, F. P. *The Earth Beneath the Sea*. Baltimore: Johns Hopkins Press, 1959.

Sverdrup, H., M. Johnson, and R. Fleming. *The Oceans, Their Physics, Chemistry, and General Biology*. Englewood Cliffs, New Jersey: Prentice-Hall, 1942.

Geologic Processes in the Earth's Crust

Billings, M. P. *Structural Geology*. Englewood Cliffs, New Jersey: Prentice-Hall, 1954. 2d ed.

Coleman, S. N. *Volcanoes New and Old*. New York: John Day Co., 1946.

Cotton, C. A. *Volcanoes as Landscape Forms*. New York: John Wiley and Sons, 1953.

Fenton, C., and M. Fenton. *Rocks and Their Stories*. New York: Doubleday & Co., 1951.

Lynch, J. *Our Trembling Earth*. New York: Dodd, Mead and Co., 1940.

Riley, C. *Our Mineral Resources*. New York: John Wiley and Sons, 1959.

Work of the Wind

Bagnold, R. *The Physics of Blown Sand and Desert Dunes*. New York: William Morrow and Co., 1942.

Kellogg, C. E. *Soil Blowing and Dust Storms*. U. S. Dept. of Agriculture Misc. Publ. 221, Washington, D. C.: U. S. Government Printing Office, 1935.

Sears, P. *Deserts on the March*. Norman, Okla.: University of Oklahoma Press, 1947. 2d ed.

Stefferud, A. *Soil*. U. S. Dept. of Agriculture, Washington, D. C.: U. S. Government Printing Office, 1957. See pp. 308–314, 321–326.

Structure of the Earth

Daly, R. A. *Strength and Structure of the Earth*. Englewood Cliffs, New Jersey: Prentice-Hall, 1940.

Flanagan, D., ed. *The Planet Earth*. New York: Simon and Schuster, 1950. See "The Interior of the Earth" by K. E. Bullen.

Gutenberg, Beno. *Internal Constitution of the Earth*. New York: Dover Publications, 1951.

Leet, L. D. *Practical Seismology and Seismic Prospecting*. New York: D. Appleton-Century Co., 1938.

Answers to Exercises

Chapter 1

1. (1)(f)   (2)(c)   (3)(b)   (4)(a)   (5)(e)   (6)(d).
2. (1)(f)   (2)(e)   (3)(a)   (4)(b)   (5)(c)   (6)(d).
3. (1) False. Cartography is an allied science of earth sciences.

(2) False. Thales is generally recognized as the first true geographer.

(3) True. Ptolemy's map showed an encouragingly narrow Atlantic Ocean, with no continents between Europe and China.

(4) False. As witness the effects of hurricanes, tornadoes, earthquakes, floods, etc.

(5) False. The plant kingdom has been "virtually untouched" by man.

Chapter 2

1. 20 square inches.
2. 260.
3. 370,000,000.
4. $\dfrac{1}{1600}$.
5. 5.8 grains (It is common practice to round off to an even integer in the last place).
6. $3.650 \times 10^3 \times 2.000 \times 10^6 = 7.300 \times 10^9 = 7,300,000,000.$
7. 250 pounds per cubic foot.
8. 17,600 miles per hour.

Chapter 3

1. $\dfrac{1}{8}$ (approximate).
2. .333 percent (approximate).
3. The earth's polar diameter is about .333 percent less than its equatorial diameter.

4. 1200 miles (approximate).

5. 3600 seconds (exactly).

6. 40 feet (approximate).

Chapter 4

1. 70°.

2. Between 10° and 20°: 2.1″. Between equator and 10°: 2.4″.

3. Between 10° and 20°: 0.4″. Between equator and 10°: 0.1″. Polar orthographic compresses land masses which are nearer the equator, while the polar stereographic enlarges such land masses.

4. $\frac{1}{2}$.

5. 11 T.

6. 30 miles.

7. 3955 miles.

Chapter 5

1. $\frac{1}{81,000}$.

2. 1 inch = 20,000 feet.

3. $\frac{1}{15,000}$.

4. 1:16.

5. 1:28280.

6. S 20° W.

7. North.

Chapter 6

1. 23½°.

2. 79° 34′ S.

3. The north pole, from about March 21 to September 22; the south pole, from about September 22 to March 21.

4. The equator; March 21.

5. 43°; 66½°; 23½°.

6. About 8° 35′.

7. (b).

Chapter 7

1. Set ahead, to read 3:00.
2. 76° 31' 15" W.
3. $+ 14^m 40^s$.
4. 12:00 noon, Wednesday.
5. About 11:27 A.M.
6. Lat. 39° 21' N; Long. 68° 45' W.
7. $+ 5^m 23^s$.
8. Ship A going westward, crossed the 180th meridian at 24^h. December 24. Ship B, traveling eastward, crossed the 180° meridian at 24^h, December 25.

Chapter 8

1. Infrared.
2. Visible light is of shorter wavelength.
3. 6.7° C.
4. 333° K.
5. 14° F and 95° F.

Chapter 9

1. 35 grams of water vapor per 1000 grams of air, including the water vapor.
2. 3.5 percent, assuming that the barometric pressure results solely from the fact that every 1000 grams of air above the instrument includes 35 grams of water vapor.
3. 60° F.
4. (a) 67 percent. (b) Becomes heavier per unit volume. (c) 25 percent.

Chapter 10

1. 90 pounds per square inch.
2. Check drawing by text.
3. Approximately 5 days.

4. Approximately 5 million cubic feet.
5. Check sketch as indicated.

Chapter 11

1. Check your answer by research.
2. Same as number 1.
3. Check your sketch with Figure 59.
4. Check your sketch with text, this chapter.
5. 20 hours.
6. Approximately 3 hours.
7. (a) Change from curved to almost straight, going counterclockwise. (b) Change from almost straight to curved, going counterclockwise. (c) Almost straight. (d) Become closer together.
8. 0.4 pounds per square foot; 40 pounds per square foot; 360 pounds per square foot.
9. Check sketch with Figure 61.
10. 8:00 A.M., next day. (Satellite will have completed 16 orbits, and station A will be back in orbital plane. A full 24 hours is needed. After 12 hours, the satellite has made 8 orbits but is on the opposite side of the earth from station A.)
11. 730 feet per second.

Chapter 12

1. 2¾ pounds of "table salt" in 100 pounds of sea water. Or, can be expressed as 2¾ pounds of "table salt" in every 1½ cubic feet of sea water.
2. Check your sketch against Figure 63.
3. 20 feet.
4. Check your answer against text of this chapter.
5. Check your answer as suggested.
6. (a) 1¾ million tons of water per square mile. (b) 24 inches of rain.
7. Approximately 100 years.
8. 260 feet, using data given. (Actual figure, allowing for slope of continental shelves, etc., is around 250 feet.)

Chapter 13

1. Compare sketch as suggested.
2. 4.

Chapter 14

1. Approximately 58° C.

2. 33 percent. Will speed up evaporation on ground surface, as compared to relative humidity of 50 percent.

3. Check your sketch against Figure 64.

Chapter 15

1. 82 feet.

2. Check your sketch with Figure 64.

3. Check your map with a published world map.

4. Compare Figure 64 as suggested.

5. 1200 miles (nautical).

6. ———

7. ———

8. ———

Chapter 16

1. 3000 feet.

2. On or about June 21; 43½°.

3. 90° N (north pole); 6 months.

4. −40°.

5. ———

Chapter 17

1. Approximately 28 percent pore space.

2. The dark-colored minerals in general are heavier than the light-colored minerals.

3. Either plaster or magnesium oxide.

Chapter 18

The exercises of this chapter are all of the reader activity type and are non-numerical, hence no answers are given.

Chapter 19

1. Equal in air space; no effect upon porosity but may have effect upon *permeability*, due to sizes of pore spaces.
2. 140 pounds per cubic foot (approximately).
3. Check your sketch with text, this chapter.
4. The water table fell, after the caverns were formed.
5. Check your answer as suggested.

Chapter 20

1. Crustal rock weighs about 170 pounds per cubic foot. Nearby mantle rock weighs about 210 pounds per cubic foot.
2. 6:1.
3. ————
4. ————
5. Check your sketch against text, this chapter.
6. 85 percent.
7. 87 percent.
8. About 8½ million years.
9. 300 years.
10. (b) About 3 miles.

Chapter 21

1. Average slope about 2 percent.
2. $\dfrac{1}{2500}$.
3. About $\dfrac{1}{10}$ of a square mile.
4. 33¼°.
5. Stereoscopic vision; the "sausage" is a composite of the views seen by either eye.
6. About ¼ of an inch.

Chapter 22

1. White (due to greater height of fall, white rocks will travel farther downslope).

2. (a) Average grade about 20 percent. (b) Mass wasting. (c) Difference in erosion due to difference of rock types at that elevation.

Chapter 23

1. 30,000 cubic feet per second.
2. 9 times.
3. Check your sketches against figures in this chapter.
4. ———
5. ———
6. Check your cross section with text, this chapter.
7. ———
8. (a) Northward. (b) Generally eastward. (c) Cutoff meander; meanders. (d) Stream *B*: about ½ mile; Stream *D*: about ¼ mile. (e) The abandoned river valley northward of point *A* should contain good soil and be easily worked.

Chapter 24

1. Suggested as a term project or as independent research.
2. (a) Cirque. (b) Tarns. (c) Col. (d) Horn. (e) Arête.

Chapter 25

1. ———
2. From right to left.
3. ———
4. Almost 300 feet.
5. Check your answer by drawing a contour map which shows the newly exposed features.
6. ———

Chapter 26

1. (a) About 2 miles. (b) About 40 percent. (c) 3 miles, 4 miles. (d) About 350 feet per mile. (e) About 200 yards.
2. Between 1 and 2 miles.

3. In a dome the outside strata are younger; in a basin the outside strata are older.

4. ———

5. About 18°.

Chapter 27

1. 30°.

2. Check your sketch with Figure 93.

3. ———

4. 2000° F.

5. ———

6. ———

Chapter 28

1. Transverse, barchan, and U-shaped dunes should have contour lines closer together on leeward slopes.

2. ———

3. 58 percent; 18 percent.

4. Hint: The three great agents of long-distance transportation are glaciers, wind, and water. Glaciation did not extend this far south.

Index

DOUBLEDAY COLLEGE COURSE GUIDES

Analytic Geometry
                         William L. Schaaf   U1 $1.95

The Calculus
                         William L. Schaaf   U5 $1.95

Essentials of Zoology
                   Leon Augustus Hausman   U3 $1.75

Fundamentals of Speech
                       George W. Hibbitt   U8 $1.45

History of English Literature to 1660
                       Martin S. Day   U10 $1.95

History of English Literature 1660 to 1837
                       Martin S. Day   U12 $1.95

History of the United States to 1865
                       James P. Shenton   U4 $1.75

Introduction to American Education
                       S. E. Frost, Jr.   U2 $1.75

Introduction to American Government
                       James Tracy Crown   U11 $1.75

An Introduction to Psychology
                       John F. Hahn   U7 $1.45

An Outline of English Composition
                       Alan B. Howes   U6 $1.45

Principles of Accounting
                       R. Dean White and
                       Floyd W. White   U9 $1.75